STORY

the Yearbook of Discovery / 1968

STORY:

Edited by
Whit and Hallie Burnett

the Yearbook of Discovery / 1968

The Best Creative Work from the Colleges
of the United States and Canada
as judged by

J. Donald Adams
Hallie Burnett
Richard Eberhart
Riley Hughes
John Luter
Clark Mills
Marianne Moore
Tad Mosel
Stanley Richards
and others
cooperating in the
STORY
COLLEGE CREATIVE AWARDS CONTEST
of 1967-1968

FOUR WINDS PRESS
NEW YORK

"Neither Here Nor There" by David B. Jones, appearing on page 241, is based on "A Report to an Academy," by Franz Kafka, copyright © 1948 by Schocken Books Inc. No use of the above adaptation may be made without the written consent of Schocken Books Inc.

"A One-Time Trip" by Barry G. Herem, appearing on page 306, was first published in Seattle Magazine, April, 1967, to whose editors acknowledgment is gratefully expressed.

Published by Four Winds Press
A Division of Scholastic Magazines, Inc., New York, N.Y.

Printed in the United States of America

Library of Congress Catalogue Card Number: 67-31285

FOREWORD

The work of the writers in this book represents the best, we believe, from today's talented youth. Here are the story tellers, poets, essayists, dramatists, biographers and journalists of this year's college generation. And if the common conception, fed by every day's headlines, is that the college population is either protesting just for the sake of protest, or half asleep on some self-immolating pad, this conception might well be in need of adjustment.

This collection cannot be said to demonstrate an abrupt and clearly defined return to artistic conservatism in the colleges of America. But the pieces published here do show that many students, whether individually committed to dissent or not, realize that in order to write effectively and creatively, they really must write, not just talk about it or dream; and that perception, experience, concentration and follow-through are a complex discipline that takes a lot of intelligence, effort and dedication to acquire.

What seems to be going on in this segment of today's college population is a growing, mature, artistic evaluation that is being turned into finished work. This takes, as it always takes, a special kind of guts: the artist's guts. And the writers in this book accept that fact and make the most of it.

We are proud to present them in STORY: THE YEARBOOK OF DISCOVERY 1968, a showcase of the young creative spirit, one we hope will serve each year to encourage, reward and publish the best writers we can discover in this college age.

And this is, of course, a College Age—of mixed and mixing ages, involving not just the graduates of secondary schools, but student-veterans, and oldsters back for graduate or refresher courses. But in the main, the writers here *are* the young—and since the short story and the poem are preeminently the domain of the young, the writers most fully represented are the story tellers and the poets.

But there are plays here, too, and biographical fragments of self-encounters in strange lands among strange people (Peace Corps Worker Theresa Stephen's "Vision Through a Veil," set in Pakistan, for example). And there are essays and articles on themes of current concern: On how it feels to find yourself back from Vietnam (Charles Coe, U.C.L.A.); on Black Power, by Stanford's Barbara Jean Savery; on the use of LSD on an Ohio college campus, surveyed in depth by David L. Bieber[1] and the *Daily Kent Stater;* and a personal "trip," related in all its kaleidoscopic detail by Barry Herem[2] of Seattle, who is also the winner of our top award in poetry.

We hear a lot these days of our being at the cultural mercy of the movies, radio and TV; that we are in a mind-bath of evanescent, visual-aural influences; and that the studied, Gutenberg reading line is passing from the scene. From the variety of expressions of experience and the individuation of language and style, it could be argued that these writers are less affected by mass electronic media than Marshall McLuhan, of Toronto and Fordham University, might imagine. Writing and reading are still going on, especially in the colleges, and it looks as if such activities will continue.

With so many categories of material, STORY this year is happy to present a wider exploration of college literary capacities than in any of its bookform predecessors. And hereafter, as an annual, sponsored by Scholastic Magazines, Inc., it will be open to practically all the creative categories flourishing in the realms of higher education.

The first STORY college collection, *(The Best College Writing,* Random House, 1961), for range, variety and regional exuberance, was, as one judge put it, "Like a bus ride across America." The next *(Prize College Stories,* Random House, 1963), revealed an internal seething which made it seem that college writers were determined to do all, tell all, and shock the nation. In the mid-Sixties, with *The Stone Soldier* (Fleet, 1964), writers were turning to a deliberate and mature preoccupation with the social side of man, and the rights and dignities inherent in him, however frustrated or in danger of violation. STORY's fourth annual combing of the colleges showed similar concern: The academic walls, which confined so much passion in an earlier year, were perforate by then with chinks which let the light and air both in and out.

(1), (2). Curiously, both these works were entered in the category of journalism, in which John Luter, Co-ordinator of the Advanced International Reporting Program at the Columbia Graduate School of Journalism, found much "that would do credit to a professional journalist." These particular entries he commended (1) for initiative, thorough research, organization and writing; and (2) for the straightforwardness and restraint of statement in the account of the author's sensations under the drug.

The ivy walls this year are in no great danger of crumbling, but the writers behind them are seeing far beyond. They are not bus conductors on a simple regional jaunt through the native homeland. They take planes these days to India. They have had experiences in Africa. One went off to nowhere and returned. Another bled in Vietnam. Still another has organized civil rights protests in the South. And withal, they have tried and, we think, succeeded, in seeing their fellow man in many and various relationships, private and social, national and worldwide.

The short story, the first love of STORY, is a form in which almost any significant predicament of the human condition may be expressed, and the significance of the current crop may well lie in the increasing emphasis on the story itself. These writers have a firm appreciation of what a good short story is, and how much it can achieve. Their successes are not accidental, as good individual short stories have sometimes been in the past—leaving the writer unable to repeat his achievement. And this new dimension of capacity may, in part, be due to the increasing excellence in the teaching of writing in the colleges, for it cannot be due to the availability of short fiction in current magazines, many of which have practically abandoned the short story—lamentably so, since the short story is the seed bed for the novelists and the playwrights of the future.

It is no accident that the first prize winner, a Jamaican-born Negro, Mike Thelwell, ran away with the short story award. He had been bucking for it in two previous contests as a student at Howard, when both his entries won an Honor Roll Publication Award (not a top prize), and his stories were printed in two STORY annuals. "The Organizer," in this collection, is experience transmuted into fiction, and that fiction shot with insight; what might have been a *parti pris* tract has been raised into a novelistic appraisal, in all its possible dramatic, human and symbolistic aspects—"transcending as it does" (as Dr. Riley Hughes pointed out) "mere reportage, particularly in the protagonist's struggle against exploitation on behalf of the movement."

The stories need no drum, nor do the poems. Each story teller had a story to tell and told it. Each poet had something to sing about and sang—and curiously and perhaps surprisingly to some, there seems to be a falling away of the sound of Ginsberg, and even Cummings, in their voices. These poets, too, are real singers, not echoes. "It would be wrong," said Clark Mills, of Fairleigh Dickinson University, "to call them 'student poets,' even though they are studying in our universities: they are poets . . . They are technically skilled, and they operate from a plentiful, fluent imagination." Of Eleanor Wait, Marianne Moore, in judging, said: "She is uninhibited, curious, retentive and takes trouble." What better might be said of a worker in the arts!

We leave you to discover how Keith Spencer and Gary Gardner manage to dramatize the changes of twisted love and turn them right side out, and how David B. Jones, from a Kafka sketch, can make a movie out of an ape in a classroom; how San Francisco, which in the days of the Dante-like city laureate George Sterling was known as the "cool gray city of love," is something entirely different to Chris Dickon of Western Reserve . . . You might do well to mark their names and the names of others in this book and see, a few years from now, how these writers turn out.

It was no surprise to STORY editors that careers begun with the first published work in STORY of Carson McCullers, J. D. Salinger, Norman Mailer and many others whose writings came out of the colleges, have since become legendary. Discovering talent is what STORY in the thirty-odd years of its existence has always stood for. There is a lot of activity in these learning, trying, testing years. And whether you are a general reader, a parent, a teacher or a student, we hope STORY, as it appears from year to year, will help provide you with some of the action.

—Whit and Hallie Burnett

For surveyors of literary geography: More manuscripts of all kinds were posted from California, the land of sunshine and celluloid, than from any other state. Not unexpectedly, the two First Award playwrights were both from the University of California at Los Angeles, though not with the same professor of the drama. Another U.C.L.A. student won a First Award in biography; Stanford students won two First Awards (one in the essay and another in motion pictures) and one Second Prize Award in the short story. One First Award in television and a Second in the motion picture were awarded to writers at San Francisco State College.

Students in New York state were the second most numerous contestants after California; Illinois students were third.

FOREWORD The Editors

ONE: THE STORY TELLERS

THE ORGANIZER — Michael Thelwell 15
1st Prize — *University of Massachusetts*

THE BILL COLLECTOR — Louis Logan 38
2d Prize — *Stanford University*

MONSERRATE — Charlotte Walker 53
3d Prize — *Syracuse University*

***Honor Roll Publication Awards

THE CHICKEN — Ernest Brawley 59
San Francisco State College

CHASTAIN ON THE X-AXIS, STEBBINS ON THE Y-AXIS — Michael Brannon 67
University of Alabama

BARREL — John F. Hathaway 75
San Diego State College

THE SLAP — Charlotte Schupan 79
Western Michigan University

MADELAINE — David Walton 85
Bowling Green State University, Ohio

A TIME FOR REASON — Derek Harris 92
San Diego State College

TWO: A GROUP OF YOUNG POETS

ELLIE: AN INVENTORY OF BEING — Eleanor Wait 103
1st and 2d Prizes shared

PLAYGROUND — Eleanor Wait 108
Chatham College, Pittsburgh

WHALES — Barry Herem 109
1st and 2d Prizes shared

AT TWELVE — Barry Herem 109

GATHER ME — Barry Herem 110
University of Washington

FUGUE: TO J. S. BACH — Karen Burke 111
3d Prize

REQUIEM — Karen Burke 113
Skidmore College

***Honor Roll Publication Awards

THERE WAS SOMETHING . . . — Cynthia Henderson 114
Marygrove College, Detroit

IF — Cynthia Henderson 114

POEM FOR CHINA — Olivia Hogue 115
University of Tulsa

TO JIM . . . DEAD IN VIETNAM — Peter Fellowes 120
Johns Hopkins University

IN A SUMMER ROOM — Marsha Brody 120
Louisiana State University

THE COOKING TIPS OF JULIA CHILD — Rene Rickabaugh 116

SOMEWHERE UNDER AN UNKNOWN LENGTH OF LOVE — Rene Rickabaugh 118
Museum Art School, Portland, Oregon

POEM TO E.E. — Patricia Schneidhorst 121

LOVE IN THE WESTERN WORLD, LESSON 12 — Patricia Schneidhorst 121

TUESDAY — Patricia Schneidhorst 122
Ohio Northern University

SCOUTING PARTY — Lawrence Kistler 123
Boston College

AFTER THE DEATH OF MY GRANDUNCLE JOSEPH PATSEY — D. W. McGinnis 124
University of Washington

BALLAD OF A TRIANGLE — Marion Pendleton 126
Community College, Muskegon, Mich.

THIS OLD MAN — Angel Abitua 127
Pan American College, Texas

WHITTLING — Hillel Schwartz 128

THE FRENCH DOORS — Hillel Schwartz 129
Brandeis University

A TIME FOR MOVING — Marjorie Allegro 130
College of Notre Dame, Baltimore

LETTER TO HIS WIFE — Geof Hewitt 131
Johns Hopkins University

LE CADEAU — Marianne Confalone 133
College of Notre Dame, Baltimore

THE GIANT YEARS — Beverly Sopp 133
College of Notre Dame, Baltimore

PREGNANT STREET — Tom Wayman 134

THE CAPES OF HORN — Tom Wayman 134
University of California, Berkeley

HAWKWEED AND ASTER — Mary Slowick 135
Marygrove College, Detroit

CEDAR KEY — Richard Mathews 136
University of Florida

THREE: TWO PLAYWRIGHTS

THE LAST LOST WEEKEND OF MISSIONARY PEALE — Keith Spencer Felton 141
1st Prize shared — *University of California at Los Angeles*

JUST LIKE IN THE MOVIES — Gary Gardner 176
1st Prize shared — *University of California at Los Angeles*

A SCREENWRITER

NEITHER HERE NOR THERE — David B. Jones 241
Stanford University

FOUR: AUTOBIOGRAPHERS, ESSAYISTS, JOURNALISTS

FIRST COMBAT — Charles Coe 277
1st Prize, Autobiography — *University of California at Los Angeles*

LSD ON THE CAMPUS — David L. Bieber 282
1st Prize, Journalism — *Kent State University, Ohio*

PILGRIMAGE TO MECCA — Barbara Jean Savery 290
1st Prize, Essay — *Stanford University*

A ONE-TIME TRIP — Barry Herem 306
2d Prize, Journalism — *University of Washington*

VISION THROUGH A VEIL — Theresa Stephens 315
2d Prize, Autobiography — *University of Arizona*

SAN FRANCISCO: SUNDIAL BY THE SEA — Chris Dickon 327
2d Prize, Essay — *Western Reserve University*

APPENDIX

THE AUTHORS AND THEIR COMMENTS 337

THE STORY COLLEGE CREATIVE AWARD WINNERS OF 1967-1968 344

AWARD WINNERS AND HONOR ROLL *** ** * 347
*Contest entries evaluated ***most distinguished, **next, *next*

THE JUDGES 351

ONE: THE STORY TELLERS

THE ORGANIZER

Michael Thelwell

The river of that name cuts in half the town of Bogue Chitto, Mississippi. All of importance is east of the river—the jail, the drugstore and Western Union, the hotel, the Greyhound station and the Confederate memorial in the tree-shaded park. West of the river one comes to a paper mill, a cemetery, a junk yard, which merges with a garbage dump, and the Negro community.

Perched on a rise overlooking the dump and cemetery on one side and the Negro shacks on the other is the Freedom House. A low, unpainted concrete structure with a huge storefront window, it had been built for use as a roadhouse in expectation of a road that had turned out to be campaign oratory. When the road failed to materialize, the owner left the state feeling, with some justification, that he had been misled, and the building remained unused until the present tenants moved in.

It is reported that when Sheriff John Sydney Hollowell was told of the new arrivals he said, "Wal, they sho' chose a mighty good place—ain't nothin' but trash nohow, an' mighty subjeck to needin' buryin'."

This sally was savored, chuckled over and repeated, rapidly making its rounds out of the jail house, to the bench sitters in the park, the loungers in the general store, to be taken home and repeated over the supper table. Thus by ten o'clock that same night it had filtered up by way of the kitchens to the tenants of the Freedom House.

"That peckerwood is a comical son-of-bitch, ain't he?" Travis Peacock asked, and the thought came to him that perhaps the first thing to be done was to board up the big storefront window. Either he forgot or changed his mind, for when the other members of his project arrived they painted "BOGUE CHITTO COMMUNITY CENTER, FREEDOM NOW" on the glass in huge black letters. Two weeks later, while everyone was at a mass meeting in the Baptist Church, someone demolished the window with three loads of buckshot. Peacock boarded it up.

Time passed.

Peacock lay on his back in the darkness listening to the clock on the town hall strike eleven. He turned on his side, then sat up and unsnapped the straps of his overalls. "Too damn tight, no wonder I can't sleep," he muttered, reached under the cot for the pint bottle that Mama Jean had slipped to him at the café that afternoon, laughing and cautioning him, "Now doan go gittin' yore head all tore up, honey."

He had no intention of getting his head "tore up," but the fiery stump likker was a comfort. He jerked to a sitting position, listening. It was just the creaking, rusty Dr. Pepper sign moaning as the wind came up. He made a note to fix the sign tomorrow: "Damn thing run me crazy soon."

He lit a cigarette and sat in the darkness listening to the squeaking sign and shaking. He had never before spent a night alone in the Freedom House. Maybe I do need that rest up North, he thought. At the last staff meeting when Truman had hinted at it he had gotten mad. "Look, if you don't like the way I'm running the project come out and say so, man." And Truman had muttered something about "owing it to the movement to take care of our health." Maybe he did need that rest.

He thought of going down to Mama Jean's or the Hightowers' and spending the night there. He pulled on his boots to go, then changed his mind. The first rule for an organizer, and maybe the hardest, was never to let the community know that you were afraid. He couldn't go, even though the people had all tried to get him to stay in the community that night. That afternoon when he was in the café Mama Jean had suggested that he stay in her son's room.

"Shoot, now, honey," she beamed, "yo' doan want to be catchin' yo' death o' cold up theah on thet cold concrete by yo'se'f."

Raf Jones had chimed in, "Yeah man, we gon' drink us some stump juice, tell some lies, and play some Georgia Skin tonight." But he had declined. And Old Mrs. Ruffin had met him and repeated her urging to come stay a few nights at her place. But that was above the call of duty. A standing joke on the project was that the two places in Bogue Chitto to avoid were, "Buddy Hollowell's jail, and Ol' Miz Ruffin's kitchen. She a nice ol' lady, but she the worse cook in Mississippi. Man, that ol' lady burn Kool-aid."

As the afternoon progressed and he received two more invitations, he realized that the community was worried. They knew that the other three staff members were in Atlanta for a meeting and they didn't want him spending a night alone in the office.

By his watch it was nearly midnight. He took a drink and lit another cigarette. Maybe they'd skip tonight. He was tempted to take the phone off the hook. "Hell no," he muttered. "I ain't going give them that satisfaction." But what did it mean if the phone didn't ring? At least when they on the phone you know they ain't sneaking around outside with a can of kerosene.

He got off the cot and went into the front room, the "office." It was the big public part of the building with a couple of desks, a table, chairs, mimeo machine and a few old typewriters, and in one section a blackboard where small meetings and literacy classes were held. He sat at a desk with the phone, staring at the boarded-up window.

"Ring, you son-ovva-bitch, ring. You kept me up, now ring." He calmed himself down by reading the posters. A black fist holding a broken chain. "Freedom." Goddamn you, ring. Another poster, "Pearl River County Voters' League: One Man One Vote." Would it be a man or a woman this time? It was five after midnight. They were late. That was unusual.

Maybe they wouldn't call tonight. They always seemed to know what was happening. Maybe they thought that everyone was gone to Atlanta. Suppose they thought that and came to wreck the office? Peacock was still, listening. He was certain that he heard the sounds of movement outside. He went into the storeroom, tripped over a box of old clothes and swore. He came back with the shotgun just as the phone rang, piercingly loud. He dropped the gun and jumped for the phone.

"Pearl River County Voters' League, can we help you?" His voice is steady and that gives him some satisfaction.

There is a low laugh coming over the receiver. "Heh, heh, heh."

"Hello, you are late tonight," Travis says.

"Nigger," the voice asks, "you alone up theah, ain'tchu?"

It's a man's voice. Good. The women are hysterical and foul-mouthed.

"You alone up theah?" The voice persists. Travis' nervousness has become anger. He starts to say, "No Charlie, I ain't alone, yo' Momma's here with me." But restrains himself.

"I'm not alone, there are three of us here." He says and laughs, yeah me, Jesus and mah shotgun.

"Ah know you alone. Thet pointy-head nigger an' the Jew-boy gone to Atlanta. Heh, heh."

"If you think so, come up and find out." Peacock invited in an even voice. "Why don't you do that?" There was a pause.

"We comin' direckly, boy, an' you can sell the shithouse, cause hit's going to be yore ass." Peacock doesn't answer. He stands holding the phone listening to the hoarse breathing from the other end. "Heh, heh. Nigger, yo' subjeck to bein' blowed up." Click. The phone goes dead and Peacock, shaking violently, stands listening to his own breathing.

Somehow that final click is the most terrifying part. As long as you can feel that there is a human being on the other end, despite the obscenity and the threats, you have some contact. Peacock broke the shotgun and loaded it. The phone rings. Briefly he debates not answering it but he knows he has to. With Ray and Mac on the road, he has to; they could be in trouble. He picks up the phone.

"Hello." That demented chuckling.

"Knowed yo' wasn't sleepin', Nigger. Ain't nevah goin' sleep no mo'."

"If I don't, neither will you, brother."

"Boy, yo' subjeck to bein' blowed up." Click.

Well, hope that's over for the night. But it isn't. They're going to take turns calling. He went to get what was left of the bottle wishing he could remove the phone from the hook. They must rotate the telephone duty, everyone volunteering to give up a night's sleep on a regular basis. Damn.

Peacock began to regret his decision not to go to the meeting. It would have been nice to see everyone again and find how things were on other projects. In Alabama, things looked pretty mean. But so were things here. That was one of the reasons he had stayed. As project director he thought that he should stay with the community in case some crisis broke. Where did his responsibility end?

Sitting there waiting for the phone to ring, he began to leaf idly through the progress report that he had sent to the meeting. He had done a damn good organizing job. The community was together, and had really strong local leadership, whose skill and competence were increasing rapidly.

Morale was high. They had formed a voters' organization and elected Jesse Lee Hightower chairman. He was a good man with real leadership potential for the entire state. And every act of intimidation seemed to increase his determination and that of the community. After the deacon board of the New Hope Baptist Church had been informed that the insurance of the church would not be renewed, they had met and voted to continue to hold meetings there. A week later the church was a total loss. The Sheriff attributed its destruction to a mysterious and very active arsonist called Faulty Wiring who had been wreaking havoc with other Negro churches in the state.

Then Mama Jean's café came under fire. She had been publicly displaying posters and announcements. The merchants in town cut off her credit, and refused to sell her supplies for cash. She had been selling beer and wine for fifteen years with the approval of three sheriffs, although the county was allegedly dry. Now she was charged with the illegal sale of alcohol and a hearing scheduled for the purpose of cancelling her license.

When the news reached Peacock he had been worried. The huge, loud, tough-talking woman was a leader and a symbol in the community—it was Mama Jean and Jesse who had been the first to go across the river to try to register to vote—Mama Jean wearing her floppy, terrible flowered hat, gloves and long black coat in the summer heat. They had been met by the Sheriff and three deputies.

"This office is closed till four o'clock."

"We come to register, Sheriff Hollowell."

"This office is closed."

"Why, thass all right, honey." Mama Jean's gold teeth were flashing. "Usses done waited a hunnerd yeahs, be plumb easy to wait till fo' o'clock." And she swept into the hall, marched to the only chair available and composed herself to wait. Hollowell and his deputies, obviously not prepared for that, had remained muttering veiled threats and caressing their guns. All knew the office would not open that afternoon.

Without her and the Hightowers, Peacock could never have gotten started in the community. If she broke, the community would crumble overnight. So he had been very worried when he ran to her café that afternoon. He was somewhat surprised to find her behind the bar laughing and joking.

"Mama Jean, what are you going to do?"

"Whut ah'm gon' do? Do 'bout whut, honey?" She was looking at him as though surprised at the question.

"Didn't they cut your credit? I heard . . ."

"Oh shush now, take mo'n thet li'l bitty ol' sto'keeper to stop Mama Jean. Jes' doan yo' fret yo'se'f none, heah. Ah be keepin' on keepin' on like ah always done." And she had. No more was heard about the illegal sale of liquor, and twice a week she got into Jesse Lee's pickup truck and drove into Louisiana to buy supplies. She claimed it was much cheaper.

Then the town council tripled the tax assessment on her café. Peacock got her a lawyer, and she was challenging the assessment, even threatening to file a damage suit.

"Damn," Peacock muttered, "if that lady was thirty years younger I swear I'd ask her to marry me." Thinking of Mama Jean cheered him. Some of the people in that poverty-stricken, hard-pressed community were so great, like the Hightowers and the Joneses, he felt warm with pride and love; it was as if he had returned to a home he had never known, but always missed.

He had lived with the Hightowers at first, while he met the people and learned the community. He felt closer to them than to his natural family who now seemed to him shadowy figures leading barren and futile lives in their Northern suburb.

He thought of Miss Vickie, Jesse's wife, a small fragile appearing woman always hovering around her burly husband, expressing her support by small, thoughtful acts. And the two kids, Richie and Fannie Lou who was extremely bright and curious beneath her shyness. Peacock loaned her books and had long talks with her, constantly being surprised at the range and breadth of her curiosity. The Negro school only went to the ninth grade, and she had long surpassed her teachers. She had finally quit, and was now a full-time volunteer, doing the typing and running the office.

His favorite was eight-year-old Richie, like his father a leader and a born organizer. He had created an organization to blanket the community with leaflets. Then he had badgered and begged until Miss Vickie bought him a denim jacket and overalls "like Travis'." A hell of an organizer he will be when he grows up, Peacock reflected.

Peacock noticed that his bottle was almost empty. He could feel the effects of the liquor, particularly potent after his recent tension.

"Hell, no wonder, you sittin' here getting so sentimental. A sixteen-year-old girl has a crush on you, her kid brother thinks you are Jesus, and your leader complex runs away again." But he felt easier now and tired. He went into the back room and stretched out on the cot, feeling his limbs relax as he gave in to exhaustion. But his mind wouldn't turn off.

He was in that half-way zone between sleep and wakefulness in which thoughts disguise themselves as dreams, when he heard the sound. That is, he sensed it, a kind of silent, dull reverberation, that reached his mind before the sound came to him—the heavy, somehow ponderous boom of dynamite. Silence, then a yapping, howling chorus as every dog in town began to bark.

Peacock froze on the cot. *Oh God. Oh God. Let it be a church, not anyone's house.*

He wanted to pull on his boots but was paralyzed. His stomach felt empty and weak. He retched and puked up all the hot acid liquor. His fear returned and he began to shake violently. Somebody's dead. They killed someone. Mama Jean. I don't want to know. I can't go. He sat there smelling his vomit, until he heard the pounding on the door. "Travis, ho, Travis!"

He stumbled into the front room, going for the door. Then he returned for the shotgun. His voice came as a hoarse whisper and it took two efforts to make himself audible. "Who is it?"

"Us, Raf Jones and Sweezy. We alone."

Peacock knew the men. They had both been fired from the paper mill after attempting to register. When there was money in the project he gave them subsistence, other times they helped Mama Jean in the café in return for meals. He opened the door. Jones and Sweezy were carrying rifles. They didn't know what had happened, either, having been outside the Freedom House when they heard the noise.

In a few moments they were running down the hill, past the edge of the cemetery towards the town and the café. Peacock was sure that the nightriders had tried for the café, but when, panting and gasping, they reached there, they found it intact. So was the little church that was now being used for meetings. Where was the explosion? A car turned into the road, going fast and raising a cloud of dust. The headlights picked them out, and they dived into the ditch. The car roared past.

"Hit's the Sher'f," Raf said. "Trouble taken place fo' sho'." They set out running in the car's dust. It passed two side roads, then turned. Peacock had no doubt where it was headed now.

"Good God Almighty." He half moaned, half shouted and stopped. The two men ran on without him, then stopped and turned.

"Yo' awright?"

Peacock nodded and waved them on. His eyes and nose were filled with dust. His chest heaved. He coughed. Whatever had happened wouldn't change before he got there. He even had a momentary urge to turn back, to run somewhere and hide, certain that something terrible and irrevocable had happened. He stood bent double in the road, clutching his sides, coughing, eyes streaming water, no longer gut-scared but filled with dread. He couldn't go on.

Wait, maybe no one had been hurt. A house can be rebuilt. He personally would go North to raise the money. He would gouge it out cent by cent from his family and their affluent and secure neighbors. If it was only the house! Then he was running again. He could smell burnt powder now. It seemed like the entire town was crowded in the road before him. He recognized faces, people, everyone was talking.

"Wha' happen? Wha' happen?"

"Whole family daid?"

"Two white fellers in a car."

Pushing his way through the crowd, Peacock realized that he was still carrying the shotgun. He didn't know what to do with it. The people would be looking to him, and if he had a gun. . . . Besides it'd be in every lousy newspaper in the country that the local representative of the organization had arrived on the scene carrying a weapon.

He pushed his way to the front of the crowd, no one called his name. Was it his imagination or were they stepping away from him? Oh God, were they blaming him?

The Sheriff's car was right in front of the house, its searchlight beaming into the living room. The front of the house was a shambles, porch completely gone, the front wall torn away. A pair of deputies stood facing the crowd carrying tear-gas guns, cumbersome, futuristic looking weapons that seemed to belong in a Flash Gordon kit. "Y'awl keep on back now. Sheriff's orduhs."

Clutching the shotgun, Peacock darted out of the crowd toward the house. One deputy turned to face him.

"Wheah yew going?"

"I'm kin," Peacock said without stopping. The deputy turned

back to the crowd which had surged forward.

Peacock ran around the house and came up to the back door. The smell of burnt powder lingered strong. At the kitchen door he stopped, looking in; the kitchen was filled with people. Mama Jean turned to the door and saw him.

"Oh Travis, Travis, honey. They done hit. They done kilt Jesse." The people gave a low moan of assent. It seemed to Travis that they were looking at him accusingly, the stranger who had brought death among them. Then Mama Jean was holding him. He clung to her without shame, comforting himself in her large, warm strength. He was sure now that there was hostility in the room. The people gathered there had kept aloof from the Voters' League, explaining that they had to avoid commitment so that they could keep their position flexible and talk with the white community. He recognized the school principal, the minister from the big Baptist church, and the undertaker. No one spoke. Then Mama Jean was leading him into the bedroom. "The fam'ly bin askin' fo' yo', Travis."

Their heads all turned to Peacock as they entered. Fanny Lou was holding Richie, their eyes big, black solemn pools in their young faces. Miss Vickie huddled on the bed, leaning forward, her back sharply curved, hunch-shouldered, clutching her clasped hands between her knees. Her face seemed set, polished from smooth black stone. When she turned her head to the door her eyes showed nothing.

"See, he come. He all right, nothing happen to him." Mama Jean's tone was soothing, meant to reassure them. But for one second Peacock heard only a reproach for his own safety and survival. *You must say something. You have to tell these folks something.*

From the next room he heard a low wailing hum. They were half humming, half singing one of those slow, dirge-like songs that was their response in times when no other response was possible. *"Shiine on Mee, Oh, shiiine on Meee . . ."*

Peacock crossed to Miss Vickie. His limbs felt heavy, as though he were moving through some heavy liquid medium, but his footsteps sounded loud. He bent and took her hands. They were limp at first, then they imprisoned his in a quick fierce grip. He was looking into her eyes for some sign of warmth, life, recognition, but most of all for some sign of absolution, forgiveness.

Jumbled phrases crowded through his mind. Trite, traditional words, phrases that were supposed to bear comfort, to move, to stir, to strengthen, and ultimately to justify and make right. But the will of which God? Whose God, that this man, this husband . . . *I am not to blame. I didn't do it.* Silently Peacock looked at her. She returned his look blankly. Then she pitched forward and her head rested on his arms.

"We will do everything . . . we must keep on . . . brave and good man . . . do what he would want us to do . . . death not in vain."

Which voice was that spewing out tired political phrases we hear too often. It couldn't have been me, please it was someone else. What hard hands she has. "Miss Vickie, I'm sorry," Peacock said, "I'm sorry."

"Hush chile. T'aint yore fault." Mama Jean's deep voice cracked. "T'aint none of us heah fault, cept we shoulda moved long time ago. Hit's a long time they been killin' us, little by little . . ."

"Ahmen," Miss Vickie said. Richie started to cry. Peacock picked him up, surprised at how light he was. The boy threw his skinny arms around Peacock's neck and buried his wet cheeks in his neck. Hugging him tightly, Travis felt his own tears starting for the first time.

"Who is comforting who?" he asked himself.

There was a soft knock on the door, and the elderly unctuous minister clad in his black suit glided in from the kitchen.

"Miz Hightower, hit's the Sher'f come to talk to you." Miss Vickie sat up, a mixture of emotions crossing her face.

"Thet 'Buddy' Hollowell have no shame. Effen he did . . ." Mama Jean began as Sheriff Hollowell strode into the room, accompanied by a man in a business suit. "Seems like some folks doan even knock fo' they come bustin' into folks' houses," Mama Jean snorted.

The Sheriff stood in the center of the room. He ran his glance over the group, fingering his jowl. He was a big, solid man, heavy-boned, thick-waisted and with enormous red hands. He was wearing his khaki uniform and a planter's Stetson. He stared at the floor just in front of Miss Vickie, and his jaw moved slowly and steadily.

"Ah just come to git a statement from the widow." His voice must have sounded subdued and apologetic in his own ears for he paused briefly and continued in a louder voice. "So theah ain't no need fer anyone else to be saying nothin'." Mama Jean snorted. Then there was dead silence in the room. Rev. Battel who had been standing in the doorway made a sidling self-effacing motion and was frozen by a glare from Mama Jean.

"Well, which a yew is the widow?" the Sheriff asked.

"Ah'm Mrs. Hightower," Miss Vickie said and pulled herself up erect. She looked at the official with an expression of quiet, intense contempt that seemed to be almost physical, coming from a depth of outrage and grief beyond her will. Peacock would swear that Miss Vickie had no knowledge of what was in her eyes. His own spirit shrank within him.

"Sheriff Hollowell," he said softly, "there's been a death in this house."

The second man flushed and removed his hat. The Sheriff gave no sign of having seen or heard anything. "Yew have another room where ah can git yore statement?" He could have been addressing anyone in the room.

"We used to." Miss Vickie said. "Anythang need to be said kin be said right here. These my husband's family and friends."

Hollowell produced a notebook and flipped his Stetson back on his head. The second man was also holding a pad. "Wal, whut happened?" Again there was a pause.

" 'What happened? What happened,' Jesus God Almighty." The words flashed through Peacock's mind, and he only realized that he had spoken when Hollowell said "Ah'm not gon' tell yew to shut up again, boy."

Miss Vickie's voice was calm and low, without inflection or emphasis. "Ah wuz sleepin' an' then ah woke up. Heard like a car drive up in the road going slow like. Hit drive past three times like they was lookin' fo' something. Ah see that Jesse Lee wun't in the bed. Ah listen fo' a spell an' didn' heah nothin' so I call out an' he answer from the front.

" 'Hit's allright, go to sleep.' But ah knew hit wuz somethin' wrong and ah started to get up . . . Then, then like the room light up an' ah feel this hot win' an' the noise an' hit was nothin' but smoke and ah heah mah daughter scream . . ." Her voice broke off and she began to sob softly. The two children began to sob too. Mama Jean turned and stared at the wall.

"Is this necessary, Sheriff?" Peacock asked.

"Boy, yew not from round heah are yew?"

"You know who I am," Peacock said. Miss Vickie began to speak.

"An' thass all. Evrah thang wuz like yo' see hit now, only the children wuz cryin' and Jesse Lee was lyin' on the floor in the front room. Ah nevah seen no car."

"Jes' one thang more, Miz Hightower." Hollowell's voice was almost gentle. "Yew know any reason fo' anyone to dew a thang lak' this?"

Peacock stared at the Sheriff incredulously.

"Same reason he got arrest three time for drunk drivin' when evrah-body know he nevah did drink," Mama Jean said.

"Ah doan know why some folks do whut they do," Miss Vickie said.

"Wal, ah'l sho let yew know soon as ah find out anything." Hollowell snapped his book. "Mighty sorry myself. Only one thang more, this gentleman heah, be wanting to ask yew a few questions." His companion seemed uncomfortable, his Adam's apple bobbing jerkily in his thin neck. His cheek twitched and he passed a hand quickly over his thinning hair. "I think I've got all I need," he began. Hollowell looked at him. "Well maybe just one thing. I'm from the Associated Press in New Orleans, happened to be passing through." He darted a quick look at the Sheriff, and spoke more rapidly. "I want you to know how sorry I am. This is a terrible, terrible thing. I want you to know that you have the sympathy of every decent person in the state, Mrs. Hightower. I hope . . . I'm sure that whoever did this will be found and punished. I was wondering if there is anything that you would like to say, any kind of personal statement . . ."

"Why can't you leave the family in peace?" Peacock was on his feet. "What more statement do you want, isn't what happened statement enough? For God's sake, what more do you want?" But Peacock's anger was not at the timid little man, but at what he knew was to come for the family—an ordeal that would be as painful as the night before them and in its own way more obscene than the brute fact of death. He was lashing out at that future and the role that he could neither escape nor resolve.

"Now ah've warned yew." The Sheriff was advancing toward him.

"Mist'r Hollowell, come quick before something happen." A deputy was standing in the door. "Hit's the niggers, yew bettah come." The deputy disappeared, followed by Hollowell and the reporter.

"Preacher," the Sheriff called over his shoulder, "mabe yew better come on." The old man followed silently, and then Peacock heard the crowd. Waves of boos and shouts came in spurts, and in between shouted angry words:

"Thet sho' doan sound good. Them folks is mad. Them peoples is afixin' to turn this town out an' ah swears thet in mah heart ah doan blame 'em."

"Ain't that the truth," Peacock said, "but I'd blame myself. You know the Safety Patrol is coming, and maybe even the Army. Them peckerwoods will shoot us down like dogs. And we gotta do something. The only people can stop them is right here in this room." He looked at Miss Vickie. She rocked back and forth and wouldn't look at him. He thought for a while that she hadn't heard. Then she spoke very softly.

"Travis, ah jes' doan know no mo'. Seems like either they gits kilt tonight or one by one nex' week. Maybe this is what hit had to come to. Ah jes' ain't straight in mah own min'."

Peacock sat down silently on the bed, his head bowed. He understood how she felt. He too longed for the swift liberating relief of wild, mindless, purging violence, ending maybe in death. But survival, what of that? Suppose he was one of the survivors. It was a nightmare that had hovered in the back of his consciousness ever since he had joined the movement—yet he saw himself limping away from the burning town, away from the dead and maimed, people to whom he had come to singing songs of freedom and rewarded with death and ashes. The organizer is always responsible. That was the second rule.

"Miss Vickie. You know how much I loved Jesse, more than my natural father. I ain't got to tell you how I feel, but you know Jesse would feel this way too. If you won't come with me to speak to the folks, lemme give them a word from you." Miss Vickie did not answer immediately. There was a new frenzy of shouting outside, louder, more hysterical than before. Peacock couldn't wait for an answer, and Mama Jean followed him as he ran out into the shouting. . . .

"Look at them peckerwoods. Look at them. See who them guns pointing at. We din' kill nobody. We din' bomb no house. Hit wuzn't us, but who the guns pointing at? Why ain't they go find the killers? Why? 'Cause they knows who they is, they brothahs an' they cousins, thass who!"

Peacock recognized Raf Jones. Himself and Sweezy and some of the younger men were grouped in front of the police car. They were armed. "Look at thet Raf, fixin' to get hisse'f kilt too." Mama Jean muttered. "Yo' right Travis, now whut is we gon' do?" They walked over to the car. Hollowell began to talk through a bull horn, his flat, nasal voice magnified and echoing through the night.

"Awright, awright. This is Sher'f Hollowell. That's enough, ah want yew to cleah these streets." Angry shouts from the crowd. "Yew good collud folks of this town know me."

"Yo' damn right we does." Raf shouted back.

"Yew know me, and ah know most of yew. Ah know yew're good, decent folk that don't want no trouble. An' this town din' have no trouble till them agitators pull in heah to disrup' and destroy whut we had. Now a man was kilt heah tonight. Ah wanna ask yew, yew all sensible folk, ah wanna ask yew. Was theah any trouble fore these trouble-makers started hangin' round heah?"

"Allus bin trouble," Raf screamed. "Allus bin killin's." The crowd roared agreement.

"An' ah want to tell yew, ah have mah own feelin's bout who done this terrible thang heah tonight. Ah tell yew, yew got evrah right to be mad. Why, hit could'a jes' as easy bin a white man got blowed up. Yew're decent folk, ah know thet. Ah know hit wasn't none o' yew did this thang. We got a good town heah. But ah want to ask yew this. Dew yew *know* anythang 'bout these outsiders yew bin harboring? What dew yew know bout them? Tell me, dew yew thank thet these race mixahs an' agitators mean this town any good? Wheah dew they come from? Right now ah only see one ov 'em. Where's the othah two raht now? Ah want yew to go home an' thank 'bout thet. Yew will git the true answers, you cain't plant corn an' hit come up cotton. Y'awl go on home now an' thank 'bout whut ah said."

The crowd was silent, shuffling sullenly. No one left. "Ah want yew to go now. Ah'm ordering yew to break this up. Stay and yew break the law. Ah've called the Safety Patrol barracks an' troopers is on the way. In ten minutes they be heah. Anyone still heah goes to jail. Yew heah me?" Silence.

"Awright, awright. Ah got someone heah yew all know. He is

one of yew, a fine collud gentleman. He got somethin' to say, then he goin' lead yew in prayer, an' that'll be awl. Step up heah, Preacher Battel." Before the old man could move Mama Jean stepped in front of him, one hand on her hip, the other wagging in his face. Peacock heard her saying, ". . . Swear 'fo' Gawd, effen yo' git up now an' start in to Tommin' fo' thet cracker, ah'm gon' run ye outta town myse'f. Yo' heah me, Charlie Battel, ah'm sick an' tard of bein' sick an' tard of yo' selling the folks out." Battel backed away before her fury. Hollowell came over fingering his gun.

"An' as fo' yo' Bo Hollowell, the onliest true thang yo' say wuz thet we knows yo'. An' ah knows yo' pappy befo' yo'. Yo' wuz none o' yo' any good. No mo' good than a rattlesnake. Whoa now, Bo Hollowell, yo' lay a han' to me an' hit's yo' las' living ack. Me 'n' Travis gon' git the folks to go home, but hit's gon' be our way. We gon' do hit cause we doan want no mo' peoples kilt, an' thass whut you fixing to do. But if hit's mo' dying tonight, t'aint only black folks gon' die."

She turned her back on him and marched over to the car, walking past an immobilized Hollowell as though he were not present. The passionate power of the fat, middle-aged woman was awesome even to Peacock, against whom it was not directed. He followed her automatically.

"Gi'mme a han' up," she demanded. She balanced herself on the fender of the car, holding Travis' shoulder for support. Silently she surveyed the crowd, her broad chest heaving, hair unkempt and standing out on her head. "Lookaheah. Hit's me, Mama Jean, an' ah ain't got much to say. But yo' all hear that rattlesnake talking 'bout outside agitators. Yo' all knowed he wuz talking 'bout Travis. Wal, maybe he is a agitator. But yo' seen the agitator in yo' white folks' washing machine. Yo' know what hit do, hit git the dirt out. Thass right, an' thass what Travis gon' do now. Listen to him, he got a message from Miss Vickie. An' he gon' git out all the dirt thet Hollowell bin asayin'." She jumped down. "Go on, son, talk some sense to the folks. Ah'm jes' too mean mad mese'f, but yo' kin tell them lak hit is."

Hollowell stepped up. "Don't look like ah got much choice." He drew his pistol from its holster. "So yew say yore piece, but remember ah'l be raht heah behind yew. Yew git them to go home now. Say one wrong word . . ." He waved his pistol suggestively.

Travis climbed onto the bonnet of the car and waved his arms for silence. The skin of his back crawled, sensitive to the slightest pressure of his shirt and waiting for the first probing touch of Hollowell's bullet. He closed his eyes and waited for the crowd's attention.

"Friends. Friends, you got to be quiet now, cause I ain't got no bull horn like Hollowell, an' I want you to hear every word." That's right, keep your voice low so they have to calm down to hear. "You all can see that house right there, least what the crackers left of it.

There's a lady inside there, a black lady. And her husband's dead. They killed her husband an' she grievin'. You know she grievin'. Seem like thass all we black folk know to do, is grieve. We always grievin', it seem like." Peacock shook his head and bowed his head as though in grief or deep thought. A woman gave a low scream, "Jesus, Jesus," and began to sob, deep, animal, racking sounds that carried into the crowd. Peacock waited, head bowed, until he heard a few more muffled sobs from the crowd.

"Yes, some o' us cryin'. Thass all right, let the good sister cry, she got reason. Will ease huh troubled heart. Lady inside thet bombed-out, burned-out house cryin' too. She cryin' right now but while her soul cry for the dead, her min' is on the livin'. She thinking 'bout you. That's the kind of lady she is. She say to tell you the time for weeping is almost over. Soon be over. She say she cryin' for her man tonight, an' she don't want to cry for her brothers and sisters tomorrow. She say they already kill one, don't give them a chance to kill no more. She say to go home peacefully."

"Why?" Raf shouted, "so they kin git the rest o' us when we lyin' up in the bed? Ah say, GIT ON WIT THE KILLIN'!" There was a roar from the people, but Peacock judged that it came mainly from Raf's little group. Raf, shut up, please. Every time you say something like that, I can just feel that cracker's finger jerking. He had to find something to divert the people. "Miss Vickie, say to go home, it's what Jesse Lee would want." A deep murmur of rejection came back.

"Jesse Lee was a fighter!" Raf yelled. This was greeted with cheers.

"Lookaheah," Travis said, raising his voice and adopting the accent of the folk. "Lookaheah, y'awl heard the Sheriff." I sure hope Hollowell doesn't loose his cool. I got to do this now. A small muscle in his back kept twitching. "Yeah, ah'm talkin' 'bout Bo Hollowell, that ugly ol' lard-ass, big belly, Bo Hollowell." Peacock held his breath. No sound came from behind him. There was scattered laughter in the crowd.

"Yeah," Peacock continued, "look at him. Ain't he the sorriest, pitifullest thang yo' evah saw? Ain't he now? Looka him. See him standing there holdin' thet gun. He scared. Yo' heard him say he called fo' the troopers. Wal, he did. Yo' know he did, cause he scared as hell. Hit's too many angry black folk heah fo' him. He scared. Look at him." Peacock turned and pointed. Hollowell was standing in front of his deputies. His Stetson was pulled down to hide his eyes, but Peacock could see the spreading black stain under his arms, and his heavy jaw grinding as he shook with barely controlled fury. But there were cheers and laughter in the crowd now.

"He scared lak a girl," Peacock shouted and forced himself to laugh. "Why ol' bad-assed Bo Hollowell standin' theah shaking jes' lak a dawg tryin' to shit a peach stone." That cracked the people up, real laughter, vindictive and punitive to the lawman, but full, deep and therapeutic to the crowd.

"Yessuh, lak a dawg tryin' to shit a peachstone," Peacock repeated, and the people hooted. Jesse, I know you understand, Peacock apologized. I got to do this. He waved for silence and got it. His voice was soft now.

"But looka heah, very close now. Sho' he scared. But he scared jes' lak them peckerwoods whut blowed up this house. An' yo' knows whoevah done it ain't even folks. They scared, they sick. Thass right. Whenevah peckerwoods git scared, niggers git kilt. Ahuh, thass lak hit is, whenevah white folks git scared, black folks git kilt. Yo watch 'at ol' big belly Bo. He scared right enough to kill me right heah." Peacock was sweating in the night breeze. I have to do it just right, one word too much and he' goin' break, he warned himself.

"See," he said, "an' when them othah crackers git heah, they goin' be scared too. They gon' start whuppin' heads an shootin' folks lak we wuz rabbits."

"Thass right."

"He right."

"Tell the truth."

"See. An' they's a lot of women an' chillun, beautiful black chillun out heah. What's gon' happen to them? Now yo' men got yo' guns. An' thass good. If Jesse Lee hada had his'n he might be alive this minute. So we gotta be ready. But whoevah stay heah now, bettah be ready to die. Thass right, *be ready to die.*"

"We dyin' right now," Raf shouted.

"That wuz true. An' hit still is. But not no mo'. Hit's a new day comin'. Hit's gotta come. A new day. Thass whut scared them peckerwoods, why they kill Jesse Lee. 'Cause Jesse was a free man. He didn't take no mess. Y'awl know that? An' he was tryin' to git y'awl to come with him. That's what scare them folks. He was a free man. His min' was free. He was not afraid."

"Tell it."

"Right. Thass right."

"Yes, brothahs an' sistuhs, thass whut scare 'em. Black folks wuz fixin' to be free. Ahuh. See, an' ol' Bo knew thet. Them peckerwoods is mighty tricky. Yo' gotta study 'em, they *awful* tricky."

"Yes Jesus, they sho' is."

"So now, lookaheah very careful now. Inside that house is this black lady, an' she mournin' fo' her husband. An' she say, Go home. She say, Go home, cause she love yo', an' she cain't stan' no mo' grievin'. Then out heah, yo' got Bo Hollowell an' his gun. He say, Go home, too. Now why would he say that? 'Cause he scared? Thass part of hit. But mostly, yo' know why he say thet, 'cause he know we sick an' tard. He know we sick an' tard o' bein' whupped." Peacock was now chanting in the sing-song cadence of the ecstatic sermon with the full participation of the people.

"Sick an tard o' being starved."

"Oh yes, oh yes."

"Sick an' tard o' being worked to death."

"Oh yes, yes Jesus."

"Sick an' tard o' bein' cheated."

"Jesus Gawd, yes."

"Sick an' tard o' bein' kilt."

"Yeah, mah brothahs an' sistuhs, that cracker know we sick an' tard, thet we sick an' tard o' *bein' sick an' tard.*"

"Tell it, tell it."

"Yeah, that cracker sure do know thet so long as we live, *we gon' be free*. He know that if he say go home, yo' gon' stay. An' yo' know somethin', even though he scared, he mad too. An' cause he scared he want yo' to go home. An' cause he mad, he kinda hope yo' gon' stay. An' yo' know why? Yo' know why that cracker, yeah look at him, yo' know why he want yo' to stay? SO HE CAN KILL SOME MO' BLACK FOLKS. Thass right. Evrahone heah know he bin sayin' he gon' come down heah an' clean the niggers out. Yo' know he say thet evrah time he git drunk."

"Thass right."

"The gospel truth."

"Yo' right, man."

Peacock waved his hands for silence. He spoke softly and clearly now as though he were revealing a great secret. He tried to inject into his voice certitude and calm authority. Yet he was tired and the slowness of his speech was not entirely for effect. His dripping body was lethargic, relaxed, and a peacefulness crept over him. For the first time he did not care about Hollowell's gun at his back.

"So whut we gon' do, mah brothers? We are going to go home like Miss Vickie say do. We going to trick ol' Bo Hollowell this time. No more black folk going to die tonight. We men with the guns going to get the women and kids home. We going to get them there safe. And then we going to stay there. When those troopers come, there ain't going to be no folks standing around for them to beat on, all right? And we are going to stay home so that if any more bomb-toting crackers come we can defend our children an' our homes, all right?"

The crowd shouted assent.

"But that's only tonight. We aren't going to let Jesse Lee Hightower jes' die like that, are we? No. Uhuh. Tomorrow night we going come back to a meeting. Tomorrow night at eight o'clock, we all going to come to a meeting an' plan and decide just what we going to do."

"Yes, we is!" the crowd roared.

"An' we going to do it all together. Us folks gotta stick together.

And you know where the meeting is going to be tomorrow night? In Rev. Battel's church, that's where. Rev'ren' say he done seen the light, an' out of respect fo' Jesse Lee, he gon' let us have the church."

Peacock listened to the cries of surprise and approval from the people. They all knew that Battel had kept himself and his church apart from the activities of the movement. Glancing behind he could see Mama Jean rocking with mirth at a thoroughly unhappy looking Preacher Battle.

"All right, so we going home now. Raf an' Sweezy, will you get everything all straight so that folks get home safe? But before we do that, one more thing. Rev'ren' Battel will give us a prayer. An' we not going pray for no forgiveness, we going to pray for justice, an' for the soul of our brother."

Battel stepped forward. "Let us bow our haids an' ask the Almighty . . ." he intoned.

"Wait," Peacock shouted. Battel stopped. Bowed heads were raised. Peacock pointed to Hollowell and his deputies. "Folks, I didn't mean to interrupt the prayer. But remember what happened here tonight. A man is dead, murdered. And I know that Sheriff Hollowell and his men don't mean no disrespect. But I believe we should ask them to remove their hats. Even if *they* don't believe in prayer."

The crowd stood stock still for a moment, a low murmur growing and thickening. The officers made no move. Peacock could not see Hollowell's face which was shaded by the brim of the Stetson.

"Jesse Lee Hightower is one black man they had to respeck in life," Mama Jean boomed, "an they bettah respeck him in death too."

Slowly the crowd was closing the distance between itself and the lawmen. It had become very quiet, the only sound that Peacock heard was the soft hum of feet on the dusty road. The people were no longer a diffuse crowd, but had become a single unit.

The click of Hollowell's pistol cocking was sharp and clear. Peacock cursed himself; it had been such a close thing and now he had torn it.

"Take them off, take off the damned hats!" He thought that he had screamed, but apparently there had been no sound. The deputy on the left took a half pace backward. Hollowell's lips moved stiffly. "Hope the bastard's praying," Peacock murmured, but he was sure that Hollowell was only threatening the deputy. But the man's nerve had broken. Peacock saw his hand moving, stealthily, unbearably slowly in the direction of his head. It sneaked up, tremulously, then, faster than a striking rattler, streaking up to snatch the hat from the head. . . . The other deputy looked at Hollowell, then at the crowd. He made his choice. Hollowell was the last. Peacock did not see it happen. But the Sheriff's hat was suddenly cradled against his leg. The crowd let out a great moaning sigh, and Battel resumed the prayer in a quavering voice. Peacock felt an arm on his shoulder. He slumped onto Mama Jean's shoulder putting his arm around her neck and they stood watching the people disperse.

"Yo' done jes' great, Travis, hit was beautiful. But yo' know them crackers jes' ain't gon' take the way yo' done them tonight. Careful how yo' walk. Like ef that Hollowell should stop yo' on the road by yo'se'f . . ." Her voice trailed off.

"I know, Mama Jean." Peacock squeezed her shoulder. "An' I'm gonna be watching him. But ain't nothing he can do for the next few weeks." And that's the truth, Peacock reflected. Come tomorrow this town is going to be so full of newsmen and TV cameras that everyone is going to be careful as hell.

"Yeah, but yo' know he ain't nevah gon' forget. He *cain't.*"

"Surprised to hear you talking like that, Mamma Jean. Way you light into him an' Battel, jes' like a duck on a June bug. Don't you know you gettin' a little old to be doing folks like that?"

"Who ol'?" She growled. "Long as ah keeps mah strength ah ain't nevah gon' be too ol'. Ef they want to stop me, they gon' have to kill me. An' ah ain't sho' but whut the ones thet gits kilt ain't the lucky ones. Whut 'bout those thet lef'?" She looked toward the broken house.

Yes, Peacock thought, what about them? Us? He watched the police car drive slowly down the road behind the last group. What about them? He wondered if the family in the house had heard him. Jesse wasn't four hours dead, and already he had cheapened and manipulated that fact. He had abstracted their grief and his own, used it, waved it in front of the crowd like a matador's cape and this was only the beginning.

Inside the house, Mama Jean took charge, bustling around collecting whatever she felt the family would need next morning. She was taking them to spend the night at her place. They still sat in the bedroom, as though they had not changed position during the time Peacock had been away. Looking at his watch, Peacock discovered that the incident outside had taken less than forty minutes. He looked up to meet Fannie Lou's eyes, big and dark with grief, staring at him. What was she thinking? Of her father? Or of him, the stranger who had come to live with them like the big brother she never had? How did they feel now? Miss Vickie used to call him her son, to introduce him to visitors that way. And he had felt closer to this family than to the family he never saw and rarely thought about. But there was nothing he could say. Everything that came to him sounded weak and inadequate, incapable of expressing the burden of his feeling. Unless he could find new words that would come fresh and living from his heart, that had never been said before, he could not say anything.

When Raf and the men came back they left for the café, Peacock walking between the mother and daughter and holding a sleepy Richie. He felt Fannie Lou's light touch on his arm.

"Travis, yo' gon' stay?" Peacock looked at her uncomprehendingly. She bit her lower lip and said quickly, "I mean tonight at Mama Jean's." Her eyes filled with tears.

"I'll be back later, but I have to go to the office first." But he knew she wasn't asking about tonight. They knew that he came from another world, and one that must seem to them far more attractive, to which he could return.

He had not told them his reason for wanting to go back to the office. He had to call the national office with a report of the evening's events and he did not want them to hear him reporting and describing their loss to unknown people.

Before he had begged and pleaded to be put on the organizing staff he had worked on the public relations staff in the national office. He had written hundreds of coldly factual reports of burnings, bombings, and murders. And the "statements," how many of those had he written, carefully worded, expressing rage, but disciplined controlled rage, phrases of grief balanced by grim determination, outrage balanced by dignity, moral indignation balanced by political demands. Every time it was the same, yet behind those phrases, the anger and the sorrow and the fear were real. So we become shapers of horror, artists of grief, giving form and shape and articulation to emotion, the same emotion, doing it so often that finally there is nothing left of that emotion but the form.

He reached the Freedom House and placed the call. Before it was completed Raf called through the door. Peacock let him and his companions in.

"The womens said we wuz to come stay with yo'." Raf explained. "We got some mens watching the café." Peacock watched them file into the office, gaunt men roughly dressed in overalls and Army surplus boots, as he was. One of them, an older man with balding gray hair and a creased face came up to him. Peacock did not know him. The man took his hand in a horny calloused grip.

"Ah knows ah ain't bin to the meetin's. Ah call myse'f keepin' outta trouble. Ah says them Freedom folk, they mean to do good, but they ain't from roun' heah, somethin' happen they be gone an' lef' us'ns in the mess. Ah wuz 'fraid, ah ain't shame to say hit. But ah seen yo' wit the laws tonight an' ah says, let the fur fly wit' the hide. Ef thet young feller kin do, ah kin do too. Ah's heah to do whatevah is to be did." Peacock was like an evangelist suffering from doubt in the face of a convert. He had heard those words before. Each time it had been a new and moving experience to see a man throwing off his burden of fear and hesitance and finding the courage to step forward. But this time the responsibility seemed too much. What was the man expecting? Reassurance, praise? The phone temporarily rescued him.

The connection was a bad one, and it was as though his voice and not another's, echoed hollowly back into his ear. "June 16th, Bogue Chitto, Miss. . . ." Peacock was staring into Richie's shock-glazed eyes. ". . . A Negro civil rights leader was killed in the blast that destroyed his home. His wife and two children were unharmed . . ." Peacock saw Miss Vickie's rigid sleepwalker's face . . . "Resentment is high in the Negro community. A crowd formed in front of the house, but the local representative of the Nonviolent Council persuaded the crowd to disperse peacefully . . ." The voice went on and on. Raf and the other men were watching him as though he had stepped into a new identity that they did not recognize.

"No," Peacock said, "I have no statement."

"But we should have something from the local movement. You are project director."

"Look, if you want a political statement, write it, that's your job. All I can say is I'm sorry." Peacock hung up the phone and sat cradling his head in his arms. He knew the office would call back. Tomorrow the networks would be in town, so would politicians, leaders of various organizations. For a few days the eyes of the country would be focused on the town and everyone would want to be included. He wanted no part of it. The secret fear of every organizer had become reality for him. How do you cope with the death of one of the people you work with?

The phone rang again. Peacock knew before he answered it that it would be Truman. Big, shaggy, imperturbable, bear-like Truman. He was the chairman and was always scrambling to keep the organization afloat, to keep the cars running, the rent paid. Before he had become administrator, he had worked in the field. He would be calling with a program to "respond" to the bombing.

"Hey, Travis, how you doing, you all right?"

"Yeah, Truman, I'm all right."

"Look, in the next couple days you are going to need help. Would you like me to come down?"

That was a normal question, but Peacock suddenly felt a need to lash out. "What do you want to come for, the publicity? To be in all the pictures, to project the organization?"

"I know you are upset, man, but I think you should apologize."

"I'm sorry, man. You know I don't mean that." No, he couldn't afford to mean it because it was too close. God, they were forcing us to be just like them. Then Truman started outlining the program. Peacock listened silently. Then he interrupted. "Stop, Truman, stop. You want to stage a circus. I can't ask the family to subject themselves to that."

"Look, Travis, I know how upset you must be. But we have

to do it. Where is the money to come from to build back the house, to educate the kids? We've gotta launch a national appeal and the family must be there."

"Yes, I'm upset. If I hadna come here . . ."

"He might still have been killed. He was organizing before you came."

"But it was me who told him to go register. I went to that courthouse with him, not you."

"Travis, I know it's tough, but it's what happens in this kind of a struggle. We've got to live with it. You got to keep telling yourself that we don't ask anyone to do anything that we don't do ourselves. You gotta remember that. You or Ray or Mac could have been in that house."

"For God's sake, Truman, don't lobby me. I know the line."

"Listen. . . . You say you want to respect the family's privacy. So do I. But what's your responsibility? The only way to stop these bombings is to make them public. Yeah, we gotta exploit it. Yeah, we gotta have the family crying on national TV. The cat's dead and nothing can undo that, but we have a responsibility to use his death against the people that killed him."

"I don't want to argue politics. That's not the issue," Peacock said.

"Travis, how can you say that? It is already an issue. And we, whether we like it or not, have to take it from there."

Peacock agreed with Truman but he could no longer respond to that category of practical, pragmatic realities.

"Besides," Truman was saying, "even if we wanted to keep everything simple and pure we can't. If you think that the other organizations won't be in town tomorrow morning, then you are crazy. You call it a circus; well, it's going to be one with or without us. Just came over the wires that Williams is calling for a hero's burial in Arlington, a mourning train to Washington, all under the auspices of *his* organization. We can sit aside and refuse to participate or get in there and fight . . ."

"Yeah," Peacock said, "fight for the corpse. Fight for the corpse and raise some money?"

"Yeah, Peacock. That too." Truman was angry now. "You know how many folks been fired that we are carrying on the payroll? When those people off your project got arrested two weeks ago, where did you call to get the thousand dollars bond? You know people only send us money when they feel guilty. And that's the same as saying when someone gets killed. What the hell do you expect us to do?"

"It's true, but it's not right. Man, all I can see now is that little house blown to hell. And that lady just sitting and staring . . . Man, I just don't know."

"Look, I know what you're going through, but if you feel that you can't organize in the situation right now, I understand that. If you want to go someplace for a while . . ."

Peacock saw what was coming. He would go off to "rest" someplace, and someone else would come in. Someone who, without his guilts and hesitations, could milk the situation for the most mileage. He was furious precisely because something in him wanted to leap at the chance. "You really think I would do that? Run away now? Screw you, Truman!"

"It may be wrong. In fact it is . . ." Peacock heard a weary sigh, ". . . but man, I don't see how else we can operate. Get some sleep, man. Tomorrow you will feel different about what has to be done when the vultures swoop down. You decide then how to operate."

"Thank you," Peacock said.

"One last thing, man. Maybe I shouldn't even say this but . . . ask yourself this question. Suppose it was you who had got it, what would you want us to do? What would you expect us to do? Then ask yourself if Jesse Lee Hightower was a lesser man than you. Freedom."

"Freedom," Peacock said and hung up.

Peacock crossed over to the door, opened it and stood looking down on the sleeping town. Later today it would be overrun. Camera crews, reporters, photographers, dignitaries. Across the country guilty and shocked people would be writing to Congressmen. Some would reach for checkbooks. And the checks would go to the first name they read in the papers, the first face they recognized on the screen. Some labor leader would announce a Hightower relief fund and kick it off with a munificent contribution. Others would follow, even unions which somehow managed to have no black members. And the churches would send collections. Some conscience-stricken soul would make the rounds of his suburban community where no black folk lived. The resulting check would somehow reflect that fact. In Washington, Jesse Lee's fate would be officially deplored and an investigation ordered. And in the middle of all this, the meaningful thing would be to try to get enough to keep going for another six months. He was known and trusted by the family and the community. They would be asking his advice on every proposal, at every development. He could stage-manage the entire proceedings for maximum effect, package the pain and the loss to ensure the greatest "exposure."

They were talking about a hero's burial. Well, he had seen the last one. He remembered the fight about which organization had priority, whose leaders would have the right to walk on the right of the bier where the cameras were set up. He remembered the night before the funeral. The "hero" lay in state, his coffin set up in the center of the room draped with a wrinkled American flag smelling of moth balls. At a table by the door an old woman sat selling memberships, buttons and pamphlets to the people who filed in. Outside, proselytes of all kinds sold or gave away their particular version of the truth. The people bought their memberships and filed past that rumpled, dingy flag.

Somehow a man's life should be reflected in the final ceremony at his death. Jesse had been a simple man, and honest. That had been his way in the world and that was how he should go out. Peacock turned and walked back into the room.

"Travis, Travis. Whut happen?" Raf sprang to his feet and was peering at him anxiously.

"I . . . I'm all right, what's the matter?"

"Wal," Raf said, "effen yo' seen yore own face jes' now hit woulda set yo' back, too. Yo' bettah take a taste." Peacock drank deeply, the hot liquor bringing tears to his eyes.

"We wuz jes' figurin'," Raf said, "whut is we gon' do now, Travis? Ah mean the movement heah in Bogue Chitto?"

Peacock sat down and shook his head. He passed his hands over his face, massaging his eyes. He shook his head again. But when he looked up the men were still looking at him questioningly.

"Well," Peacock said, "be a lot happening real quick during the next few days. Here's what I think . . . We got to start with that meeting tomorrow . . ." Peacock talked, the men listened, nodding from time to time. He kept looking at his watch. When morning came he had to go back to be with the family. Funny he hadn't thought of it before, but Miss Vickie had a great face. Be great on a poster or on TV. . . .

THE BILL COLLECTOR

Louis Logan

I worked for a collection agency in Natrona City. It was just a branch office and not as exciting as some of our larger offices where they dealt in international collections and liked to terrorize little countries. It was my first job after college and I planned to go to the top and make a mark. Maybe two marks, because I was so full of ambition then.

There were fifteen of us in the office, counting secretaries. Alden was the manager. Carter was his assistant and the best collector of all. I used to try to study Carter's style. He wasn't big but he always got results. Everyone said Carter was the finest collection man because he had such a hard heart. Even Alden would shake his head and say that Carter had the hardest heart of any collector he had ever known. When Carter returned from collections his pockets bulged with money, merchandise hung from his shoulders like strings of garlic, and blood dripped from his knuckles. The Bad-Accounts around town were scared to death of him. For some reason Carter and I got along fine and he used to assure me that someday I'd make a fine collection man too.

One day Alden and Carter sent me out to collect the Agnes Lonetree Account. "Go get her," they said. "She's two months past due on twelve hundred dollars worth of stuff."

"What kind of stuff?"

"Furniture."

"I can't haul much furniture in the car."

"We'll rent a truck. Tell her that, we'll rent a truck and come get her stuff."

"Okay," I said, preparing to leave.

"B.A.?" called Alden. "Try real hard this time to make a collection. It's four weeks now, and you still haven't made a single collection."

I turned and looked at him. His suit was too small and the desk was too small. He was a huge man who had come up the hard way in the collection business, punching noses and tearing back pockets off to get the wallets. He had repossessed cars and then had to push them back by hand because he had forgotten to get the keys too. Sitting before me, cramped and uncomfortable, was truly a self-made man, a giant, and I stood before him humble.

"I'll try, Alden," I said. "I'll try my best. I really will."

"The furniture, B.A.; the furniture or the money."

I drove over to the address given on the credit statement. But Agnes Lonetree didn't live there anymore. She had skipped. The house was locked and I couldn't kick the door down. So I questioned the neighbors. The man on the left didn't know a thing. The lady on the right stuttered.

"She left f-f-five days ago."

I thanked her.

I couldn't get into the house to look for clues so I went through the garbage can. Tipped it upside down and started from the bottom up. Napkins; Kool-aid wrappers; thirty-eight empty cans; and then I came to the good part. Some letters. They were mostly past-due notices from a hundred different businesses. Agnes was no little fish, I realized. If I could catch her, Alden and Carter would be pleased.

"F-f-find anything?" asked the neighbor lady, across the fence.

"N-n-not yet," I said.

Then I found a letter to Agnes from her mother. It was a partnership offer. Together they could skin the business world. The letter got mushy. The mother said that maybe Agnes thought she was too old for the rigors of that kind of a life. If that was so, Agnes should tell her. Meanwhile, the letter concluded, would Agnes like to leave some of her nice furniture with mother? Mother's chesterfield is worn out, darling.

"F-f-find anything yet?"

The neighbor lady was still standing there. I told myself not to stutter. "Just a letter," I said, "from her mother."

"I re-remember now," she said. "Sh-sh-she was going to live with her mother."

I didn't want to stutter in her face again, so I nodded and left without th-thanking her.

When I got to the car, I read the letter again. The mother's address was on the envelope. Mills. Mills is just outside Natrona City.

Agnes was in. She was tall and as long limbed as an elm tree and as graceful as an antelope. She was Indian; big bosoms and high cheek bones and a complexion as smooth as river stone. Her eyes and her long straight hair were black; and that old saying, familiar to me came back: if her hair was any straighter, it would fall over backwards. She was beautiful. She smiled and asked her question, just as pretty as the prairie in the spring, "What do you want?"

I asked if Mrs. Lonetree was in.

She said her mother wasn't in. Could she help me. She was the daughter.

I followed her into the kitchen and we had coffee and she explained why she couldn't pay at the moment. She had been seriously sick recently, and only now was she feeling well enough to work. Could she have more time?

"Certainly," I said. It was easy to see why her credit was so good and she owed over a hundred businesses. Her request went to the heart. In my mind, I saw businessmen fall at her feet. And at her request for credit, they showered gifts on her like autumn leaves in the wind. I saw no reason why she shouldn't be given more time to pay.

Back at the office, I told a lie.

"Alden," I said. Carter was sitting nearby and he looked up. So I told them both the lie. "She lives with her mother and her mother says she was working, so I should come back some other time."

"Well, B.A.," said Alden, "I guess you're trying. Even if you didn't collect any money today."

Carter didn't say anything, but he gave me a curious look. That night when we went to the Swing Shop for a couple of drinks, he said, "Are you sure Agnes Lonetree wasn't home?"

"That's right," I said. "She was working."

"Seems funny she'd start now. She never worked a day in her life."

I laughed as if to say, fat lot you know.

Carter wasn't convinced. "Are you sure she was working? You're not just saying it because she's beautiful and it makes you want to lie? You can tell me, old buddy, I won't tell on you."

"No, that's not it at all," I said.

"I can't understand her going to work," said Carter. "Leopards just don't change their spots." He scratched his head and changed tactics. "You have to admit she's very beautiful," he said.

"I didn't see her," I said again. "Besides beautiful girls don't b-b-bother me."

After that I went over to Agnes' house every few days and we were becoming good friends. One morning Alden asked me how the follow-up on the Lonetree Account was coming along. I said, fine. I was going by there that day.

I didn't go over right away. Agnes liked to sleep late. So I made some other calls first; over to Mountain View, down on the Sand Bar, up on Nob Hill, and finally about noon I went back down through town and out to Mills. It was early fall and all the leaves were changing color. Leaves change early in the mountain states. Soon the snow would come to Wyoming and the winds would whip it in great drifts like meringue. I also realized if I didn't start collecting bills pretty soon, I'd be out in a snowdrift come winter time.

Agnes sensed something wrong. "What is it, B.A.?"

"Alden is riding me. Wants to know when you're going to pay something on your account?"

She laughed then. Oh, the silver trickle of her laughter. "Don't you know, B.A.? Didn't I tell you my code? I never pay bills."

I shook my head in disbelief.

"That's the way it is, B.A. It's the only code I have; and I can't change it. If you don't like it, we can't be friends."

Can't be friends, I thought. Pull off my fingers first. "No, no," I said, "forget the money."

That pleased her and she came and sat beside me and said, "B.A., there is a good movie Friday night. Would you like to take me?"

I nodded, happily. Of course I wanted to take her to the movie. Of course, of course.

When I returned to the office that afternoon, I was singing. My happiest day. Alden came out of his office with Carter following close behind. Together they were a short parade.

"Hey, Songbird," said Alden. "How did the Lonetree Account go?"

He was speaking of my Agnes. A-g-n-e-s. The letters mingled with the notes on my mind. "Agnes," I said aloud.

"Agnes, no," said Alden, shaking his head. "Lonetree money, yes. How much did you get?"

"Ten dollars," I said and gave him ten dollars. A small price to pay, I thought.

"Ten dollars," he screamed. "Ten dollars," he went up and down like a basketball. "Ten dollars against twelve hundred dollars. Her payments alone are sixty-seven dollars and twenty-three cents a month." Alden rushed from the room and slammed the door. I didn't see him again until the next morning.

"Man," said Carter, "you better start hustling and collecting some money, or you're gonna get run off. The snows are going to come pretty soon and all those pretty leaves on all those pretty trees are going to fall off and you're going to be lonesome standing outside. And no Agnes Lonetree is gonna wade through a snowdrift to come hold your hand either."

I didn't say anything. The joys of the day passed swiftly. I went home and tried to sleep. I would—I swore on my heart and my soul and my head—I would collect a bill the next day.

The next morning as Alden gave me a collection list, he said, "If you come in here tonight with a song in your heart and no money in your pocket, I'm gonna cram you down the elevator shaft."

With those words ringing in my head, I went to collect bills. Down the list I went, knocking on the door of each house, but no one was home. Once I thought I saw a curtain move but no one answered my persistent knocking.

In the afternoon I went to see Mr. Nute on North Grant Street. He was behind on his car payment. His wife said he was in the garage. And that was where he was, squatting on the floor, building a bird house. I squatted too, with my back to the wall, and I could see the open garage doors like the spread wings of freedom over his back.

"Hi," I said.

"What do you want?" he asked, still driving nails.

"I came to see when you could pay something toward that car of yours, Mr. Nute?"

"No money," he said.

"When will you have some?"

"None of your business."

"If you don't pay, we'll have to take your car."

"Ain't nobody gonna take my car," said Mr. Nute, taking a firmer grip on his hammer.

"I might have to," I said.

"Do, and I'll put dents in your head," he said, looking at me for the first time.

"Oh, I don't mean today. I mean sometime I might have to."

"Good," said Mr. Nute. "I thought you meant today," and he went back to building his bird house.

Back at the office I told Alden about my day. There had been no one home all day except Mr. Nute and he was going to put dents in my head if I repossessed his car.

Alden's eyes lighted up. "Oh, I would have liked that," he said. I could tell Alden had been an infighter in the old days.

"I would have thrown sawdust in his eyes and then given him a combination. When he was out, I would have nailed him spread-eagle to the garage floor with his own hammer. That's how you collect bills, boy. Fight fire with fire."

I said, I guessed so.

"You don't like collecting bills, do you?" he asked suddenly.

"No," I said. "I feel sorry for the people and listen to their stories."

"Those stories are all lies."

"Some of them probably are," I agreed. "Maybe I'm just not cut out to be a bill collector."

I expected him to agree with me and say my check would be ready the following morning. But he didn't, he did a surprising thing.

"B.A., I'm going to give you another chance. I'm going to make you a skip-tracer and you won't have to come in contact with the people anymore. You just figure out where the skips went and furnish us with the addresses. We'll do the rest." He nudged Carter and they grinned like hatchet men.

"I'll break their bones," said Carter.

"I'll hang them up and cut their throats," said Alden.

"Yeah. Yeah. Yeah." They sang and danced around the room.

"I wish I had been there when Mr. Nute pulled that hammer," said Carter. "I'd've shoved it up his ass."

"I did that once," said Alden. "Guy pulled a knife and I took it and shoved it up his ass."

"What happened?" I asked.

"Doctor who tried to get it out, lost three fingers."

Alden went into his office and returned with the Official Skip-Tracers Manual. It had seven hundred and twelve pages and contained over nine thousand terrible, underhanded, devious tricks of tracing down and capturing dirty, rotten, low-down skippers.

"Guard this book with your life," said Alden. "Don't let its contents be known to anyone or we'll all go to jail."

I called Agnes and told her about my promotion. "That's wonderful," she said. "You weren't a very good bill collector anyway."

"I know it," I said.

"Who'll take your place?"

"A fellow in the office."

"I hope he's as nice as you."

"I don't think he is," I said, a little bit jealous. "I should warn you. He's a good bill collector and apt to be brutal."

"Who is he?"

"Carter."

"Oh," she said, and it sounded far away.

"Do you know him?" I asked.

"Yes," she said. "I know him and he is just as terrible as his reputation."

I was concerned for Agnes at that moment. I had seen Carter return from where others had failed and his pockets bulged with the collected money. I began to wonder how Agnes, the best of the bad credit artists, would fare against terrible Carter, the best of the bill collectors. A main bout no doubt, and scheduled for the very next morning.

"What are you going to do?" I asked.

"Skip," she said.

I told her I would have to skip-trace her. But I would always give her fair warning before the collectors closed in.

She thanked me, and we said good-bye.

When I got to the office the next morning, Carter was sitting on my desk.

"Thanks a hell of a lot," he said sarcastically.

"What's the matter?"

"I went to Agnes Lonetree's house this morning. She skipped last night."

"That's too bad," I said.

"That's what I thought you'd say."

Carter had been friendly before that incident but now he turned cool. I hardly noticed for I threw myself into my work, and page by page I memorized the skip-tracing manual.

"Hi there," I'd say on the telephone. "Are you Bill's sister?" knowing full well it was his mother.

"No, I'm his mother. Who is this?"

"B.A., ma'am. I was in the Army with Bill and he loaned me a suitcase. I'll return it if you'll tell me where he lives."

"All right, Mr. B.A. By the way, any friend of Bill's is a friend of the family. Can you come over for dinner?"

"Yes," I'd say. "Now if you'll give me Bill's address."

"Twelve-twelve Smoggy Place, Trenton, New Jersey."

And that was the way I operated. Smooth, and they loved it. I'd pick up the phone again and dial, Trenton, New Jersey.

"Hello, National Collection, Trenton Branch. Got a skip for you. On Smoggy Place."

By the time I had memorized my way to the middle of the book, I was finding eighty per cent of the skips.

Alden was delighted. "You're a natural born skip-tracer," he said. Then he'd tell Carter, "That B.A.'s got a nose for tracking down no-good skippers."

"He sure has," said Carter.

"A real nose like a bird dog."

Alden started calling me that. "How many bad birds you get today, Birddog?"

"Six."

"That's the limit. I don't want to hear of you going over six birds a day." Then he'd sit back in his chair and rub his stomach, savoring the pleasure of an efficient office.

Carter said, "Birddog, you're as good at catching skips as I am at collecting bills. Let's be friends again."

"Fine," I said and we shook hands.

Alden stood up. "I'm going to buy you two dinner," he said. "I never had such a good staff and I want to celebrate."

We went to the Riverside Club that night. It was a mile up stream from town and they had a good floor show. We had drinks and a nice dinner. Then more drinks. Alden said, "That Birddog eats high class. He must be pedigreed."

A few couples were dancing out in front of us and I wished that Agnes and I were among them. It was now two weeks past the night we were supposed to have had our date.

"I haven't been this happy," said Alden, "since I first got married and lived in California."

About a week after that Alden called me into his office. "What kind of leads do you have on the Lonetree Account?"

"Pretty good ones," I said.

"Good, you better spend a little time on that account and let some of the others ride for a while."

I went back to my desk and called Agnes' mother. I thought I might as well practice my skip-tracing so I disguised my voice.

"Hi there," I said. "Is Agnes home?"

"No."

"That's too bad. You must be her mother?"

"That's right. I'm her mother. Who are you?"

"Bill Quicksilver."

"Bill Quicksilver?"

"Yes. A good friend of Agnes. I have some money for her."

"Money? You say money? She could use some monev."

"Well, actually it's a check. A cashier's check and if I could find her, I'd mail it to her."

"I'll give it to her," said the mother.

"I can't do that, Mrs. Lonetree. I have to mail it to her personally."

"Well," she hung on the phone trying to decide whether to give me the address or not. "Well," she said. "Agnes sure could use the money. She is living at 2323 Canyon View Road, South Rim, New Mexico."

"Mrs. Lonetree?" I said.

"Yes?"

"This is B.A. I was just teasing you."

"What did you do that for?"

"I was practicing my skip-tracing."

"I would have given you the address."

"I know that but I need the practice. I'm calling her now. You have anything for me to tell her?"

""Tell her her mother says take care of herself."

After we hung up, I called New Mexico. When Agnes picked up the phone, I said, "You're surrounded. You can't get away this time."

"What?"

"You are Miss Agnes Lonetree, aren't you. The famous bad-credit artist?"

"Yes."

"Hi, this is B.A."

"Oh, B.A." she said. "You're crazy scaring me like that."

"Yeah, I know," I said. "How are you doing down there?"

"I'm tired of this place."

"Good," I said. "I'm supposed to find you today. How long will it take you to get out of there?"

"Half an hour."

"Fine. I'll turn you in after lunch. You should be gone by then."

"Thank you, B.A."

"That's okay."

"I'm sorry we didn't go to the show that night."

"So am I," I said. "But we'll make it sometime."

"Maybe when you get a vacation, we can meet somewhere."

"I'd like that," I said.

That's the way Agnes and I worked it. I would warn her first and then call the collection agency. A few days later the agency would write us and say they were sorry, but Miss Lonetree had skipped just before their collector made contact.

About the third time that happened, Alden was ready to go out of his mind. He marched up and down the floor shaking the letter. "It costs twenty-five bucks each time a collection agency handles one of our accounts. Twenty-five bucks," he said.

"We'll catch her," said Carter firmly.

"I hope so," said Alden.

"The odds are against her," said Carter. "Nobody beats the odds. Sooner or later, we get everybody."

Which was true. But the way Carter said it sent shivers up my back. We did sooner or later get everybody. But that day I would have made a private bet that we would never catch Agnes in a million years.

"Sooner or later we're going to get an honest collector," said Alden. "One who won't let her go. I've got a lot of confidence in Birddog and sooner or later, when he flushes her, the right collector is going to be there."

"If I ever get a hold on her," said Carter, "I'll break the bitch's legs, then we'll see how much skipping she does."

It was fantastic the amount of success we were having in the office. The amount which we eventually wrote off as uncollectable was only three per cent. We were fixed on that percentage and couldn't go below it because a certain percentage of the people we were after died and their accounts were uninsured. It was an exciting moment for Alden and Carter when they learned of the death of one of our accounts.

When I located a skip, I'd put his name, address and amount owed on a three by five card and drop it on Alden's desk. If it happened to be a dead one, I'd put his name, amount owed and where the remains were located.

When I dropped a dead-card on Alden's desk, he'd look up and a kind of mood would come out of his slowly building smile. The girls would stop typing and sit quietly and the others on the telephones would hang up in mid-sentence. Then Alden would come up out of his desk, slow and fluid, easy like smoke; and all the eyes in the room would watch as Carter got up from his desk too and joined Alden. Together they crossed the room on tip-toes to the file cabinets. Carter stood at a discreet distance while Alden slowly pulled the big file drawer out like a coffin.

If the deceased had insurance, they would whoopee and dance around; and the girls would go back to typing and the others would ring back their numbers on the phone. If however, there was no insurance and the amount was lost, Alden and Carter would return to their desks and sit down heavily.

Business in the office went along pretty smoothly that fall. I was catching skips, left and right; and Carter was collecting money at his usual high rate. In October and November, I located two skips who had been on the books five years. Alden said he was almost as happy as when he first got married. When he talked about it he would go as soft as a teddy bear. "We lived in San Francisco then," he said, "and every Sunday we'd take a bottle of wine and picnic lunch to the Golden Gate Park."

But the Lonetree Account worked against his total ecstasy. It was like a sharp stick. "If we ever collect on Agnes Lonetree," he said, "I'll be the happiest man in the world. We'll have a party."

"Yeah, that'd be all right," I said, trying to sound enthusiastic.

He announced it to the whole office. We'd have a party at the Riverside Club when the Lonetree Account was cleared up. Everyone clapped and began planning for the party.

I stayed in close contact with Agnes during this period and kept her moving around. I didn't want someone to accidently find her. From South Rim, New Mexico, she moved to Monahan, Texas, and then to Corpus Christi. She said she liked it best in Corpus Christi. Then she went to West Virginia, Oklahoma City, Washington, D.C., and Hastings, Nebraska. She said her credit was good all the way. So good in fact, it was now difficult to find a trailer large enough to haul all her stuff.

Sterling, Colorado; Tucson, Arizona; Barstow, California. On and on she traveled, happy and gorging herself on credit. The trailer was bigger now and heavily loaded. She said the Renault no longer controlled it. Gold Hill, Nevada; Moab, Utah; Sunnyvale, California. On and on she went; and now I was pushing harder because the office had increased its efforts to find her. Her length of stay in each town shortened and she began to tire.

Little complaints at first. Then protesting, more and more. Once in Drain, Oregon, she said she couldn't go on. Was going back to Corpus Christi and get a job. Never move again.

A chill ran up my back. Run, run, I said. The hounds are on the heels of the hare. She hung up crying.

Carter and I fell into the habit of having a drink after work. Our work was closely allied and there was always something needing further discussion; so we'd go out for drinks, talk it over and often end up drinking all night.

After the other places closed, we'd go down to the Sand Bar. Park on one of the dark streets and go in to the after-hours club. From the outside it was hard to tell it was a club at all. It looked like a little house all dark in front. But inside it was crowded and they called it the Cozy Club. The only light in the room was furnished by beer advertisement signs which revolved, or jumped up and down or flashed you blind with lights going off in flash holes; and sometimes there'd be a little bit of light coming from behind the bar.

It was a close club, small and there were too many tables for the space. Sometimes there was live music, local talent, and sometimes just a jukebox. The people would stay there all night listening to the music and drinking good stuff, for which, in spite of the risk, the management charged only a nickle or dime above the uptown prices.

Most of the clientele were colored. I recognized a few. A few recognized me. But everybody knew Carter. That's the way it is with a bill collector. When we sat down, we got good service and it was before anyone else. They'd come running up and say, "Good evening, Mr. Carter. What will you have, Mr. Carter?"

Alden said Carter was the only man who ever worked for the company who could collect the Sand Bar. He'd come back from collecting down there with his pockets full of part payments, a five, a ten from each account, but he'd bring that in and he'd get a firm promise for the rest. And when that day arrived, he'd go back and get the rest.

So we'd sit there and listen to the music and talk till morning. Sometimes we'd come out to the broad daylight. Then we'd walk out of the Sand Bar and up Center Street to the Wonder Bar. There we'd be served by a sleepy bartender who had just opened up and was drinking coffee. Sometimes other customers were already there, drinking beer and listening to the lonesome Western music.

Sometimes we'd sit in the club all night and do very little talking. The business of collecting money would fade away and I'd think of Agnes. With the music and the drinks it was easy to forget the business. But I'd be jerked back. Because Carter would call someone over and buy him a drink. When he started to take a sip, Carter would ask very casually when he planned to come by and make that payment. Carter never forgot his business of collecting bills. I would. And several times I almost told him about Agnes and me.

Carter could disarm a person in a minute by taking them into his confidence.

"What do you think of Alden?" he asked.

"Okay, I guess."

"He's weak," said Carter. "He was okay as a bill collector. Because that was something he could touch. The people, the money. But in the office is something else. The problems of an office you can't touch; they are of the air and if he didn't have us, he'd have ulcers."

I had never heard him put Alden down before.

"You know," he continued, "we're artists in a way. We thrive on the loose ends of elusive things." It sounded great over bourbon and water in the Cozy Club. He let me think about that for a long time. I was wide open when he asked the question, "How's your girl friend?"

"What girl friend?" I asked.

"Agnes Lonetree."

I didn't fall off my chair but I tumbled in my mind. My mouth dropped open. He had opened me up with one hand and then let me have it with the other.

"Forget it," he smiled confidently. "A guy gets to thinking out loud sometimes. Gets to thinking maybe she's being tipped-off. But that ain't it. She's Indian; and everybody knows Indians can smell and hear things two days off."

Then he winked and I sweat cold.

The next morning I was nervous and jumpy. I wondered if Carter had talked to Alden. To calm myself, I picked a skip at random and began to work it. Of the over nine thousand skip-tracing tricks in my book, I chose the most terrible one of all to use. That was how ugly I was that morning. I called the skip's only living relative, his sister.

"Hello, Mrs. Wilson?"

"Yes."

"This is the morgue." I gave her both barrels. "We believe we have your brother, Buddy McKay. Will you please come in and identify him?" Silence. I had used the meanest and the greatest skip-tracing trick of them all. It scares them stiff. If they know anything, they will scream it out in the first horror-struck moment.

"It can't be him," she cried. In the very desperateness of her voice, she allowed that it could be him. She had no control over it. "He's working out at the Pumpkin Buttes and staying in the hotel there. He called yesterday."

"Well, I hope we're wrong, ma'am," I said and hung up. She was crying and praying the last I knew.

I filled out the three-by-five card. Buddy McKay, Pumpkin Buttes Hotel, $195.00 for a car. And I dropped it on Alden's desk. Alden smiled when he read it. "Thanks, Birddog." That afternoon Carter went out to the Pumpkin Buttes Hotel and got the car.

I didn't feel any better for my viciousness; and it didn't do any good to pace the floor so I called Agnes in Sandpoint, Idaho. She answered with a tired voice. I snapped like a whip. Get-get-get. She began to wail, as Indian women used to wail when their bucks were killed by the white men. I was too nervous to work after that so I went out for coffee.

When Agnes was in the South, Alden had decided to distribute wanted posters down there. So I moved her up the East Coast. Then he wanted to distribute posters there, too, with a five-by-seven picture on them. It was like a chess game for me. Carter suggested instead of wasting posters in the East, we should put them in the Great Lakes area. That way people would be prepared for her when she came through.

I bought a map, four by six feet, and put it up in my room. I plotted Agnes' moves from there. With posters up in the North Central States, I shuffled her through Nebraska. Right up the middle. Two days later Carter started to plug up the middle, and put up some posters in Colorado. So I swerved Agnes down to Arizona.

Alden was jumping mad. "Nationwide, worldwide, I don't care what you do. Send out the flyers."

Carter was calm. He just sat there looking at me. And after the meeting, at his suggestion, we went out for drinks. It became a habit until the night he showed me the purpose of his friendship; and I became the chief suspect in Carter's mind.

As the days went by I got more and more jumpy. Carter would come up to my desk, smile slow and easy and say, "You want a drink, Birddog?"

I tried to remain calm. "No-no-no-no," I'd say, shaking my head violently.

When he left, I'd call her up. "Get, Get," I'd say.

She'd be panting. "I just got here."

"Get-get," I'd say wildly. "Go to Spokane."

Then she'd start to whimper and cry. Or whine out, "Sometimes I think I'd be better off if I had never met you."

That would have hurt me at one time. It would have twisted in my stomach only the month before. But not now. I didn't care anymore. The name of the game was to win.

"Get-get."

"Where?" she cried.

"Burns, Oregon," I'd scream and slam down the receiver. People sitting near me would turn and stare.

One day I walked by Carter's desk. His back was to me. What I heard froze me in my steps. He was trying to skip-trace Agnes. In front of him was the manual and he was going through one of the tricks, step by step with his finger.

"Hello," he said into the telephone. "Is Agnes there?" Pause.

"That's too bad, I have a check for her." Another pause. "You're her mother?" Then a laugh. "You think I'm putting you on. You think I'm B.A. pulling your leg again?" He laughed. Agnes' mother thought she was talking to me. "You're right, honey," he said, "this is good old B.A. talking. Where is old honey-poo Agnes these days anyway?"

I acted fast. Before she had a chance to answer, I jumped in. "Carter," I said, slapping him on the back, "let's go have that drink you been inviting me for."

The phone came away from his ear. "Hello, B.A.," he said. We both heard the click, when Agnes' mother hung up. I stumbled away.

"Yeah," he called after me, "we'll sure have to go get us a drink now."

I didn't know how long I could stand it. Could go on. I think I would have been relieved if the truth had come out. If I had been labeled the fraud I was. But it didn't. Carter kept his silence as if he had other things in mind.

How long? I wondered. How long? I called Agnes all the time. Kept her on the move. Up in the air like a bird. She'd alight and I'd swoosh her up again. Carter sat at his desk and stared across the room at me. Five, ten, fifteen minutes at a time, he'd stare, fixed on me as if watching my transformation.

Agnes stopped crying at the last. And her voice sounded hollow on the phone.

I'd say, "Go."

"Where?" she'd ask.

"Boise." Then I'd look up at a staring Carter.

"Change that," I'd say.

"Where to?"

"Coeur d' Alene, Idaho."

It all came to an end on a Friday morning. One of the girls said, "Mr. B.A. On four, please."

It was the sheriff of Coeur d' Alene County, calling to say Agnes had been killed in an auto accident. Called me because my name was written all over the inside of the car. On the headliner, on the dash, carved into the steering wheel. He said she came off that long hill coming into Coeur d' Alene and was out of control all the way. "That big trailer was like a dog, shaking that little Renault car like a rat."

I said I was sorry and would call her mother. Relief came slow. My hand shook as I filled out the three-by-five card and handed it in to Alden. Out in the hall I leaned against the water cooler and heard the noise of the office die down to a point as if someone had pinched it off tight.

My hand on the water cooler spigot did not let go and the cup filled up and spilled over. Never again would I be stared at. Never again would I live in such crisis.

Inside the office I heard Alden and Carter whoop and yell and begin to dance. And the others were screaming, "Party, party." By then relief had burst upon me like flood waters. Turbulence everywhere and I held to the water cooler as if it were a bobbing buoy.

Carter came out and put his hand on my shoulder. "I'm sorry," he said. I pulled away. But there was no reason for that. No reason to distrust him anymore.

So when he put his hand on my shoulder the second time, I did not move.

"It was a tough one," he said. "A baptism in blood almost." He spoke with feeling. "But you'll make a fine collection man now."

MONSERRATE

Charlotte Walker

Gazing down at the mountain unfurling beneath him, Andrés stood at a pitched angle in the back of the *funicular,* the same cog railway car he had taken up the mountain from Bogotá when he was a boy. He had liked excursions then, being unnoticed and free to respond to things or not, as it pleased him. Now excursions were too involved, too many people had to be considered. But this day his sister Francisca had organized the outing, and his American wife and small daughter—his two *gringas*—had been quiet, a little frightened by the steep ascent, so that he was left in peace with his thoughts. But the thoughts themselves were not peaceful. It was his first visit home since he had become an American citizen, and he felt suspended between the two countries, like this *funicular* car moving dizzily up Monserrate.

He thought of his first ride up the *funicular* as a boy of twelve. They had just moved to Bogotá from the coast, and he had been very ill after his first exposure to the damp, cold air that seeped into the houses and even between the sheets of these hard beds. Now Andrés gripped the post which was all that kept him from tumbling out of the car and rolling down the mountainside. As a boy he had clung to it with both hands, releasing one hand now and then to lean out with arm extended, trying to taste the feeling of fall. Papa had brought a paper and read most of the ride, not noticing Andrés' tricks.

"How green it all is!" said Laura, his wife, her American voice breaking into his thoughts. Andrés nodded. The slopes were as green as the emeralds from Colombian mines. Green inside the earth and green on top of it. He had not thought of it until he came back from the United States, where nothing of nature was as green as these mountains, or the *llanos* outside the city.

"*Pelo verde y venas verdes*—Colombia!" said Francisca, rolling out the words proudly. She had always had a way of coming next to his thoughts, Francisca.

Laura looked at him inquiringly. "She says Colombia has green skin and green veins," he told her. "She means the grass on the mountains and the emeralds in the mines." At times like this, he felt they were no more to each other than tourist and native guide.

"Is it from a poem?" Laura asked.

"It is only from Francisca," his sister answered shyly, in English.

The railway began a great grinding noise as they entered the final stage of the lift, passing through a dark concrete structure, then stopping with a harsh digging in of brakes and gears. It sounded the same as on Andrés' first ride—as if the whole thing were about to slip and go careening backward, hurling itself like a meteor into the center of Bogotá.

Susan and Laura clung together, their faces alike, each trying to hide the fear that was obvious in their eyes. Francisca roared with laughter.

"You think we go down the hill again. You too, my brother! So funny!" She stood up. "Here, I carry Susan out," she added, reaching for the little girl.

Andrés saw Laura draw back. Why was she so mistrustful? As if his sister did not love Susita too. "Here, I'll take her," he said, and pulled Susan away from his wife.

"We must go to the Church of Monserrate first," said Francisca, "and pray God the car will not fall on the way down!" She laughed again; this time they all laughed.

A group of *gamines,* the street urchins of Bogotá, crowded about the passengers as they got off the *funicular.* These tough, homeless little boys, sons of maids and prostitutes, were everywhere in the city, fending for themselves, leaving room at home for younger ones. Since his return this summer, Andrés had a strange feeling about them. He remembered a maid at home, a girl named Marcia, who had been sent away because she was pregnant, the year before he entered college. He had been angry with his parents for sending her away, knowing they suspected whose child it might be. He had made elaborate plans to find her and marry her, she had been good to him, what happened between them had been real. But he had forgotten soon enough when his father offered him the chance to study in the States. Now it came back to him. He did not think of Marcia so much, but of the child, who might be any of these boys. When they thrust their hard, dirty palms before him, he would search their faces for some resemblance to himself, and always seem to find it. Sometimes a feeling so painful would come upon him that he could not even stop to hand them some coins, but would stride away from them angrily.

He walked quickly past them now, holding Susan on his shoulder, above their grasping hands. She strained at his arms as he walked, until he put her down and she went scampering toward the steps that led upward to the church. Andrés loved to see how pretty his little daughter was. He would have chosen a dark Colombian son, but since he had been given this *hija dorada,* this golden daughter, he cherished her. She was the only creature in the world who did not misunderstand him; like him, she belonged to two countries. She had the *gringa* blondness of her mother—he had thought Laura's blond hair beautiful, but did not expect her to give him blond children—but she also had the sloe eyes and long cheeks of the Alvarez. And her skin was pale gold. It would never be disfigured by brown sun spots, the way Laura's skin was every summer.

He quickened his gait to match Susita's little leaps up the steps. "Come, Papa," she invited, reaching up for his hand.

"Venga," he corrected her. *"Tienes que hablar español, m'hi jita."*

"What, Papa?" Susita did not look up, was concentrating on the ascent to each step. *"Ven-ga."* Right foot, left foot. *"Ven-ga."* They were at the top of the stairs, and he stopped with her to wait for Francisca and Laura. The church in front of them was white-washed stucco, beautifully cared for. He liked to see things kept neat and clean like this. The tiles of the roof hung over the edge of the walls above him, and he saw a small bird fly out from one of them. They entered through a great carved doorway, and found that the main aisle was taken up by a family of supplicants.

The mother, a fat, shabbily dressed woman, was in front, walking forward on her knees. Her four children all knelt behind her, each of them carrying a lighted candle and inching forward slowly on his bony knees. The smallest one was no bigger than Susita, and the candle in his little hand wobbled from side to side, flickering dangerously. Andrés hoped Laura would not notice them, but knew she already had, by the way she glanced at him.

"That child may set fire to himself!" she whispered. "Why do they allow it?"

How sensible and responsible Americans were. She was right, of course. The child with the candle made him wince also, he had become so American himself. But he would answer like a Colombian. "His father is probably dying," he told her as sternly as he could in a whisper. "They are asking God to save their father."

"With a human sacrifice?" Laura said. He ignored her. Of all the women in the Americas, how had he chosen the one with the sharpest tongue?

"Come," said Francisca. "I show you my *Cristo."* She led them over the shining tile floor and up to the nearest side aisle, till they came to some steps behind the altar. Andrés remembered it all clearly as he walked behind the others, though he had not thought of this church in years. Yes, there was the *Cristo* in the glass coffin, resting on a little balcony behind the altar. They climbed up to it and stood around the sparkling glass, with the too-realistic *corpus-christi* inside.

"Look, Laura," Francisca said. "A miracle. The *Cristo* is weeping."

"But it can't be!" Laura stared at it more closely, then turned to Andrés. "It is made of glass, isn't it? The tear on his cheek?"

For an atheist, his wife was so impressionable! He did not answer her, but stared at the enameled cheek with its one glass tear below the right eye. He had been twelve and Francisca fifteen when she first told him the same thing. Did she really believe it herself? She had given him a fright that had sent him to confession for many months afterward. Only when Carlitos told him it was glass had he realized the trickery. Not that he objected to trickery, when it brought people to God. But did Francisca really believe in the tear? And if the tear was not glass, but real, then was not the blood dripping from the thorns on the forehead real blood, and the blood on the palms also? Why did Francisca speak only of the tear?

Laura spoke again, insistently. "It isn't a real miracle, is it Andrés?"

"No one knows," he said. Perhaps she might be converted yet, by their Colombian churches and their statues with tears. Perhaps even an intellectual *gringa* could know God here. Did he know God here? A foolish question.

Francisca was pointing to the walls along the side behind the altar, where dozens of crutches were fastened in a haphazard latticework. "Proofs of miracles," she said. Francisca was ardent, she was transformed here from her usual plain self. He could not bear to answer any more of Laura's question. He would leave her and Susan to Francisca.

"I want to get some air," he told them. "I'll walk around awhile and meet you in front of the church. I want to get some pictures." He walked back to the front of the church, brushing against the fat little priest with the polished forehead who had always been there. His dangling camera bumped against his knee as he genuflected on the way out.

He took the path among the life-sized stations of the cross, where pilgrims knelt before each statue. He walked quickly past, pausing only before the replica of the Pieta, where a dark young woman knelt on the ground. She wore a handsome wool suit, a black lace shawl over her head. She would get runs in her stockings there, and nylons so expensive in Colombia. But Laura was always getting runs in her stockings too, with no prayers to redeem them. He walked on swiftly. There was something disturbing about so many life-sized Christs in one place.

The path grew narrower and weedier, and led to the edge of the mountain. Pebbles scraped and rolled under his feet as he walked to the edge and observed the steep green fall to the city. He looked down the green slopes, across the eucalyptus trees, to where the buildings began. First the small huts of the poor, then the old houses from Colonial days, then the modern business buildings scattered among older ones. The bull ring still there, shambling, ugly, enduring as the Coliseum. He would take Laura to see the *corrida,* if only he could rely on her not to take the part of the bull, as Americans do. He did not need to see it for himself any more. It was part of him. The *toro* and the *torero,* they pawed and swooped inside him vividly enough, endlessly. Am I the *toro* or the *torero,* he had asked himself as a boy. He was both.

In the center of the city, the big buildings. The banks. Of course the banks. Tall and modern, bold architecture. The Tequendama Hotel, American of course. But I am American, he thought. I traded my country for the land of golden opportunity, for triple the salary, for a blond wife and baby, for the comfort of not being murdered on a weekend in the country. La Violencia. His country, home of La Violencia. The news of it had seeped into his American life, never letting him forget what he had left. "Colombian Bus Attacked by Bandits. Twenty-four People Beheaded and Mutilated." Political violence turned into butchery for the hell of it, butchery as a life's work. But what could he have done about it, even if he had stayed? He was only one man.

His eyes scanned the city. Between the new buildings were the old, streets and streets of the ugly old houses, of beautiful Colonial sections, showing through here and there. The Plaza de Bolivar. They could be proud of that at least. Bolivar's statue small in the middle of it, the pigeons all around—he couldn't see them from here, yet his mind added them, they were so much a part of it. Then the impressive capitol building. The State greater than the Liberator; as it should be. But as it was? Well, as Bolivar would have wished it, just the same. And the Cathedral at right angles to it. The little closed-down ancient church between them. He had loved it best of all before they closed it.

"Señor Gringo! Do you have a few centavos for us?" The voice was shrill, yet commanding. His heart jumped, his camera fell to the end of its strap.

"Señor?"

He looked around at three middle-sized urchins. "What are you doing up here?"

"We climb, Señor." The tallest boy, about eleven or twelve, grinned at him. They stood blocking his way, the precipice behind him. He was in their power. They were small and undernourished, but one push and he'd lose his balance, fall over the side. They'd want his camera first, though, and that would mean a struggle. They wouldn't dare, unless they hated him enough. They could hate him.

They should. He had left them, hadn't he? Left them to beg all over Bogotá. The tall one might be his own son, he had the long face, the sloe eyes. But so were they all, all the *gamines*—his abandoned sons.

"What can you give us, Señor? Are you tired? Do you want help over to the *funicular?*" The tone of the tall one, the boy his son's age, was friendly. The other two boys had not spoken, only watched.

Andrés grinned at them. He had abandoned them, yet he was a *gamin* himself, as homeless as they were. "No. No, *gracias.* Here. Take this." He gave them a handful of coins. They could have had his life, but he would not show it. Probably they didn't know. Probably they did.

THE CHICKEN

Ernest Brawley

Mandio and Jerry and me surfed Steamer Lane in Santa Cruz in the morning and then the surf went down so we thought we'd take a ride up to Frisco. When we made it we changed clothes in the men's head of a Texaco station and went down to Market Street. Took in a movie, hit a couple of bars where they didn't check ID's, walked around, nothing much. I never did like Market Street anyway. Too many Hawaiian shirts and hairy chests, too many Gobs and Jarheads and GI's, too many fruits, too many Slants and Spics and Spades, too many sweaty Kikes with shiny silk shirts and white on white ties. It always reminded me of LA.

Somebody said why don't we go up the hill so we got in the car and drove up to Broadway and that's where we met the chicken. She was bopping out of a little bar that had a fat neon pig running and wiggling his tail above the door. We sort of brodied up making a lot of noise and Jerry said, Hey, babe, come here a minute, and she looked around very cool not surprised and Jerry went again come here with his finger at her and said it, Come here, beautiful, and she ran over to the car and leaned on the door and said, Hi, and Jerry said, Hi, baby, hop in, and she did, in the back seat with Jerry and Mandio, and we drove off. We couldn't believe our luck.

And she wasn't bad either, a small chicken with a nice little bod, sandy hair that I don't think was out of the bottle, great big eyes, I forget the color, and a sort of baby pug nose. Very nice. She smiled a lot too but her teeth were in pretty bad shape. They were crooked and sort of tobacco-stained. And her skin was a little too white, unhealthy looking. You could tell she dug the tans and the long Gremmy hair and the woody-wagon and the boards on the top. She looked young. Probably not much older than us. It was about two in the morning and she said, It's too early, I don't feel like going home early, do you? What you guys want to do? And Mandio said, Three guesses and she laughed but Jerry said, Come on Mandio quit it, why don't we have a beer and think it over? She said, Okay and Jerry tapped us all a hooker and then he started hustling. You could always tell when he was hustling because his whole style changed. He made his voice deeper, talked smooth, soft, cool. I guess he was pretty suave. He said, What's your name? and she said, What's it matter? And he said, You're right, what's it matter? Chicken, do you live around here? How long? Where's the haps, pretty mama? She said, We could go up to Twin Peaks. And we said, What's Twin Peaks? And she said, It's a big hill, the highest in the city. It's nice up there. We could drink, look at the lights from the bay, and the cops don't bug you. Jerry said, Okay, let's go. I could tell he was excited. I was too.

When we got up to this place we sat there drinking and bull-shitting for about a half hour. The view wasn't bad. The chicken showed us all the bridges and which was which and the lights from Marin County and the East Bay. Then Mandio and me got out of the car to take a little stroll but before we could split she said, You might as well stick around, won't do you any good. I know the scene. You guys leave us alone then when this cat does what he wants to do the next one comes along and does what's on his mind and then the next one and before the gig is finished I'm so full of what all you cats got on your little minds I can hardly walk. She didn't seem to be sore or anything in fact she even laughed when she said it. But she really had us figured. We sort of forced a giggle, got back in the car and cracked a couple of more hookers.

After a while Mandio leaned over and whispered, This is getting to be a drag. Three cats? Why don't we drop Jerry? I looked in the back. He had his arm around her and they were blowing in each other's ear and like that. I said, Why not? I backed the car around and started down the hill. Jerry said, Where we going? And I thought a second and said, To the beach. He said, Why there? And I said, Why anywhere? He never said another word all the way out.

Splitting on Jerry wasn't as bad as it sounds. Or maybe it was, I guess it depends on the way you look at it. He didn't have a permanent home or anything. He was more or less like us. Only not as smart. He lived on the beach most of the time, traveling around up and down the coast from Santa Cruz to Mazatlan. He only worked once in a while glassing surfboards or something. All he had were his trunks and the clothes on his back. He didn't even have a surfboard of his own anymore. He was always borrowing ours. Dropping him in Frisco wouldn't hang him up in the least, nothing new to him. He didn't care much where he was most of the time anyway as long as it was near the ocean. We knew he had a little bread. He'd get along.

When he got down to the beach he played right into our hands. I guess the poor bastard trusted us. Even with the chicken in the game. He said he had to take a leak, got out and walked a little ways down the beach. We just drove off. Laughing like hell.

And it didn't seem to bother the chicken at all. She was laughing too. Didn't even ask why we did it. Pretty soon she climbed over the seat and got in between us. A sandwich, Mandio said, and we all split a gut. Then we got to talking, I asked her where she was from and she said Ventura and kept on talking. At first we asked her a lot of questions but she was handling things so good that after awhile we didn't say anything and just listened to her.

She'd run away from home when she was sixteen. Her old man wasn't mean and she didn't have a stepmother and she wasn't knocked up, she just ran away. Went to LA, got a job as a car-hop in Culver City, met a sailor there. His name was Billy McNeer. From West Virginia. They got married. He was based in San Diego and they lived for a year and a half in a quonset hut project. He used to be away at sea from four to six months at a time. She played around but who could blame her? She had the allotment checks so she didn't have to work and she never worked, she said, unless it was absolutely necessary, but she got a little bored. There was no grass in the project and thousands of screaming kids and San Diego is a dirty city anyway. They got a divorce. She had an aunt in Kingman, Arizona, who ran an all-night diner on Highway 66. She rode the Greyhound out there and got a job. But she was always fighting with her aunt and Kingman was dead anyway. She went back to LA again and met a guy who was a fruit tramp—Not fruit tramp, he used to say, Fruit Tourist! He had a kind of interesting life, traveling and all. Pretty soon she took up with him. They went over to Covina and picked oranges for half the winter, then in February they came up to Stockton to top celery, stayed a month and then went down to the Imperial Valley for the winter crop of tomatoes. He used to have an old green '39 Chevy and a little home-made house trailer only eighteen feet long. When summer came they worked their way back up the Central Valley. Ten, twelve hours a day. Picking peaches, pears, lettuce, tomatoes all the way up the San Joaquin. Dusty little towns like Colusa, Hanford, Delano, Porterville, Corcorran. Hotter than hell, even at night. It got to be a drag. She had a little money saved so she hitch-hiked over to Frisco one day without saying goodby. His name was Roy.

She got a job as a waitress at Foster's Cafeteria and an apartment on Green Street a few doors down from the "Anxious Asp." She liked North Beach, she said, because the people were so beautifully sick. Sooner or later she was going to move over to Fillmore in the Negro district, she said, because she liked Spades. I don't know, she said, I want to see it all I guess. She studied pottery at City College night school. Her ambition was to have her own little potter's studio. She was really good with her hands, she said, she could do anything and Mandio said—Oh yeah! And we all laughed.

That was her whole story. When she finished she started asking questions about us and since just awhile before we'd pulled a couple of minor capers and didn't want to get too specific about all that names, addresses jazz we told her about lots of funny things that happened when we were kids in Tracy, about good old Georgie and Barry Napolean and Norman Redding and Joey Serpa and Yuri Zelinsky and the old '36 Ford Mandio got one summer from working the apricot packing shed, The Jungle Cruiser, we used to call it and about how we used to load it up with kids and take BB guns and slingshots and dirt clods and go hunting bums down under the San Joaquin River bridge—white bums, nigger bums, Spics—scared green every time they saw the old Jungle Cruiser come bumping across the tomato and asparagus patches or even down the railroad tracks, down the black bottoms and out onto the mud flats and all us kids barefoot and grabbing trophies: hot cans of potato soup and coffee water, greasy pots, half empty bottles of Port and Muscatel, kicking over the pots, letting out screams of victory, howling like a bunch of wolves, drinking up the wine, pouring the coffee onto the mud . . .

And we told her about Mexican Joe, the dirtiest man in the world, and his little house in the city dump and about the big sparkling water containers he stole and filled with wine he made from rotten grapes he got from the vineyards, and about how one day we happened to roll by in the Cruiser when Joe wasn't home and tore down his little cardboard house and drank up all his wine and broke all his bottles and about how he cussed and yelled out in Spic talk and chased us all over the property when he came home and caught us drunk, laying around on the wreckage of his house and how when he couldn't catch us he cried, the tears like mud running down his ugly dirty face into his thin patchy old black beard and made us feel sorry for him and we said, We're sorry Joe and we really were and I even offered him the Jungle Cruiser to pay for the damage because by this time we'd all put so much time and work and change into the Cruiser that we thought of it as all of ours and how Mandio said, Not my car, by God, you ain't giving my car to that dirty Spic, and jumped in and ran it off and left us there to walk the six miles back into town and how Mexican Joe really got peed off then and came up with a .22 from somewhere and started firing and we ran like hell and it was only because Spics and Indians are the world's lousiest shots that we made it out of there alive . . .

We told her lots of stories about us when we were kids, when it was all safe and in the past, we even made some up for her and sometimes a thing I'd say wouldn't quite jibe with what Mandio was saying and I guess she knew because she was a very smart girl, you could tell from the way she laughed at everything and the way she came back quick without having to think when you said something and the way I guess that she just didn't give a damn and never pulled us up when we lied. Everything seemed like it was okay with her. That's how I could tell.

We beat around for hours in the car talking up a storm, telling dirty jokes, I remember Mandio told the one about the cat who was in China during the war and had a really horny wife back in the States that he wanted to stay true to him. And we were drinking beer and listening to the Spade station from West Oakland with a disc-jockey named Bruce and after every song he'd yell out "GREEEAT HOOGA-MOOGA! AAAH *AM* THE BRUCE!" And we were singing too, singing R and R with the radio—We were singing . . . "Well do'ya do'ya do'ya do'ya wanna dance, do'ya do'ya do'ya do'ya wannadance, oh baby, do'ya wanna da-a-ance?"—Everything was going along fine, everyone was happy. Mandio and me, everyone! The chicken threw back her head on the seat and started laughing. We're all happy, she was yelling, everyone's happy. And she put her arms around us and said, Aren't we? Aren't we? And pretty soon Mandio started laughing, then me, and we were laughing so hard we had to stop the car on a hill on Union Street, laughing like a bunch of hyenas and we were laughing about the sun which we were sure was up now but that we couldn't see through the summertime fog, about the sound of the beer cans when they rolled down the hill, and then the chicken really began to wail, putting us on, putting everything and everybody in the world on and we were going out of our minds about what she was saying about all the wonderful little people who were getting up now to go to work all over the city and about their fat wives and baby-fat kids, and how they were all kissing goodby, about the whole world waking up around us, peeping from behind blinds to watch us, about the bald-headed old men running the world between them, about the number of children conceived last night all over the world. Where? she said. Anywhere! You name it, she said. In taxi-cabs, bathtubs, stairwells, convent-gardens, gunny-sacks? About poor poor Jerry back there at Ocean Beach, about Mandio pissing in the street and about the skinny paperboy with buck-teeth and black and white saddle shoes who laughed when he saw him. About how bitching beautiful it was, she said, to be unclean, uncombed, unslept, unsatisfied but not unsexed (like all the rest of them climbing out of their safe little beds), eighteen and nineteen years old and dead drunk in the cold Frisco morning fog ten years ago.

She turned us on with her talk, she really did, she really turned us on. It was wild, we were winging, we opened the doors and screamed and yelled and hooted and shrieked and sang, we jumped out and danced and stamped and whirled. We'll defy everything, the chicken said, everything! But when the first threats were thrown our way, when the windows and doors started opening and little men in pajamas started shaking their fists at us, we split for the car, laughing at our own chickenoutedness, laughing when it wouldn't start, laughing as we pushed it over the rise, Mandio and me, the chicken driving, laughing when it finally caught and started, laughing as we chased it and jumped in, and then away we went up and down and all around those

Frisco hills, aiming at every stray cat and barking dog we saw. The chicken said it and we believed it—we were swinging. Let's split, Mandio said, let's go somewhere, let's flee!

So we drove north over the Golden Gate, but it was the same. Mandio said, Let's keep moving. Let's go to Tahoe. Have you ever seen it? The chicken said, No. It's bitching beautiful, he said. Sunny all day long and trees like you've never seen. And the water's so clear, man, you'll never believe it. It's like flying, like floating on air! And the chicken said, Okay.

Mandio and me only had about fifteen dollars between us but the chicken had a hundred and twenty. Two weeks' salary. She'd just got paid and she didn't mind treating us, she said, and screw the job!

It took us a long time to get to Sacramento and by the time we did we were all pretty shot. I pulled up at the Greyhound bus depot. I knew we could get cleaned up there. Mandio was curled up in the back seat, the chicken was in front with her forehead up against the window, fogging it, watching the people walking by. I rousted them out and we went in.

When Mandio and me got back out to the lobby the chicken wasn't back yet so we passed the time reading war magazines on the big rack. There was this one article about some cat who was a hero in the war, killed some forty-odd. When he got out after the war he kept right on killing, "went berserk," they said, killed another eight or ten people before they finally got him. I showed it to Mandio and he couldn't laugh enough about it, thought it was the funniest thing in the world.

It took the chicken a long time but when she finally came out she really looked sharp. She had her hair pulled back in a sort of pony-tail which looked very good and she'd powdered the dark circles out from under her eyes and I was thinking how great she'd look if she'd only done something about the teeth. When we got out to the car Mandio told her he had an aunt in town and that maybe we could go over and sack out for an hour or two or at least get some chow and I knew then what he had on his mind and I could've said something then but I didn't. She said, Okay. It seemed like everything was okay with her.

We drove along to a nice street with a lot of sycamore trees and shade and older wooden houses. Then we pulled our usual caper. Mandio stopped the car and went up to a door and knocked, if somebody was home he asked for Mrs. Venegoni and they would say she didn't live there and we'd move down the block. After about four tries Mandio found a place where no one was home. He walked back to the car and told the chicken he hadn't been exactly sure which house was his aunt's but he thought this one was it. She must be at work, he said, so he'd have to look for the key. Then he went back and looked around for the key that this kind of older middle-class cat has always got hidden outside somewhere in case they lose it or something. He looked under the doormat and in the bushes and under the eaves of the porch and finally came up with it. It'd been hidden under a pot in a flower box hanging beneath the front window. As soon as we got in I flopped on the sofa. Mandio took the chicken out to the kitchen and pretended to show her where everything was.

When they had breakfast ready the chicken came in and woke me up. I noticed they'd turned on the air-conditioning. I'd forgotten. Sacramento is very hot in summer. Breakfast was good, ham and eggs. We ate quick and nobody said much. When we were done Mandio and me took our coffee out to the living room and left the chicken to do the dishes. She didn't seem to mind, I could hear her singing to herself as she was working: "Well do'ya do'ya do'ya do'ya wanna dance, oh baby, do'ya wanna da-a-ance . . ."

Mandio said, We're not going to get anywhere this way. There's two bedrooms here. Why don't you sack out in the back one till I finish. He was grinning. I said, How come you first? And he said, Somebody has to go first, what you want to do, flip coins? And anyway don't worry, it'll still be there when you get to it, and I said okay.

I walked back to the bedroom and waited while sitting in a wicker chair trying to read an old *Reader's Digest*. But I couldn't concentrate. In a few minutes I heard them go into the other bedroom.

When Mandio came back he said, All right, man, I told you, it's still there. I walked down the hall and opened the door. I was sort of nervous. The chicken's hair was all mussed up and all she had on was a pair of panties . . . but she was smiling.

When we got out to the living room Mandio was laying on the floor with his head propped up on the leg of the sofa watching TV and I guess he was a little sore because we'd taken a lot longer than he had and he said, You guys just about ready to go? And the chicken just laughed at him and said, Yeah, why not?

Mandio wanted to drive. He took Highway 40 west out of town, back toward Frisco. Nobody said anything.

At the top of Waldo Grade the chicken asked if we couldn't stop for the view. Mandio pulled over on the shoulder and she ran across the freeway through the traffic to look at the cities of Richmond, Berkeley and Oakland all white and shiny in the sun like they were just flooding over the hills and right down into the bay.

She left her purse in the car and Mandio spotted it even though I tried to hide it with my leg and he dropped the car in low and started to split on her and I said, Don't, and he said, Why not? And I said, She'll probably give us some bread if we ask her or maybe she'll even come down the coast with us and he said, Bullshit, and I thought about grabbing the wheel and stopping the bastard but I didn't.

When we were crossing back over the Golden Gate, Mandio was all the time talking about the way the chicken hadn't even noticed us make it on her, staring out over the bay like she was. And even if she had she couldn't have got back across the freeway in time to catch us, and even if she'd caught us she couldn't do anything about it, and she was just a slut anyway, and now we were 120 ahead, 120 clams ahead, and he'd been determined to cop the 120 ever since she told us about it and it was better this way anyway, we would've gotten it one way or another and it's always cooler to avoid violence if you can. So she was actually better off, if you look at it that way. And now the south swell would be booming in off the Pacific at Dana Point and Wind and Sea and The Trestles and we could surf for at least a couple of months on the kind of bread we had now, but I was all the time looking for our old morning fog, and I found it way out at sea, just a low gray line on the other side of the Farallone Islands.

CHASTAIN ON THE X-AXIS, STEBBINS ON THE Y-AXIS

Michael Brannon

It was a hot day in May at the end of the semester when Professor Chastain and I finally fought it out in front of the entire Economics 3 class. Even now I can still remember the sweat that ran down my forehead, burning my eyes, blinding my held back rage.

The classroom was full that day. Students had brought their friends; even some assistant instructors had come to see the battle. Everyone sensed that the storm which had been building between us for so long now, must surely burst forth on this the last day of class. They knew that Chastain had tossed down the gauntlet; they also knew that I would pick it up. What else could I do?

Our little war had begun simply enough at the very first class meeting, a cold rainy day in January. When Professor Chastain came into the room, I was surprised that he looked as old as he did. I had heard him called "the best *young* economics theoretician in the country." *Young?* He was completely bald and his eyes seemed as cold as the January day outside. Although I knew he was no more than thirty-five years old I nevertheless thought when I heard him speak that he was the oldest man I'd ever met. His voice was dry and brittle, and he spoke without the slightest trace of feeling.

Professor Chastain began by saying, "Economics 3 is a course in Basic Economic Theory. Due to a shortage of teachers in the Department, I am required to teach this undergraduate course. Certain things will also be required of you. You will be expected to know and understand everything which I write or draw on this blackboard. You will be tested accordingly. There is no textbook for this course. If you cannot keep up, you are in the wrong course. Perhaps, you should not be in a university at all. If you fail, I shall give you an F. Class will begin exactly at ten minutes after the hour. If you are late, you will find upon your arrival that I have closed the door; do not open it; you are absent. I will not bother to lock the door, because I am certain that if you find it closed, you will have the courtesy not to intrude. You may not cut my class more than four times. If you are so foolish as to exceed four cuts, you will receive a penalty F. Are there any questions?"

I had a question, but I did not ask it. I wanted to know why Professor Chastain was such a bastard. I also wanted to know why I, an Art major, had been so stupid as to sign up for his class. Either all of my classmates were Economics majors or else they had chosen, as I had, to remain silent and drop the course as soon as possible.

"If there are no questions from the class, then I have one for you: How many of you are not Economics majors?"

Three other students and I raised our hands.

"The four who raised their hands will please remain after I have dismissed the rest of the class. Class is dismissed."

Amid the shuffle of chairs and feet, the four of us slowly made our way to the front of the classroom. Up close, Professor Chastain looked even colder than he had before.

"I suggest that you four gentlemen make arrangements to change into another section, taught by some other instructor."

"Yes, sir," the other three students said, nodding their heads and leaving the room as quickly and gracefully as they could.

"Is there any rule which prevents non-Economics majors from taking this course from you?" I asked.

"What is your name?" he asked, not answering my question.

"Jack Stebbins."

"No, Mr. Stebbins, there is no such rule, but I think you would be wise to follow the others' example."

"I just got out of four years of the Navy, sir," I told him. "I'm a little tired of following. I'll stay in here, if you don't mind."

"I do mind, Mr. Stebbins. I spent four years in the Marines and I fought in Korea. Discipline is important to me and you seem a little rebellious. What is your major, Mr. Stebbins?"

"Art."

"Art?"

"Yes, sir."

"This is clearly the wrong class for you, Mr. Stebbins."

"I'll stay anyway."

"You may find it too hard for you."

"I'll stay anyway," I repeated.

"Very well then, Mr. Stebbins. I'll see you tomorrow."

"Yes, sir."

I should have dropped Economics 3 that very day. I was not prepared for a war. I was still weak. Four years in the Navy had drained me of most of my meanness. I had served two years in Vietnam on River Patrol boats. Some men, when they see their friends die, learn how not to feel emotions such as love or pity or sadness. Some men when they are forced to kill, learn how to hate, or else they learn how to blank out all feeling. I was not one of those men. I brought a great sadness home with me. Physically I was healthy and whole. Mentally and emotionally, however, I was unprepared for what was to come. Or so I thought, that first day.

In the weeks that followed, Professor Chastain came to represent all that I hated in life. If someone did not know the answer to a question, he would harangue the student concerning the unfitness of most of the student body to participate in academic discussions. He called on me every day. I began to devote all of my time to his course. I let my other subjects slide. They no longer seemed to matter.

Chastain would ask me a question. I would answer it. He would then proceed to point out how I might have extended my answer to include other points. Soon when he asked me a question, I managed to extend my answers until they involved adjacent topics of relatively remote importance.

He then tried a new tack; "You are wandering, Mr. Stebbins. If you don't know the answer, simply say so, do not wander and take time which belongs to your classmates." I realized at this point that I could never win as long as I was under attack. I decided to take the offensive. Henceforth, I would choose the field of battle.

One day when he was illustrating a simple change of expenditure graph, he said, "Suppose you have a rise in expenditure, such as increased hospital bills caused by your wife having cancer, you would then . . ."

I raised my hand.

"Yes, Mr. Stebbins."

"If the line represents a woman dying of cancer, could the economist consider the feelings of the persons involved?"

"I'm afraid I don't understand your question, Mr. Stebbins. What possible relevance can . . ."

"I just wondered if you would graph feelings on the x-axis or y-axis. I realize, of course, that economic models don't need to take feelings into consideration, but I just thought if you could graph a woman dying of cancer, you could probably graph feelings also, if you wanted to."

Most of the class laughed, an uneasy laugh, but a laugh. It was the first laugh of the semester. I determined that it would not be the last.

Chastain took the bait. "Anything can be graphed, Mr. Stebbins, anything. Actually I am glad you raised your pseudo-humorous question. Economics today has become as scientific as the natural sciences, simply because we have been able to construct mathematically valid models which exclude sentimentality. Therefore, the answer to your question is that Economics is a pure science because we are able to eliminate 'feeling', as you put it, from our models. Although as I said before, anything can be graphed."

"Professor," I asked, "after class, would you mind graphing the war in Vietnam for me."

This time everyone laughed, except Chastain. His expression did not change.

"I would be glad to, Mr. Stebbins. Please remain after class. I am certain the rest of your classmates are not interested in such a graph. They are Economics majors, not Art majors."

The class laughed again.

"Class is dismissed."

They were still laughing and smiling and winking at me as they left the room.

Professor Chastain walked to the back of the room and closed the door. I remained seated.

"I will be brief, Mr. Stebbins," he said. "Do you wish to pass this course?"

"Yes, sir."

"If you continue with your present attitude, you will fail Economics 3."

"Regardless of how I do on tests?"

"Regardless of that."

"If I shut up, do I get an A?"

"I'm threatening you, Mr. Stebbins, not bribing you."

I laughed. "Yes, sir, I can see that."

"Do you believe me?"

"Yes, sir. I believe you."

"Very well, then Mr. Stebbins. I'll see you tomorrow."

After the dying woman incident, Professor Chastain did not call on me. I asked no questions. I turned my attention to my other studies. My grades were good, but I could not afford to fail anything. I was doing four years of work in three years. If I did not fail any course, I would finish in one more year. Perhaps Professor Chastain knew that. I was ashamed of myself at first for submitting meekly to his ultimatum. However, I soon became involved in my art work again and I rationalized the entire situation away, by telling myself how petty it all was. In Vietnam men were still dying. All over the world there were people struggling just to survive. Every day people lost to death the race that we all run. I had become involved in a petty squabble of no importance.

I began to stay up late every night working on three paintings. I worked first on one, then another. Each of the three seemed to fill some special need inside me. The first painting was the smallest of the three. In Vietnam I had once seen a peasant sitting cross-legged in the dusty road in front of his hut. He was sawing a piece of wood. I was unable to forget his face. The first painting was of the old man. I painted him lying on his back on the ground. He was dead. His eyes were open and his mouth had a strange twisted expression. There was an open wound, as from a shell fragment in his stomach. Men were standing around him, but you could only see their feet. Some wore Army boots; some wore Ho Chi Minh sandals, strips of rubber tires on their feet. The ground beneath the old man was brown and barren.

The second painting was of three little girls playing in Balboa Park in San Diego. I had seen them there, the first day I was back in the States from Vietnam. They had brought me laughter and tenderness at a time when I thought I could feel only a sort of bitter sadness.

The third painting, the largest of the three, was the result of my fight with Professor Chastain. In the background I painted a steel and plastic city, with ribbon-like highways encircling it. Around the city was a large area of burned, leveled, blackened dirt. In the foreground I painted daffodils and grasses that stopped as soon as they touched the blackened area surrounding the city. The city was the city of science and I made it as sterile as I could. I decided to entitle it "Exiled from the Kingdom."

I finished the third and last of my paintings two weeks before the end of the semester. It was the same day that I met Professor Chastain outside the classroom for the first time. I had taken my paintings to an art dealer with whom I had become friends. I met Professor Chastain as I was coming out of the gallery.

"Good afternoon, Professor."

"Good afternoon, Mr. Stebbins."

"I hope you have been enjoying teaching us more—the undergraduates, that is—lately," I stammered. It was a mistake.

"If you are referring to your silence, Mr. Stebbins, the answer is yes. I have enjoyed that immensely."

"I decided our argument was petty," I told him.

"Art and sentimentality are always petty, Mr. Stebbins. True science never is."

"I thought we were both being rather trivial. Didn't you?"

"Only you, Mr. Stebbins, were being trivial. Good day."

The next day in Economics class Professor Chastain was discussing the construction of a model for international trade. "Let us first assume that transportation between countries is instantaneous."

"Professor Chastain," I said, raising my hand.

"Yes, Mr. Stebbins."

"Will it hurt our model any, if we assume something that has no basis in reality?"

"No, Mr. Stebbins, it won't hurt our model. Do you mind if I proceed?"

"No, sir, go ahead."

"Thank you, Mr. Stebbins."

"Next, we shall assume that no artificial barriers to trade exist."

"That isn't very likely, is it?" I asked.

"This is an assumption, Mr. Stebbins."

"Oh, I see. Go ahead."

"Next we shall assume that labor costs are the same in all countries."

"Professor Chastain."

"Mr. Stebbins?"

"Doesn't it bother you to construct a ridiculous model composed of ridiculous assumptions?"

"Mr. Stebbins, if you cannot maintain a serious attitude in this class, you may leave the room."

"Yes, sir."

It got worse. On the next to the last class day, Professor Chastain informed me that if I interrupted the class again, I would find it impossible to pass the course. This time he said it in front of the entire class. I don't think he meant to say it in front of everybody. I think he was mad, not angry, but mentally deranged. Of course, I was too by this time. But that afternoon I learned that all three of my paintings had been sold—for one hundred dollars each! I was insanely happy. I decided to keep silent the next day. My fellow students would be shocked. They were certain I would pick up the gauntlet. What else could I do? They were wrong. I was above all that now. I was a successful painter, at last.

The classroom was full that day. Students had brought their friends; even some assistant instructors had come to see the battle. Everyone sensed that the storm which had been building between us for so long now must surely burst forth on this, the last day of class.

Professor Chastain must have been awake all night waiting for this moment. His eyes were red and he seemed even more irritable than usual. He lectured for a half an hour and I said nothing. Everyone seemed to be waiting. Finally Chastain could stand it no longer.

"Mr. Stebbins."

"Yes, sir."

"Have you no choice comments for the class, today."

"I don't believe I am allowed comments any more, am I sir?"

"No, that's right. You're not allowed them, Mr. Stebbins." He smiled.

What the hell did I care? Oh what the hell, I said to myself. Chastain was still smiling. Then I did it.

"Professor Chastain."

"Yes, yes, yes, Mr. Stebbins. Something?"

"I know your mathematical proofs are abstract, and logical, and exact and all that; what I want to know is, what are your approximate graphs, Professor Chastain? Are your illustrations science, too? Or are they art, Professor?"

"I wouldn't know, Mr. Stebbins. You're supposed to be the artist, aren't you? You tell me. Are they art?"

"They certainly don't seem to be concerned with beauty, do they, Professor? Of course, they aren't exactly ugly either. They are not life-like at all. Maybe they are a bastard science. At any rate, I certainly don't find them very beautiful."

Then, at last, the bubble that was Chastain had been pricked. He burst.

"There is no beauty, Mr. Stebbins. Nor does ugliness exist. There is only order and disorder; that which unites and that which does not. Do you understand? Answers are either valid and consistent, or else they are sentimental nonsense, trash, useless junk—like your remarks, Mr. Stebbins—like your performance in my class."

"I am amazed at how much you know, Professor Chastain," I replied. "Perhaps your knowledge alone will get us through. The whole human race might be able to subsist on your graphs. Take away our blood and fill us with chalk dust. Change our flesh into a blackboard and let us have order, unity, validity. Save us from having to live an uncertain life, Professor; just plot it all and tell us which intersection is significant and which one is mathematically absurd."

"Class is dismissed."

When the time came to take the final, I couldn't make up my mind to go or not. I tossed a coin and lost, so I went and took the final. When I handed my test booklet in, Professor Chastain handed me a piece of paper with an address on it.

"It's my address. Will you come over for a beer tonight?"

"Sir?"

"I'm serious," he said. "Come by about 7:30. Will you be there?"

"Uh, yeah, yeah, I'll be there."

I rang his front door bell at seven-thirty. He opened the door. He was wearing a sport shirt and blue-jeans. Blue-jeans!

"Come in, Stebbins, come in."

"Good evening, Professor Chastain."

"Call me, Bob," he said.

What the hell! I thought, "Call me Jack, then. I don't care."

"Have a beer," he said, pulling the pull top off the can.

I noticed that he had a beer opener on the coffee table in front of us. I thought it strange, but then decided that everybody has a beer opener lying around somewhere or another. My mind wasn't working too well.

I drank my beer. I waited for him to speak. Say something trite, I thought. He did.

"We've had our differences, Jack, but I want to forget about them. Wipe the slate clean, so to speak."

"Okay," I said.

"When I went in the Marines, I wanted to be an artist."

"I thought you were born an economic theoretician," I said.

"No," he said, letting the sarcasm slip by, "I wanted to be an artist. I saw a lot of beautiful things in those days. I wanted to capture it all."

"What happened?"

"I went off to war. I saw a lot of ugly things, painful things. I didn't see anything beautiful anymore. I had to teach myself that nothing is intrinsically ugly, or beautiful either, for that matter. It was all in the way I saw it. After a while nothing was ugly to me. I could look right at it, and it didn't bother me, at all."

"You lost the beauty, because you didn't want the ugliness?"

"No. That's not quite it. Beauty and ugliness didn't exist."

"They existed as feelings in you. Beauty and ugliness are not inherent qualities in the object, but they are words that describe feelings in you."

"Not any more, they don't," he replied. "That's why I asked you over here tonight, Jack. I don't think you sufficiently understand how I feel about art now."

"I think I understand it," I said. "I just don't accept it."

"Do you believe that I hate art?"

"No, I don't guess I believe that, not really."

"See. I was right, Jack. You still don't sufficiently understand how I feel. Come in here in the dining room," he said.

"See, Jack, you can graph anything."

I followed him into the dining room. My three paintings were hung on his dining room wall, the old man, the little girls, the city, all there on his wall. I had been wrong. I had persecuted him. How could I have been so blind? He was not at all like I thought he was. Then, I saw the beer opener in his hand. He ripped a cross on each of my three paintings.

I didn't touch him. I just walked out of his house. He gave me an F in his course. I could have gone to see the Dean, but it really didn't matter. I didn't want to stay there anymore. I used his $300 to go to another state, another school. My G.I. Bill was still good. I would start over again.

Professor Chastain taught me something I was never able to get the knack of in Vietnam. He taught me how to hate. Even now sometimes, I still dream of him. I dream we meet somewhere and we are alone. I put my hands around his throat and I strangle him.

BARREL

John Hathaway

He needed a barrel, a simple, ordinary everyday type of wooden staved barrel with iron straps holding it together. The china had to go to Suzie. It sat stacked in the stripped living room as the only reminder. As soon as he had it packed and shipped off to that address in St. Louis it would be all finished: the divorce, the property settlement, the whole damn marriage.

He looked out of place in the dark musty warehouse. He stood in a small pool of light from a lone window waiting for the foreman to notice him. He hadn't worked for five weeks, but he was still dressed in his gray suit, out of habit.

The foreman looked up from his desk, which was really nothing more than a couple of stacked crates, and asked, "What can I do for ya, buddy?"

"I'm looking for a barrel," he said, "A fairly large wooden one."

"We got 'em," was the answer. "Standard price of twelve bucks each. Some of 'em ain't very good, but we let ya pick your own."

He reached into his pocket and felt what he knew he would find there, two dollar bills and some small change. The divorce had been expensive, especially without a job.

"Twelve dollars? Isn't that a little high?" he asked.

"High? Look, buddy, those are used barrels. A new one would cost ya fifteen or more," the foreman rasped.

"Oh, I see. Well, I guess I won't be needing a barrel after all. . . ." a lie; he saw the stacks of china back in the living room. "Thank you for your help," another lie; the guy hadn't been any help at all.

He tried other places, but the foreman had been right. Twelve dollars was about the cheapest you could buy a barrel for. He never paid any twelve bucks for the ones he used to roll in as a kid. . . .

In the barrel, with your eyes shut. Your buddies laughing outside, you tingling with the anticipation of your trip. You feel your body lurch and you open your eyes and look out the top and the ground has twisted into the sky . . . and what had been the blazing blue sky was now friendly grass. The world outside begins to spin faster and faster as you roll down the steep knoll. The barrel protects you from the world gone chaotic outside . . . grass to sky . . . sky to grass . . . over and over . . . and over . . .

He stopped walking and squeezed his eyes shut and he remembered. Those days had been the good ones. . . .

"Hey Tommy! C'mon, we're goin' rolling!"

"Sure, wait for me, fellas. Last one to the Fort's a rotten egg."

He was the rotten egg, but he didn't mind. A guy could forget a lot at the Fort, a nagging mother, a mean father, a bitchy teacher. It stood in the back corner of the vacant lot across the street from the Torrance Hill park. The Fort had been built by generations of kids from the old neighborhood, each generation making its own contribution in the form of an additional room or secret passage. As a result the Fort was a hodge-podge of bits and pieces of wood stolen over the years and incorporated into the main design. The many pounds of nails driven into it guaranteed its solidarity.

Inside the Fort was another world. Tiny splays of sunlight broke through the many chinks in the rough walls and onto the cool dirt floor, scattering their little touches of warmth over a fellow sitting in the coolness of the Fort.

The Fort was always the meeting place after school. And invariably they would decide to go barrel rolling across the street on Torrance Hill.

He wondered if kids still rolled down the Hill in barrels. They must. It was such a wonderful sensation that surely it wasn't lost with his generation.

He stopped his slow walking. They always kept the barrels in the Fort; there was a special room for them hidden behind a wall that moved. If the neighborhood kids still rolled in barrels, they must keep them in the Fort. It was worth a look, he was so desperate.

He started walking again, this time with a grim determination and a direction.

He found himself standing in front of the Fort. It was deserted now because school wasn't out, but it hadn't changed. The older sections were gray from abuse from the weather, while the newer additions still retained their original raw wood colors. He walked around to the rear where the "secret" entrance was. However, when he saw the small door it seemed much more obvious than he remembered.

He got down on his hands and knees and pushed the door open with his head, and then followed in with the rest of his body.

He leaned against a crate to allow his tired eyes to become accustomed to the darkness. The small storeroom was across the room from where he sat. He crawled across and pushed the wall. It gave slightly. He gave a harder push and the swinging wall broke free of the loose dirt from the floor which held it.

The storeroom was darker because the kids who had built it (he had been one) had been much more careful with its construction. Unlike the rest of the Fort, the storeroom walls did not have the many little openings which allowed shafts of sunlight in. It was cooler, too; this had always been his favorite room in summertime.

He couldn't miss the three barrels standing in the corner. They were empty, of course, and as his eyes grew accustomed to the darker room he could see the scars in their sides where they had protected their young riders from the world they were escaping. He picked the middle one. It was scarred like the rest, but all its staves seemed solid.

He remembered how much trouble it had been to move barrels as a kid; it always took two or three of them to roll one up the Hill. But the ease he had in moving this one amazed him. He'd forgotten that he was bigger and stronger now.

He pushed the barrel out of the Fort, and stood blinking in the sunlight as he inspected it. He saw that it was indeed a good barrel. The staves were all solid and none of the metal bands that held them in place were broken. It would protect that damn china perfectly.

Almost effortessly he swung it over his shoulder and headed for his house, less than half a mile away.

He took the short cut across the park. . . .

. . . and found himself standing at the summit of Torrance Hill, with its grassy banks sloping gracefully below him.

"G'wan, Tommy! I dare ya to roll down the steep side!"

He swung around and the weight of the barrel almost caused him to lose his balance.

"Who said that?" he demanded.

The empty slopes of Torrance Hill held no answer.

"I double-dare you, Tommy!"

Nobody. It had to be his imagination. But . . . it had been fun in those days to roll in his "airplane," spinning out of control, with him, the valiant pilot, struggling for the controls. . . .

He put the barrel down and looked around. Nobody. It was a pretty good-sized barrel. He should have no trouble getting inside it. What about his suit? He looked down at himself. The dirt of the Fort clung in great smears on the shimmering gray. What the hell, a little more dirt wouldn't hurt.

He laid the barrel on its side and sat down in front of it.

His capsule lay ready, waiting to project him into the limitless confines of stellar space. Colonel Thomas Smith grabbed the edge of the hatchway, lifted his body, and slid in.

Barrels hadn't changed, he noted wryly. Each was still a different world, any world its inhabitant wished to call it.

He poked his head out the top and saw that he was still poised above the slope. He lurched toward the base of the hill, and felt the barrel shift with his weight. He lurched once more and the hill took over. The barrel began to roll and he pressed his hands, knees, and body in all directions to brace himself. He watched out the top of the barrel and saw the world he hated disappear into a blur of blue and green nothingness. . . .

Inside, Colonel Thomas Smith struggled for the controls of his space capsule, which was plummeting out of control.

THE SLAP

Charlotte Schupan

My senses told me what day of the week it was. Seeing the blur of the newsprint spread over the kitchen floor, hearing the now silent, yet still-ringing grinder, a fading rhythm in my ears, smelling the foreign odor of fish skins and carrots boiling in a big pot, it was Friday. I was really home.

Sitting at the kitchen table sipping breakfast coffee, I realized that this table wouldn't be used for dinner tonight. It was the Sabbath she was preparing for, the Sabbath to be warm and beautiful. The family would eat in the dining room because it was Friday night, the holiday sanctifying family love and unity with God. Disappointments, anger, or unhappiness were intruders, unwelcome to walk into the house on the Sabbath.

What I had to tell her had to be told before sundown, before the prayers over the candles, which closed the doors to all intruders, except death. As I watched her dissecting a large hen with the precision of a surgeon, I began to feel nauseous.

"So maybe she'll pick herself up and take another cup of coffee, it shouldn't get cold?"

Mama rarely talked directly to anyone. It was as if she were asking the tail of the chicken or the bulging eyes of the fish lying on the newspaper waiting to be rolled into the garbage.

I got up, walked to the stove, turned my head away from the boiling fishheads, and filled my cup.

I walked nearer the sink so I could watch what she was doing. The chicken lay neatly in a pan and she was pouring seasoning by measuring some in the palm of her hand.

"Ma! How do you know how much?"

"How do you know? You know by practice. You know how much salt, how much pepper, whatever you like, you know. You'll know, you'll sprinkle a little of this, a little of that . . . like life, it will turn out right."

She smiled at me as if she had made a joke and the punch line was a secret enigma beyond my understanding.

She picked up the chopping bowl where the freshly ground fish mingled with bits of onions, and began pounding with an iron blade that had been her Mother's and would undoubtedly become mine. The loose skin of her upper arm moved rapidly in time with the chopping. Suddenly she stopped.

"Oh God! My feet hurt, my arm is falling off. I'll rest awhile, I'll sit. Maybe my daughter's tongue will unlock, she'll tell me about the university, we'll talk awhile. The coffee is still hot?"

I jumped up and got her a clean cup. I poured the steaming brew to the very top, what she called a full cup of coffee. Anything else was half a cup, and if you didn't pour a full cup, you were selfish and miserly. I set the cup in front of her. Mamma reached for a sugar cube, placed it in her mouth, and sipped the coffee through the cube.

"School is all right I guess. I like my classes . . . I see a lot of Marc."

She nodded approval. As she reached for another lump of sugar, I caught her hand in mine.

"Mamma, I want to talk to you. I want to quit college for awhile. Mamma. . . . Mamma, I want to get married."

"That's nice! Just a half year left to finish and she wants to get married!"

"You know Marc and I have gone together for over two years, it isn't like we just met. He starts his residency next semester at Stanford Hospital, that's four hundred miles away. We'll never get to see each other. We don't want to be apart. Marc wants us to get married."

"Ah, ha! So it's Marc who wants my daughter to quit, an education she doesn't need? Marc, the big eye doctor."

"Opthalmologist, Mamma, not eye doctor."

"He's an eye doctor. What's the matter, he doesn't like children? He doesn't want to be a children's doctor like your brother, Milton. It isn't good enough for him maybe?"

"That's what he wants to do. He doesn't really want me to quit school, I'll go back."

"Your Papa will cry. You didn't think about that? He'll cry because his baby is running away from him to jump in bed with a man. . . . a stranger."

"We love each other, we want to be together. We're not babies."

"She's not a baby! The big grown up woman. What does she know of love? She thinks maybe love is a man and a bed."

Momentary anger stirred within me. What did she understand about Marc and me? What had she ever told me of love, of sex? My original introduction to the subject had been an ugly reflection mirrored in my brain from my early years in junior high school.

It was after a gym class. Usually I hurried to the dull, half-lighted locker room, grabbing my basket of clothing, heading for the semi-seclusion of the water-stained shower curtain. I'd undress, wash quickly, and leave the water running so the others would believe the shower stall was still in use. I'd dry my body with the hard gray towel supplied by the school and dress in my street clothes before leaving the little cubicle.

But this day I was held up. When I got out to the locker room most of the girls had left. The smell of steam and sweat was overpowering, the dim room became a grotesque dungeon. I walked to the mirror over the wash basin to comb my hair and when I took the towel to wipe away the steam, in the circle of brightness I saw two girls standing at the back of the room. They couldn't see me, because of a slight jut in the room. Motionless I watched and listened.

The overdeveloped girl had everything on but her sweater, I could see her breasts bulging against her undershirt. She had just finished with the four letters and the ugly word was sprawled over the whole back wall in bright red lipstick.

The skinny girl stood stark naked, unamused and whining.

"I hope somebody catches ya, Jackie. . . . Come on, where ya hide my clothes? Ma wants me right home. . . . Come on, I'll really get it."

"Aw, shut up, baby. . . . That's what ya are, a Goddamn baby. Here's your damn clothes . . . your dirty clothes."

Jackie leaned down and pulled a bunch of wet towels out of the hamper, then she pulled out the girl's clothes she had hidden at the bottom and threw them at her.

The skinny girl began to scrabble into them. She continued to complain, "Gee Jackie! Everything's a mess . . . you're a mess . . . you're dirty, Jackie . . . just plain dirt."

Jackie's face was scarlet, furious that her friend wouldn't go along with the joke.

"What da ya mean, I'm dirty? If I'm dirt so are you, and your Ma too. Where in the hell do you think you came from? You think your Ma and Pa just sleep in bed? You dumb baby. Well, they don't. That's what they do."

Jackie pointed to the bold print on the wall.

The skinny girl didn't answer, she just stared at the wall a moment, then she started making choking sounds. She was really crying as she passed me. I could hear her shoe laces flapping against the concrete as she ran out the door and down the corridor.

"That dumb dirty baby," Jackie was saying over and over. Then she picked up her sweater, pulled it over her head as she walked toward the mirror. As her head came out of the sweater she caught my reflection in the glass. She just glared at me. Slowly she put her arms into the sweater. Her mouth was working, "That goes for you too . . . ya dirty Jew." She slammed out the door.

Stunned, I turned and looked at the back wall, and the ugly

red letters. I was drawn to the wall. Impulsively, with the hard gray towel in my hand, I began to rub furiously trying to smear the letters off the wall and out of my mind.

The Spring sun seemed to blind me as I left the school building. Everything seemed blurred as I started the six blocks toward home. I wanted to tell Mamma what had happened. Suddenly I was at our front door, exhausted, panting, I had run all the way as if a stranger was following me. I entered the house, closed the door and locked it.

I heard her call my name from the kitchen and yell something about cake and milk, but I couldn't face her. I couldn't go to her. The stranger was no longer behind me, but in the house. I unlocked the door.

Going upstairs, I headed for my parent's bedroom. From the doorway I looked into the bright clean room, saw the neat double bed with its snow white coverlet. I knew Jackie was a liar, but the words, "Where do you think you came from" and "That goes for you too," burned in my brain. I hated Jackie. In a childish way I must have hated Mamma and Papa too, because I remember that night at the Sabbath table I couldn't look at either of them. . . .

"Mamma," I said now, remembering, "you know, you never talked to me about love. What do I know of love? The only love I understood was for you, Papa and Milton. It was so nice, that warm wonderful feeling. Then one day something happened at school, and I lost you. I couldn't talk to you, I couldn't even look at you and Papa. You weren't perfect anymore . . . Mama, I think I even hated you both."

"You hated your Papa and me? The commandments say honor your. . . ."

"I know, Ma. I didn't understand. . . ."

She got up from the table, stirred the boiling water, brought the coffee pot back to the table and filled my cup to the very top, pouring what was left for herself, a half a cup. She sighed deeply and sat down, placing the empty coffee pot on the table.

"Why, asks my daughter? So I'm perfect, I know everything? No, who told *me?* My mama, *alev-hasholem,* never told me anything. It's like I said before, you live love, you practice and measure with the good and bad of life. Living with the good and bad becomes love, then love becomes the way you live."

"But you never said anything about love or emotions with a man. And you knew, Mamma . . . you knew."

"Sylvia, what's the matter? Can I feel for you? I should know what you love, or hate or fear?"

I wanted her to say something, anything to ease my mind. I wanted her to put into words what I was feeling. I wanted her to make everything all right; it was absurd, but I couldn't help it.

"Once you felt for me, you felt my pain, my fear. I suppose it was love, but you never told me."

"That's so unnatural? A mother wants to take pain and fear for her child, but it's not possible."

"One day you did! That day I came home from school in the middle of the morning feeling sick and dizzy, not understanding what was happening to my body. I came right into this kitchen, Grandma—"

"Alev-hasholem!"

"—May she rest in peace—was sitting right where you are now. When I told you about myself, you told her I was no longer a child, but a woman. She picked up her hand as if to slap me. Remember? She tried to slap me across the face and you stopped her. That was the first time I ever heard you yell at your mother. I was frightened."

Her face softened. "Yes, I remember, I stopped her. I remembered how hard she had hit me across the face many, many years before, I was frightened. I didn't want that you should feel punished like I thought I was."

"But Ma! Why did she hit you? Didn't you ever ask?"

"Did you ever ask before this moment? This moment you're asking me everything. Yesterday you knew everything. All children think they know everything. Tell me, did you ever ask me anything, Sylvia?"

"I'm asking now, Mamma," I was beginning to raise my voice.

"Sh! Sh! It was just an old wives' tale. From mother to daughter, from woman to woman."

"Old wives' tale?"

"The slap was to be hard, painful. Then came the prayer from a mother's lips . . . Dear God, my child is now a woman, protect her, may this pain be the only pain between us now as women; may her pain through life . . . through childbirth, be no greater than the pain I've just inflicted . . . Amen."

For what seemed to be a long time there was a stillness in the room, only the bubbling pot on the stove was talking out loud. The room darkened as the morning sun went behind a cloud. Mamma got up slowly and turned the light on in the kitchen. She walked back to the sink and the chopping bowl; now a gentle soft scraping, picking, sound began. She was trying to get her work done, but still wanted to hear my voice. And my voice must have amused her.

I was completely unaware that for a brief moment I was expressing myself as she did, talking to her and the cup in my hand.

"She sent me out of the house, away to college, all she said was, 'Sylvia be a good girl. Enjoy all the gifts of life, live each day with learning and goodness.' "

"So that was wrong advice? You'll get me four eggs from the ice box, please?"

I got up and took the eggs to her, setting them on the sink.

"No, Mamma, it wasn't wrong. But what is goodness? What I feel for Marc, how much I want to be with him, isn't that good?"

"It's a beginning my child, just a beginning. Later you'll see that the wanting is just a selfish beginning. Marriage with love is a woman's life."

I wanted to tell her, I wanted to shut out her words, but she went on.

"Sylvia, believe me, you'll finish your education. That's what we want for you, Papa and me. Marriage will come . . . with Marc? So let it be Marc. First things first, finish school. Your mother is dumb, an education she never got. For you we want more."

Inside I was weeping . . . Oh Mamma! Mamma, you dumb? All the damn books in the world can't help me now, just your wisdom, your measure, your practice of life. But Mamma, maybe you should have let Grandma slap me. Maybe then . . . my eyes were closed so I wouldn't see the pain on her face.

"I'm going to marry Marc. I'm going to marry him as soon as possible, I love him and need him. Mamma! I'm going to have his child."

The scraping noise stopped. I felt the numbness in the room. I opened my eyes, and she was staring at me.

"I'm sorry," I whispered.

She stood there staring, unbelief on her chalk white face.

"It's true, I'm sorry." That's all I could seem to mumble.

Mamma raised her hand. I saw it coming and I could not move. The slap was sharper, more painful than anything I had ever remembered. We were both crying; I had never seen her cry before. I reached out to put my arms around her. For a second I thought she jerked away from my touch, but then I felt her arms tighten on me. How long we stood I do not know, but the room became bright again, the sunlight blaring through the windows.

She released herself, wiped her eyes on her apron as she walked to the light switch and I heard it click. Watching her, I stood mute, waiting for her lashing words, but there was nothing.

She lowered the heat under the boiling water, reached for the heavy brass candlesticks in the cupboard and set them down on the counter top. Color came back to her tired face as she studied the candlesticks side by side. Reaching in a drawer she pulled out a clean, bright apron. Still not looking directly at me, she tossed the apron into my hands.

"Come, my daughter," she said quietly, "so you're going to be a married woman? I'll show you how to prepare for the Sabbath."

MADELAINE

David Walton

"Look," Frank said, "I'm an old breast man from way back, but that's not the problem."

He was a breast man. The whole apartment was crowded with pictures of naked women, with a forest of nipples closing around us, in every tint from pink to dark tan.

The pictures were in color, featuring the cover girls and centerfold girls from every magazine published since Frank had entered puberty.

In one corner of the room a stereo was playing an album by the Supremes, with the volume so high that it was one steady throb, punctured only by the wail of "Bay-bee, bay-bee, bay-beee. . . ."

"The problem is Madelaine. I think I'm impotent."

"What?" I shouted.

"I said I think I'm impotent."

"Look, could you turn that thing down a little?"

He turned it down enough for us to hear each other without missing anything that might happen on the record. "I don't know what to do," Frank said, giving me one of his cigarettes. "Things are just falling apart all around me. You know me, Harry, you know what I'm like—we're from the same hometown."

I didn't say anything. I knew exactly what he was like.

"Madelaine has been living with me for five months now," Frank told me, giving me his man-of-the-world smile but still keeping his eyebrows carefully knitted. "And she's really great. You've met Madelaine, of course."

"Afraid not."

"You'll have to meet her. We don't see enough of each other." He stared at one wall. "She has breasts like two pink mountains in the morning sunshine, like mounds of clean sand waiting for the tide, like—"

"You say you're impotent?"

"You know me, Harry, we're from the same hometown. You know what I'm like. Actually I think it's only Madelaine."

"Madelaine."

"She's too good for me, I mean, really. She'll do anything for me, and I don't deserve it, I don't deserve it at all. When she first moved in here, I was crazy about her. I even took all the pictures down from the wall. I was willing to treat her good—take her places, buy her drinks, cigarettes, go on walks with her. Just about anything she wanted. But she only wanted to stay here and make love."

"Ummum."

"Well, there's nothing wrong with that, really," Frank said, spreading his hands as though to catch a basketball. "But then she wanted to cook for me and sew my clothes and do my wash and shine my shoes. I have the best polished shoes on campus. She made sure that I got up for all my classes and she insisted that I put all my pictures back up again. It cost me two dollars for the tape to put them all back."

"Yeah?" One thing about Frank. He can be an interesting conversationalist, in spite of all his faults. He has a way of getting your attention.

"How are you supposed to live with a girl who lives only for you?" He lit a cigarette. "I started getting moody and had long times that I just sat and listened to records and wouldn't talk at all. But she just sat with me and held my hands and said that she understood. And then I started having temper fits and hit her a couple times—not real hard or anything, you understand, I'm not that kind of a guy. But she just said that it didn't hurt and she forgave me." He sat back and stared at one wall. "The only time I feel comfortable anymore is when she goes for a walk."

"Yeah?" I said. I glanced at my watch and then lit another of Frank's cigarettes. I was beginning to get bored, the same way I feel in a class when a professor makes his point and then has to go over it seven or eight more times. The record player clicked.

Frank folded his hands behind his head and crossed his legs. "So then it got harder and harder to make love to her, because she does anything and never complains and really doesn't make any demands. I mean, she's great practice for getting married. I just can't understand what's wrong with me. It's the best thing that ever happened to me, but it just isn't working. So I think it must be that I'm impotent."

"Oh, yeah?"

"But on the other hand, I don't think I've lost any of my powers and I still feel the same way about things. I mean, I still take pleasure in my pictures and I still feel the same way when I go to a bar where there's a lot of girls. I think it must just be Madelaine."

"Oh."

Frank frowned and did diverse things to make himself look worried. "What do you think I should do?"

"Gee, I don't know," I said, staring at my cigarette and thinking, just thinking. "Why don't you go for a walk and let me think about it for a while."

"But Madelaine will be back from the store soon."

"Oh, yeah?"

"And she'll want to cook my supper and make sure that my shoes are shined and then she'll sit down on the arm of my chair and rub my neck while I study for my geography test and then she'll make up the bed so that we can make love. How are you supposed to live with a girl who lives only for you?"

"You say she's good looking?"

"Great, just absolutely great. You've probably noticed her around campus and wondered who she was. Really great breasts."

"Like two mountains in the morning sunshine, I think you said."

"She's a great little number, hardly any wear on her. She's really built solid—they don't make them like her anymore. There's a lot of action left in her." He shook his hair back from his forehead. "But what do you think I should do?"

"What?"

"What do you think I should do?"

"Well—why don't you just go for a walk and think things over, and I'll sit here and think about it for a while and see what comes up."

"You think that's best?"

"Sure." I crushed my cigarette in the ash tray and rubbed my pants legs. "I find a good healthy walk always helps the circulation and eases the digestion."

"Well, look—there's beer in the refrigerator and you probably know how to work the stereo, don't you?"

"I'll make out."

Frank took my hand and shook it firmly, with the type of grip you get at a fraternity rush party. "You're a great guy, Harry, I knew I could count on you. I knew you'd be able to help me out—a friend in need, boy, I'll say."

"Have a good walk."

He turned back half way out the door. "She's a great girl," he said. "No trouble at all, a really satisfactory girl."

"See you later."

I lit another cigarette after he left and studied some of the pictures on the wall. One thing about Frank and me. We could always communicate clearly with each other. While I waited I went into the bathroom and combed my hair and smoothed my shirt into my pants. Fifteen minutes later Madelaine came in. She was morning sunlight. Everything about her was morning sunlight.

"I'm Harry Gordon," I said, helping her with the grocery bags she carried. "I'm a friend of Frank's. He had to step out for a few minutes and he said I could stay here and listen to records."

"Frank does have good records. I'm Madelaine." She accepted one of my cigarettes and sat on the couch.

"I get lonely sometimes," I said, lighting the cigarette for her. Our hands touched. She met my eyes. "Frank's from my hometown. I live all alone on campus—I have my own place. And it gets pretty lonely. I mean, I just sit there sometimes and stare at the walls and the place does get to be pretty much of a mess. You know how it is when a guy's all by himself. I have no talent for cooking or cleaning or even for polishing my own shoes."

"Frank went out?"

"That's right."

"He left you here?"

"That's right."

"All alone."

"I'm not alone now." I sat beside her on the couch. "Tell me, would you like to move in with me?" She dragged at her cigarette and looked at me and did not say anything. "Actually I'm a very warm and sincere person," I said, "and I don't demand too much from people. I just like the basics of life—a good clean room, some quiet music, my neck rubbed while I'm studying, my bed made up before I go to sleep. And I hardly ever get moody or testy or slap people around or anything."

She flicked ashes into the ash tray and examined the walls and shifted her breasts slightly. "Sure, why not. I don't mind."

So we loaded her two suitcases and the bags from the grocery store into my car and we went home and had a good meal and washed the dishes together and then later she polished my shoes and rubbed my neck while I studied for a test. After that we kissed a while, making signals, touching until it was time to smile together as we turned down the bed. It was the end to the evening. It was morning sunlight and it was heaven.

And it stayed like heaven for a full three months. She was a good cook. And she did polish shoes well—I had the best polished shoes on campus. And she was beautiful, in her way. And she was understanding—even when she got moody, she was understanding. And kind. And considerate. And warm. I had nothing, really absolutely nothing in the world that I could possibly, in the wildest stretch of my imagination, in my most extravagant fantasy, even begin to complain about.

Although she did not talk much, she would talk when I wanted to—even though she did it as though she were shining shoes. She was willing to discuss any subject with me. We would go to a movie, like maybe we would go to see "Doctor Zhivago," and on the way out she would say, "I think that's terrible, him going to see that other woman while his wife was pregnant." When we discussed human values, she would say, "I can't understand why people hate Jews, after they've contributed so much to our cultural experience." When I would say, "Look, do you think all this is really working out?" she would say, "Why don't you come over beside me and we'll talk about it." When I would say, "There's this new book I'm reading" she would say, "I think you have a nice body." And always, there was really no girl who could cook so well or smile so well or rub a neck so well and still look so great all day.

I guess my realest moment with Madelaine was in late March, just when the weather broke. She stood at the front window, letting the air flow onto her hair. She had just washed her hair that morning and it was soft. And when she turned, her eyes were soft, too. Her hair mussed loosely and I watched the quiet, soft curves of her body relax as she leaned against the wall.

"Why did you come with me?" I asked her.

She smiled her smile and straightened her hair a little with one hand. "Because I like you."

"Why the others, then?"

"You aren't going to hold the others against me, are you?"

"No, I just want to ask you why. Did you like the others like me—do you like everyone like you like me?"

She smiled her smile and smoothed her hair down with her hand. "You asked me to come here," she said. "I didn't ask to come."

"No one made you come," I said. She had been starting over toward me but instead she went to sit on the couch. "You could have stayed with Frank."

"No, Frank was finished with me." She took one of my cigarettes and lit it herself. "I always know when a guy is finished with me. Like last year—last year I was dating a guy in a fraternity, a real nice guy. I had a place with two other girls, and he used to come over to see me while they were out. We had some good times." She studied her cigarette and straightened the seams of her slacks. "One night he went back to his fraternity house and there was a pledge visiting from another chapter, from another college. So my guy sent him over to see me."

She looked at me, taking a bit of tobacco off her tongue with her fingernail. "You know," she said, "in the fraternities it's a courtesy to find a girl for a guy in from another school." I still did not say anything. "That was his way of telling me he was finished."

She went to the window, standing smoking her cigarette and letting the breeze muss her hair loose. "This place seems empty, bare, have you noticed?" She looked at me, smiling her smile. "You're quiet now. Would you like me to give you a happy?"

I think that was when I realized I was getting tired of Madelaine. Her answer to everything was to smile and give somebody a happy. And if she couldn't solve everything with lovemaking, she got depressed and took a walk. Living with her was like having one of those big old wind clocks—the kind that you get tired of before you get used to it.

But I never treated her bad. I never hit her or talked mean or even said anything to tell her I was tired—I think I have that much to my credit. I have thought everything over very carefully and am sure that I can't blame myself for Madelaine. I gave her a place to stay and paid the bills and satisfied her needs and was always reasonably good to her. I don't think she could have expected much more of me.

But I was tired of her, and desperate to know what to do about it. She knew about it, I suppose—there were times that she would cry after we had made love, and she was always going for her walks. It was over two months before summer vacation.

And then I heard from faithful Frank. He appeared like the god who solved all the problems in a stupid Greek play we had to read in a literature class. About a week after spring vacation he called me while Madelaine was doing the dishes, saying, "Harry, I wonder if you could stop over tomorrow afternoon to talk to me. I'd really appreciate it, because I have a lot of things on my mind and I need somebody that I know real well—somebody who's been close to me for a long time, who will understand me and be able to give me some good advice."

"Yeah," I said, "yeah, sure, I'll stop over."

"About four? How would that be?"

"Yeah, sure."

I went back to my chair, back to my studying—but instead I explored the feel of my ear lobe and stared at the pictures Madelaine had taped on the wall. "Was that your mother again, dear?" she called from the kitchen.

I could hear her stacking the dishes and I thought how warm it would make me feel to see dirty dishes in the kitchen again.

In a few minutes I felt her presence in the doorway behind me. Then I heard the water drain down the sink and I could feel her at the doorway again. After a moment she drifted behind my chair and rubbed my neck. "I understand," she said. "Whatever makes you unhappy, I understand it."

I caught her hand. "One of my old friends is stopping over tomorrow afternoon," I said.

"Yes."

"I may have to be out when he first gets here."

"Out?"

"If I'm out, will you keep him company until I get back?"

"Yes, dear."

I kissed her hand. "Give me a cigarette, will you?"

"Yes—" She turned. "Where are they?"

"On the desk, I think. None there?"

"I don't see any."

"I guess I've finished the pack, then." I looked around the apartment. "I'd hate to go out for some now."

She looked around the apartment. "I was just thinking I'd like to go out for a walk. Why don't you let me get you some?"

"That would be nice, real nice."

She put on her jacket and went into the bathroom for a while. When she came out her hair was neat and combed and she looked at me for a moment and then leaned to kiss me, her eyes closed. Neither of us said anything. She just walked out, not looking back.

I stretched and yawned and sat in my chair for a few minutes, just looking at the pictures on the wall. It was quiet in the apartment—very, very quiet. After a while I got up and called my friend John and said, "Listen, John, this is Harry. I've got this problem that's bothering me—I'm beginning to think I'm impotent, as a matter of fact. And I was wondering, since we used to room together and are so close friends and everything, I was wondering if you'd mind stopping over tomorrow afternoon and talking to me for a while."

I felt better then, just like a kid who has learned a new football play. I felt so good that I went out for a walk myself—making sure that I went a different direction from where Madelaine would be. I enjoyed the night for a half hour or so and then I thought I would go back to the apartment and give Madelaine one last, good happy.

When I got back, the place was lighted and warm and tidy. I tried to imagine what it would be like in a week—dusty, disordered, beer bottles on the desk, dirty dishes in the sink.

The bathroom door was closed, with a strip of light at the bottom of the frame. I went into the bathroom and found Madelaine dead in the bathtub, with her wrists slashed and the blood running down the drain but hardly splattered around the tub or walls at all. I looked at her for a few minutes, hardly able to move, not touching her. Then I went back into the other room and got a cigarette.

There was hardly a touch of her anywhere in the apartment and there was no note, no explanation. I went through her drawers and there were only her clothes and her cosmetics. All the brands and all the styles were nothing and said nothing. I felt sick that she had done it with me.

I didn't call anyone just then, but I went back to the bathroom and sat at the edge of the tub and watched Madelaine lying there dead. I felt nothing really, because I had never loved her and I had never actually known her, but I could not understand why she had to do it. I just sat at the edge of the tub, smoking the cigarette and trying to make her open eyes go closed.

A TIME FOR REASON

Derek Harris

The moon went down behind the farmhouse and it seemed as if the veldt itself had turned into a limitless sea of motion. It was so quiet the sound of a lizard's tongue could be heard as it flicked out to snare a fly.

In the darkness below the old house the Mau Mau were gathering, staring up at the high two-storied building, wondering how close they dared approach, looking at the shadows in the windows that looked back.

"We're safe here, don't worry," Brian Williamson told his son. "They'll never attack us here. Our lights are good and we are protected by sandbags and barbed wire to keep them away from the house. Besides I'm the best shot in the country and they know it. We'll take turns keeping watch and let them see we're not sleeping."

It was not the first time that the Mau Mau had attacked. But lately the raids had increased, and Williamson had been forced to send the farm workers back to their villages, letting the farm go to ruin rather than face the risk of being killed by them.

Twice before they had attacked his farm, but both times his communications were good and help had arrived in plenty of time. But this time he had been careless and his communications were broken. He knew his farm had become a symbol, a symbol of the "Goddam White Man," to be crushed at any cost. There were more of them than ever before and only four men to defend the farm. Four men and no help on the way.

"Not a very pleasant welcome home for you, Son."

Later, when the first light was showing through the windows, Kidogo, the head man, woke Williamson and told him that Jomo had gone. Williamson got up quickly.

"Jomo? Your own son . . ."

"I let him go, Bwana. I could not stop him. He would not listen." Williamson looked away from him.

"Your own son. They tried to kill him because he would not take the Oath, but he stayed by us. I . . . I can't believe it." All loyalties were collapsing around him. Trust no one. Your servant is your executioner. Williamson said sadly:

"Kidogo. It's just another indication of how strong they really are." He thought to himself, "I was like his own father. His father is my friend and I raised him with my own son as his brother. No matter how much we try, we'll never understand what goes on inside their heads. I can't believe he's gone to join them, yet I know how tightly his loyalty was stretched. We never know how big the gulf is between blacks and whites until we try to look across it."

The voice of his own son, Paul, cut into his thoughts. Paul, who was like Jomo's brother, not his master. "I can't understand. What did we fail to teach him?" he asked.

"The only thing we failed to teach him is that the world is getting smaller and that he has to conform to our ways," Williamson said.

Paul did not want to argue. "Or we to theirs," he said. "After all, it's their country."

Williamson looked at him in surprise. "Whose country?"

"Well, the Wogs' . . ."

His temper was beginning to mount. This argument coming from his son. Williamson said angrily. "Hell, do you know how many whites were born out here? You were! What are you, an African or an Englishman? You were born here but your mother took you to England and filled you with English ideas that don't count out here. How can you preach equality and rights in a country where the people don't understand the meanings of the words, let alone how to practice them! And what the hell do you mean by 'their country'? We took it from the Germans, who took it from the Portuguese, who took it from the Arabs. Before that . . . who knows who took it from who? Who has the proper claim, the Swahili? The Zulus? The Bantu? The Somalis, or those who worked the land, who turned it from swamp and desert into the farms we're fighting for today. It's *our* land, *ours!*" He stopped suddenly, looking at Paul; then said, "We've built something worth having and they're trying to take it away from us. It's as simple as that."

"Is it?" said Paul quietly. "What started all this trouble, I don't mean just this, but the unrest all over Africa?"

"Until now," his father answered, "the white man's rule in Africa has never been disputed. But now, he's beginning to dispute it himself. The African is just doing what the white man is doing—copying him as he always has."

"Are you trying to tell me that those Africans out there are just copying us?" Paul asked.

"You, yes! Me, no. I'm a better man than any of that bunch

out there, and so are you. The difference is that I won't deny it while you cry about how cruelly we have used the blacks. The old Boers had the right idea—they beat them publicly in the square, and there was no more trouble because they knew their reward would be pain. The British stopped all this and the blacks knew they could do what they wanted. The British took away the authority of the tribe and tribal leaders, and the young bucks left their weak villages and were corrupted by the whites. Do you think that the white man, with his military knowledge and might, can't stop these murderers? Of course not! But I'll tell you why we don't. It's because people like you wallow in their own self-accusations and become their own worst enemies. It's people like you who started that movement out there, a movement started by whites, not blacks, it's a movement downhill and there's no stopping it!"

"If what you say is true, why don't you order them to leave?" Paul said.

"Now you're looking for common sense in that bunch and I'm not sure you'll find it there," his father answered. "What common ground could we argue on?"

"You could try. They might listen."

Williamson sighed. "I wish you were right, Son, but I know damn well you're not."

Paul made a hopeless gesture. "Perhaps."

Jomo was shocked to see the Mau Mau. They were painted like the warriors his father had told him about and many were strangers, from tribes he could not even recognize. All had the mark of the Mau Mau slashed on their arms and many had harsh scars down their cheeks; some even had their teeth filed like the "eaters of men."

He was not afraid of them when they threw him to the ground. He heard a voice ask, "Did you come to take the Oath? How many guns did you bring? Did you kill the white man, Boy?"

He twisted around and saw who was speaking. The man was the leader, short and stocky, with thick legs and arms and dressed in an odd assortment of khaki uniform pieces looted from government warehouses.

"Answer me, Boy!"

"Let me get up and I will speak." He was pulled roughly to his feet. "I came to tell you to go away," he said, "to tell you that you cannot take this house. They are well-armed and will kill many of you. It is better that you go and leave them."

The leader slapped him and said again, "How many guns?"

"The two white men are great hunters, and my father has learned to shoot. They have many guns and much ammunition."

The leader laughed. "Three men, and we are an army! We are the hidden people, the drinkers of blood. The Mau Mau can hear a bird breathing. We can see an ant move in the dark, we can follow spoor so well that we track footprints on solid rock. You still want us to go away?"

"It would be better," Jomo said steadily.

"Now you will fight with us against them."

"No, I will not fight with you or against you or with them or against them."

"You are either for us or with them, Boy."

"No, I will not fight, my master trusts me."

"I will let you go back and steal their guns . . ."

"No, I will not kill my master."

"Then you die, servant to the white man."

The leader gestured and two warriors forced Jomo's head down. When the machete flashed, it sliced neatly through his neck. The warriors laughed and let his torso fall to the ground. Then they returned to the fire to joke and boast of their valor in the coming battle.

The sun had come up fast on the empty veldt, driving away the night's cold moisture, and in less than an hour the earth was dry again.

Williamson had gone to find Kidogo and discovered him on the top veranda in the front of the house. Kidogo pointed out into the veldt. "There and there," he said. "We are getting old, Bwana, but my eyes have counted more than fifty of them. Many have rifles, very many."

Williamson studied the area around the house with his binoculars. "Hell, I can't see them even with my glasses!" He turned to Kidogo. "What are they waiting for, why don't they attack?"

Kidogo thought, making a careful estimate, so as not to be a fool in his master's eyes. He said at last, "I think they are waiting for the Oath Giver, the Mau Mau priest. They are waiting until someone tells them to attack us. If they are told to wait, they will—but they will attack. Our blood is to be drunk, this they have been promised. They will probably try to force their way in tonight as soon as the moon is down."

When the sun went down and the night set in, a despondency settled slowly on Williamson. He frowned up at the moon, low on the horizon, and thought, "Ten more minutes and it'll be as black as pitch out there."

Suddenly Paul called out, "I think they're coming . . ."

In another moment the firing began, erratic, unsteady, harmless. Nothing could be seen but the flashes of their rifles. Williamson began counting the seconds: "Three . . . four . . . five . . . six . . . seven . . ." When he reached ten, Paul threw the switch that controlled the searchlights and they gazed out on a picture of arrested motion. Ten Mau

Mau were caught moving toward the house, startled into immobility, their weapons unready, staring in surprise at the lights. Suddenly the picture exploded. The Mau Mau began firing and one of them, faster than the others, broke into a run, hurled himself over the barbed wire with a fantastic effort, and made it to the lower veranda before his face was shot away by the blast of a magazine shotgun fired by Kidogo. Another group of eight or nine was out on the flank, farther away.

"All right," Williamson yelled, "let's take them now before any more make it to the house!" They fired quickly, expertly, and few of their shots missed the mark. The attack broke up as the Mau Mau changed their minds and ran back for cover, leaving five dead before the house.

Paul whispered, "Five in less than a minute." But his father was not listening. Williamson was worried, surprised at the intensity of the attack. He said, "I'd have sworn they wouldn't dare. They're stronger than we thought." Kidogo touched him on the shoulder.

"Bwana," he said, pointing, "they are sitting by their fire there. Waiting."

"Waiting for what?" Paul asked.

"The Oath Giver," said Kidogo.

The leader of the Mau Mau was binding a rag around his arm, trying to stop the bleeding bullet wound. He stared into the darkness and then turned and walked to the fire. "Get up," he said to his men, "our friend is coming." He could sense the fear in them. "Don't have any fear, he is our friend. I sent for him to help us. With his help they will not stop us again."

"How many men do you have?" the Oath Giver asked. It was his first question.

"Fifty-three, and we have thirty-four rifles and many spears and machetes," answered the leader.

"And five have died. You need my help. Bring me sand, fire, some feathers, and the eyes of a dead man," he ordered. Then he called out, "Do not fear the bullets of the white man, my magic will make you invisible and he will not be able to see you."

The things he ordered were brought. He burned the feathers in the fire, and as the smoke rose he sprinkled sand and some powder from a pouch into the fire and watched as the fire burned red for a moment. Then he took in his fist the two wet eyeballs that had been brought to him and crushed them. As the juice ran from his fists he said, "As I kill the sight in my hands, so do I kill the sight of the white men . . ." He repeated the words five times and then there was nothing but silence.

The sun had been up a long time. It was midday. And then

suddenly they came, an attack in full day. The strength of it filled them with dismay. Two hundred yards away, thirty or forty of the Mau Mau broke cover all together, and at the same time a volley of shots came from the distant rocks.

There was only one thing to do. They picked up their rifles and methodically began to fire at the attacking Mau Mau. A tall Somali twisted and fell as he was hit. Another was hit in the face by a shot from Kidogo on the roof. A Bantu threw a spear that entered the window and hit Paul in the leg, and Williamson fired and saw the Bantu fall. Paul was firing fast.

As suddenly as it started, the attack stopped. Paul poured whiskey into his wound, and then looked out the window. The Mau Mau had fallen back, the ground littered with their dead; wherever he looked there were bleeding men on the hard ground and a few were hung up on the barbed wire. The living were looking for cover among the scattered rocks.

The leader of the Mau Mau was in a bad mood. His arm was giving him trouble and he had lost twenty men because his priest's magic had failed. He was watching the silhouette of the farmhouse, stark and silent in the evening sky. Close beside him sat one of the warriors from a nearby village.

"To the east of the house," the warrior was saying, "there is a *wadi* that passes close to the barbed wire and is very near the house too."

"Why did you not tell me this earlier? Now the night has come."

"Only at night can the valley be reached."

"Can a man reach this *wadi* without being seen?"

"I reached it during the battle, when the white men were busy at the front of the house."

"You know my son, Osanga?" asked the leader.

"I know him."

"Send him to me, with four of my best warriors."

Osanga was much taller than his father. He was as tall as a Masai or a Watusi. He had spent his entire life by his father's side, caring for him and fighting with him. Now he came and sat before his father, waiting to be told what to do.

When all the warriors had arrived the leader pointed in the direction of the *wadi* and said, "When it is dark we will go to the *wadi* that runs close by the house to the east, and from there two of you will enter the house without being seen and kill the white men. If you fail we will charge them again, but this time from a distance of only fifty paces. In the house you will use only machetes. There must be no shooting, they must be found one by one and killed silently so the others will not know. My son will be one of those who enters. I will lead the group that stays in support."

Osanga was happy. "We have a good man to support us," he said, "and tonight all our enemies will be killed!"

Paul heard a faint sound upstairs and thought, "It's only Kidogo . . .yet . . ." He ran upstairs and fell over a body. When he groped at it in the dark he felt the stickiness of blood on his hands, and when he rolled the body over in the dim light, he saw that it was Kidogo. And then he was conscious of the sound of a man's shallow breathing—a man hiding close by in the shadows.

In the sudden flurry of sound and movement, he threw up his rifle to protect his head and a machete cut deep into his left arm. He lashed out and heard a body crash to the floor.

He threw himself on the man, his fingers finding the throat, and silently he began to choke away the life. He could feel the bones in the neck, and he crushed his hands together so hard they almost met. He saw the machete on the floor beside him, the blood on it his own. He reached for it and slashed downward, ending the life of Osanga.

Afterwards he did not remember the violence, his own violence and hatred. The machete was still in his hand and he threw it to the floor. He heard a sound in the doorway and turned quickly.

His father was there beside him. In his left hand he gripped his long hunting knife, red with blood. He said quietly, "There was another one below. He's dead now. I think there were only these two—any others would have made more noise. But we had better search the house."

"Kidogo is dead," Paul said.

"We have been together forty years," his father sighed. "He was my friend." Paul looked at him and said nothing.

"It wasn't anyone's fault," his father said. "There just weren't enough of us to watch the whole house. As soon as it's light we'll have to find out how they got in."

All night long the leader and his men had waited in the gulley. The men were silent, afraid. They looked at their leader, knowing the love he had for his son. They were afraid because the magic of the Oath Giver had failed. Afraid, too, because now they were sure he would make them rush the house and they would die as the others had died. Suddenly one of them said, "Look there, the white man and Osanga!"

The leader looked across to the house and saw Williamson throw down the body of Osanga from the veranda. Williamson called, "Mau Mau! Come from your hiding places and listen to me! You cannot take this house because it is too strong!" He pointed to the body below him and shouted, "There is your man who came to kill and he is dead. I give him back to you so you will know that what I say is true. Leave here before more die!" Then he turned and went back into the house.

The leader screamed and ran to the body of his son, took the lifeless form in his arms, and rocked it back and forth, weeping. Here was a young man who would have been a great leader and now he was dead.

Paul raised his rifle and squinted down the barrel at the grieving man. His face was filled with hatred. Suddenly his father knocked the gun out of his hands. "NO, Paul."

"Dammit!" Paul screamed. "That's their leader, look at his uniform!"

"No."

"But they killed Kidogo and probably Jomo. They kill us and we have to kill them.

"No."

"What would you do then?"

"Maybe the time has come for reason. Now is the time to find out."

The leader looked up when Williamson stood beside him. "Your son?" Williamson asked.

"My son, my family, all that is left of it."

"And this is the price you pay . . . for what?"

The leader did not answer for a minute. Then he said quietly, "I do not know."

"Take your son and bury him, and we will bury our dead, and then you must take your men away from here. Take them back to their villages and have them count their dead."

The leader of the Mau Mau picked up the body of his son in his thick arms, turned, and walked back to his waiting men.

Williamson did not turn back to the house until the Mau Mau began moving away. The battle, for the moment, was over.

TWO: A GROUP OF YOUNG POETS

ELLIE: AN INVENTORY OF BEING

Eleanor Wait

I am Ellie.

I am twenty years old.

I am a student, but never a co-ed.
A girl, afraid to be a woman.

If I stand very tall I am 65 inches high.
I have blue eyes streaked with gray
And tarnished brown hair
That gets in them.
Sometimes I wear it in a bun and am Emily Dickinson or
Louisa Alcott
Or in pigtails, and play hopscotch in front of Mellon Institute.
Or just let it hang,
And run down Chapel Hill anyway.

I am a student, and a lady, and a child;
Almost a woman, but always a girl.

I love rare steak and burnt potato chips.

I am older than Neenie,
Younger than Lea;
I love the smell of Arpege and mud flats.

I drink tea with lemon and sugar with coffee.

Daffodils laugh, but blue-bells depress me.
I'm afraid of trolls.

I like raisins in oatmeal, and in the sun.
I work best under pressure.

I like shiny fingernails and jazz, but
I hate Altman's and mini-skirts.

I like small rooms lined with books, and braided rugs, and
Pillows, because I like to sit on the floor.

I like fountain pens and brown notebooks and blue ink and
I don't believe in god, but I don't tell anyone anymore,
And my children will go to church,
Because I love Christmas.

I love pearls.
I like garnets better than rubies,
And topaz more than diamonds.
But someday I want a diamond
And a gold band
Forever.

But not just now.

Someday I want a girl named Jeannie and a boy named Mike —
But they'll have to wait.
Because I want to be a person first.

Subject to change.

I believe that women are more than equal, but keep quiet
about it.
I know there are 435 members of the House of Representatives
But I don't understand why more of them aren't Negroes and women.

Rachel Carson and Margaret Chase Smith were my high school
ideals.
Now I'd add (quietly) Jean Kerr.

I'm an anti-feminist.
I love to travel alone.

I'm crazy about noodles and tuna fish and pizza with pepperoni
and Jello.
I hate clutter, unless it's books.

I love cosy slippers and lacy underwear and going barefoot
in the mud.
I make spaghetti in a popcorn popper, and always add paprika.
I am in love with chipmunks, pigeons, and 4 x 6 envelopes.
I read Dickens and Ferlinghetti.

I love wind and rain and snowmen
And Baroque music and Barbra Streisand, even if she's trite.
And I don't like earrings or hair spray or soap operas and
I adore commercials.

I love fireplaces with real fires, and front porches with
creaky swings, and noisy typewriters.

I like strawberry milkshakes and frosted lipsticks.
I'd like to be cultured, but I love WABC and
I daydream at the symphony.

I love to get dressed up, but I don't waste time doing it.
I hate alarm clocks and television sets. But I couldn't live
without them.

I'd rather walk than ride. But I'll drive anywhere.

I'm honest to a proudly self-conscious fault, and I'm
Corrupt to a deeper meaning.
I wish sex were legal — but I went through a phase of
wishing human sacrifice were too.

I don't want to grow up, but I'm scared to stay young.

I eat too much, sometimes, and talk too much, often, and
Wish I could sleep too much, always.

If the world were a stage I'd feel more comfortable in it.

I'm a loner, but I love being lonely.
I'm a conformist, except when I think.
I have horrible nightmares, and wild daydreams,
And I couldn't live without either.

I spend too much money on velvet hair ribbons and funny cards
and books of plays.
Hamlet and Antigone are my ideals, but
Creon and I are one.

I think too fast.
I hate greasepaint, but I love crowds.

I love Degas, but I don't think I like horses or ballet.
I've always wanted to be the first woman president, and a
marine biologist, and a literary lionness,
And an archaeologist,
But I'm allergic to dust.

I don't want anyone to understand me,
But people think they do, and
They're probably right.

If I were rich the first place I'd go would be Scotland.
The second would be Stratford.
And the third would be Disneyland.

I need someone to need me, because then I need them too.
I'm a deadly realist, but I pretend to be idealistic.
I used to think there was no such thing as love.
Now I'm not so sure.

I never want to go to the moon, but I'd love to see penguins.
I've always felt that horses were incomplete zebras.

I'm funny.
But most of the time it's intentional.

I get migraine heartaches.

I either love or hate October and March; I haven't decided yet.
I like men who know that women are people too,
And I hate crew cuts and red hair.

I'm a drama major because there are only five of us.
I support the minority, but
If I were Jewish, I'd be conservative.
If I were a Democrat, I'd be liberal.
I'm in favor of staying in Viet Nam,
But I hate war.

I may be in love, and it scares me.
But he doesn't.

I love to see the sun rise, but hate to get up in the morning.

I'm perennially frustrated because I can't know everything,
And I'm annually concerned about self.

My name is Ellie, and this is 1967.

PLAYGROUND

Eleanor Wait

Step
on a crack,
Break
your mother's back.
A hop
And a hop
And a
Skip
Skip
Skip.
I want a lick
of your popsicle stick
Red rover,
red rover,
Let Mary come over.
Concentrate, Miss! concentrate
Miss
tress Mary
Quite contrary.
The sun is high
In the sky
And I want a piece
Of your mother's pie.
One
Two
Three
Four
Open the door.
I want more.

Come'on Joey
Start'er
Start'er!
We want a pitcher,
Not
a glass
of wa
ter.
And hop
And hop
And run
Sheep
Run.

WHALES

Barry Herem

The whales go by in December.

I watch them from the cliffs,
Seeing them pass . . . in twos, in threes, in herds.
The great-fluked whales pass.
And they are so great, these solemn beasts,
Gray or spotted with heavy shoulders pressed upon
            the yielding sea
            as they go,
Past the crags of the land,
Down the edge of the sea.
        And in their time the geese go south,
        The lemming swarm,
        Grunion run,
        Bears burrow,
        And cocoons are spun.
        The salmon search for the certain stream,
            Ermine bloom in the snow.
But I have spied whales from the cliffs,
                                        great whales,
And watch them pass down away,
            down the edge of the sea.

AT TWELVE

Barry Herem

My sister has long arms,
Some call them gangling at her age,
I find them lovely — very Gi Gi
        (that's her name).

She swings them when she walks
    down our suburban street from school
And they remind me of two topsy-turvy metronomes
    that
Click along in separate twos
    and
Counterpoint the heels of her shoes.

She has a grace that's all her own
with her light and almost
skinny arms,
But brother can she swing a ball!
They are not weak, those arms, I know,
We've fought enough and scuffled,
pulling hair.
I find she eats her spinach.

Right now
her predilections don't imply her sex,
But her arms do.
She slings them straight across her head
when she is always
"prematurely"
marched to bed
And then they are a wreath of youth,
white, drooping petulance
that promises to bloom.
And when she sleeps they intermingle with her hair.

GATHER ME

Barry Herem

As you would divided stalks of grain,
you may gather me that way,
All my particulars.
When I am slumped, care-creased, and very tired,
then gather me.
When I grieve,
When I turn away most, baring my back,
then gather me.
Gather me when my legs are down
And when my eyes are gray,
When I lean away gather me as you would some leaves
on cool
September mornings.
Bring me to your breast when I refuse to speak,
Bring me as you would some bloom,
up to your lips,
And gather me in spite of taciturnity and tears.

FUGUE: TO J. S. BACH

Karen Burke

The last pew in St. Thomas Church
Is reserved for three parishioners who,
Punctually five minutes late each Sunday,
Thread their way through the aisles
In plain view of the congregation.

Enter Basso,
Flinging open the left front door;
Compact, complete within himself,
He revels in the resonance of
Leather soles on solid floor.
Never glancing sideways,
He lands triumphantly
In the first seat
In the last pew

of St. Thomas Church, where,
Instantly the congregation shifts its focus
Forward, heralding the arrival of Alto.
Slightly younger, slimly profiled, and
Having paused his measured time
Within the vestibule,
He now appears to trace his pattern
Down the center aisle
Toward the second seat
In the last pew

of St. Thomas Church, where
Two will now perform
An episodic carol in duet.
Mid-duet, the congregation eyes the door
In expectation:
Enter stretto, tripping staccato
Through the right front door;
Soprano, dancing over sacred floor
Toward the amen corner of the room,
Where her comrades carol
In a joyful way
In the last pew

of St. Thomas Church. And now
There are three, though seeming more than three,
Parishioners, who resolve their differences
In full hearing range of the congregation;
Three, signifying more than stating,
And exulting in restraint of unity
From their place
In the final Gothic pew
Of Baroque St. Thomas Church.

After a brief but extremely productive life as musician and composer, Mozart died while composing the "Lacrimosa" chorus of his Requiem Mass. A pupil, Süssmayr, later completed the composition in Mozart's original style.

REQUIEM

Karen Burke

I am told
You were classic and correct,
Declaring each chord the rightful heir
To its predecessor.
You listen now, perhaps,
While the court judges your choices
Inevitable;
As though Music hovers, unheard,
Awaiting a hand to release it from silence,
Or voice to echo.
The verdict, Mozart: earthly instrument,
Divinely taught.

"Lacrimosa" . . .

Tears, tones,
Flowing into sacrificial phrase.
Pity us, who seek a name
For what must be forever nameless;
We ponder ethos — pathos,
Bestowing you with equipoise.

"Dies illa" . . .

On that day,
Did you weep for us?
Wrapped in final sorrow,
You may not have seen your comrade
Waiting to rescue you mid-phrase,
Bring you to deserved completion.
His tears, and ours, mingled with yours
Already fading into paper,
As he gently plied the pen from still-warm fingers
And blotted the ink spattered across the page.

THERE WAS SOMETHING

Cynthia Henderson

There was something I wanted to say
But a milkweed seed lit ever-lightly on my nose
I blew it off
and ran the whole length of the field . . .

There *was* something I wanted to say
But a piece of tune hopped piggyback onto the thought
and rode away with it . . .

There was *something* I wanted to say
But a funny boy with big bright laughing eyes dared me to a race
I'm breathless! . . .
Oh, it can wait.

IF

Cynthia Henderson

If you'd tied a wisp of dandelion around my waist,
I'd have sung you a wildflower song,
But you must have me vine-trussed.

Well, sing to yourself
    my friend
Or find yourself a housebroken rose
To sing to you
at day's end.

POEM FOR CHINA

Olivia Hogue

Surely the Red Guard has not
destroyed all the books in the Imperial library.
I am convinced that in the back of some converted
building now devoted to the archival party,
the old scrolls are still rolled, waiting
for the scholars to return.

Somewhere there are whole maps and treatises
upon the nine burning cities, records of trade
in the blue oxide, the old locations of petuntze
and the feldspars, and the comments of Lao-Tzu upon
the prunus vase which held the flowering branch.

Only the ancient potters have ever known the real
porcelain, only in China were there fields of
white clay waiting for the variant, dynastic wheels.
Do his potters work in the new commune, or does Mao
too eat off his version of Melmac? Oh China, China,
you live on the white belly, have you praised
God or the prunus vase lately?

Somewhere there is a good spy
who must infiltrate the walls of the new library
and walk past the political stacks to the back room
and efficiently and calmly microfilm all the scripts.
He will see that they are smuggled out the usual routes
until they reach the outer mailbags. We must all
look under the postage stamps of all the letters
we receive from now on, who knows that he is not the
end of the network, and may not be the recipient of
dictionaries and records.

I am convinced that if I read them with calm and
deliberation, page by page through to the end, I shall
understand Chinese and be able to browse in the imported
library, acquainting myself with the unknown potters, and
poets of Han, knowing absolutely all the old terms, and
reading for pleasure, one word after another.

THE COOKING TIPS OF JULIA CHILD

Rene Rickabaugh

1

This is the old
mixer I like to use
to mix everything
up in
between the beater blades with
a rubber spatula and all the jewels
of Golconda's ladies
plus the savors of Murial Gustaphony
for she rises in the loaves of my eggs omelet
once-over. Sprinkle
in ground round plus
a pound from your heart's chambers
for flavor
then smear out the
lumps you
will find it helpful. Roll out
dough 3/16 inch thick,
powder, rub
down with slick braided-black crow's wing rolled
in soda crumbs and add liver with any
of your own trappings for
that will give
it the touch of Doreen Bleakney
who can stuff lobsters with the
weeds of her own smile
and give a rug shampoo at
the same time
with a bonbon shining in
her teeth.

2

Now you are ready to flip the switch
in order to toss the pot of your
Blendette Kitchen Helper.
And get used to this business of tossing the pot,
for it eases the ham into place
without creasing your elements.
At this point you can also remove your
spattered bottom, and using a
Swansdown whip, beat the body vigorously.
Throw in a six-pack of wings, then pierce
a cross in the closed end
of your padded flap, and simmer the legs
in gumbo. For this I shall use my
favorite loop-and-dart spooner,
and carefully baste the momentum of the heart.

3

Shape dough around anything
handy like
this horse-shoe pan then
trim with
ravioli wheel for
it leaves the edge
buckled, pressed, and
pink curly
especially if you
shake an angel with her harp
behind the bark-black alder-dark
corridor doors,
constantly singing with a high
red voice of the "drums
of the forest, gloria on the
highest, adeste to the Lord
of tarts, dominum,"
then frost and serve with roses for
you have honored Lucy Cake
and the White Fathers.

SOMEWHERE UNDER AN UNKNOWN LENGTH OF LOVE

Rene Rickabaugh

The rare Harietta-Bird is a bare-knuckled flusher
readily identified when fanning the muscle of her frontal buffer.
Somewhere under an unknown length of love,
she slims the fatty midriff of her silent symmetry
and swelters in the fevers of divinity. While hunting
her domain, proceed with caution. Do not refrain
from 'tween-meal treats or the fires of hot devotion, but lie
in the original position of glory
as you gargle the passion of her holy timber
which is tender, and repairs you with the lumber of its splendor.

Full-grown queen grunts with cheek
barbs or freckled kissing-grunts are often spotted as a
snapper variety of the terrific savage gorilla-grunt.
In lofty-flavored crafts and bated steeps
we see him wear the baggage of cool deeps and hark
among the slur of turbid cinders. Spring settles
to the bottom very fast, but passion always lingers.
(Listen, and you will hear the silent clouds
forever softly hover over boulders. Somewhere before
desire becomes tedious in the mind,
a tender true-ankled aphid is crunching
geranium shoulders.)

The Springtail Luna is usually the first footed sinker
to appear after the turn of the deer. He is
a livestock fugitive with free-moving molars,
sprocketed shoulders, and a terminal ear.
Somewhere under an unknown length of love, the walrus has dragged
a belly-full of fainted tuskers
while the snail extended with unchartered capacity
a random mouth over the jelly-roll
which it did not understand at that moment
of fierce velocity touching quite tastily,
somewhere before any experience lunching so fearlessly.

These unreal dramas quicken and are here.
And so I will be where I will not be,
in reckless winds that are and are not near. Beside
my tomb, the grass is growing late.
And flushing beauty does not hesitate
to bicker, but barely warbles in the huffy dark
a human chirp, and hears the daisies bark.
Sweet Donna drops her legs into a canyon,
removes her arms, and cries for some companion.
(Oh what brave prince will save
this lovely maiden from sure death?)
Stay tuned for an unknown length of love to grace
her breath while we take pause
in deep and gentle tremor to impart
that there's more whitening power
in heaven than the regular, brand X heart.

Nowhere before any experience have you
touched this season. Feel it truly
while the Harietta-Bird is fanning her footed sinker,
while the walrus is lunching with fugitive molars
forever and only yesterday,
while a reckless grunt over the ocean cruises in
the last rising of Spring that is turning now
and never into primeval bruises,
somewhere and always under an unknown length of love.

TO JIM...DEAD IN VIETNAM

Peter Fellowes

Why couldn't you have shot baskets
all those years or spent the time
rooting on Chicago's Cubs or Blackhawks,
your loves, instead of Latin.

How could you know
those anguished hours of recitation,
your red face buried
keeping six lines ahead in Vergil,
were hell, for nothing in return.
You hated yourself through all four years
to cross the world, then die.

IN A SUMMER ROOM

Marsha Brody

Why are your eyes unquiet?
You used to be content
To lie asleep on quilted spreads
After the stories we'd invent,
And lazy in the afternoon,
Laugh at the empty hours we'd spent.

Will you believe me if I say
There's nothing more outside?
Be glad of summer organdy
And slatted blinds that hide
The sun from your half-wakened face.
It was a dream voice cried.

And in the morning, as before,
I'll bring you fresh-brewed tea,
And we will talk of gentle things
And listen to the sea,
The only other sound you hear,
A voiceless memory.

POEM TO e.e.

Patricia Schneidhorst

On reading all of E. E. Cummings'
"Sonnets — Realities" — in one sitting

What's-your-name
my love
this unspontaneous night
of shall I say
love?
(our preposterous bodies cling moistly
from utter exhaustion)
is over.
thank god for morning

LOVE IN THE WESTERN WORLD, LESSON 12

Patricia Schneidhorst

Men and Women: in general they
are faithful and true to their spouses each day.
In spite of temptation, they do what is right;
— they go home to their wives and their husbands at night.
Not for any good motives (the lesson is sad),
but for lack of a comfortable place to be bad.

TUESDAY

Patricia Schneidhorst

So this is how it is, then.
No shouting, no sudden moment of decision,
no certainty;
the day chosen
because that's the day the movers can come.
No tears;
only those swallowed or shed so long ago
that only numbness is there.
No meaning;
our whole attention given to
who shall get the refrigerator,
the cradle, the books, the cat.
The children wander blankly
through the liberated dust.
A lost shoe is found, too late.
Your back is turned; there is
no final confrontation.
My arms are heavy as I close the door
at last.
Even the sky is sullen.
The clock does not strike
as I descend the stairs.
Having let go, there is no release;
only a tired turning away,
this time forever.

SCOUTING PARTY

Lawrence Kistler

I wait upon the hillside; nothing moves
But gently flapping leaves and the slow
Collapse and heave of faded-denim lungs.

Along the valley, sedentary pools
Remain from courses and fine channels dug
By beaver. Here, when young I brought my tools,

A rod of beech, string, safety-pins — and knew
No limit to my catch. The bites were strong
And fought the line that held me to the edge.

I sweep the meadow with scarecrow eyes —
Broods of sparrows fail to stir the fields
And no gay toss of underbrush tracks squirrels;

The sky has died, a muslin cloth thrown damp
Upon the mountains, numbing whirl
Of birds, the flight of atoms, river's flow.

And on one bark-stripped spur of neutral ash
Kingfisher sits, rattling his song
To woo the minnows from the cove, alone

With me in this pale and glaring valley
This still-born universe shaded by trees.

AFTER THE DEATH OF MY GRANDUNCLE JOSEPH PATSEY

D. W. McGinnis

I

As we sat with you one summer evening,
you with a bottle of beer in one hand,
and a steaming mussel in the other,
told the story of Kwatee, the Changer.
Your grandchildren sat in a huddle,
awed by your heavy-lumbered frame
and demonic shadow painted in the sand by fire.
When your laughter cracked in the pine logs
that smelled of kelp and seaweed,
we knew the story followed the seasons.

Seven years have passed since I last saw
the fishnets that hung through winter
to drape across the common stream.
What cold winter afternoon was it
when your pantomime told the story of the black elk
who was only caught in dreams,
and the Chinook salmon held in a net,
and because of his bronze eyes and flapping defiance,
you threw him back into the sea?
Or the morning we heard you shout profanity
at the heap of crab shells you had fallen on
that had been discarded the night before,
after the all-night feast?
We still don't know how you managed this fall.

Today, your home is covered with forest flowers
and ferns, and the little animals of stone
you carved and lined to your front door
are mirror dreams of your children's children.

What is all this without you, granduncle?
How long before the story that grew in the flames,
did you first begin to die?
Was it when you lived in the square circle?
Is it true that today your sons lie stripped
down to their hides, charred stumps in a cedar forest,
old roots in the soil of many seasons?

II

Sometime in old age, I will look up at Mount Taoppish
like my granduncle did before they threw him
back into the foliage of blue coral and red sand,
salted bones for the crabs and fish,
and see him wave to me as he watches salmon fin
the Quinault river rapids on their way to spawn
in the Ho-Had-Hun creek beds.

Later in the darkening sunset I see him follow
the winds down the mountain to where pacific seas
roll red sand through the coral reefs of blue bones,
and then feel our similar and different clay,
and die like the men of cedar in his stories,
rain-soaked and restless.

BALLAD OF A TRIANGLE

Marion Pendleton

"Now the air is sweet with lilac scent,
Why are you so full of merriment,
Mother, O my mother!
And wear a smile full content,
Mother, O my mother?"
"For your father's love, my dear, I smile,
For the love of your father, I smile."

"Now the maple leaves are turning brown,
Why is it that you wear a frown,
Mother, O my mother?"
"Your father stayed the night in town,
Daughter, O my daughter!
Your father stayed the night in town,
And that is why I wear a frown."

"Now that the branches all are bare,
Why do you lie on your bed there,
Mother, O my mother?
And wear a look of anguished care,
Mother, O my mother?"
"Because of your father I languish, dear.
Because of your father I languish here."

"Though the weather freezes to the core,
I saw him in the village store,
Mother, O my mother,
And he's as healthy as before,
Mother, O my mother!
His eye is bright, his step is light,
And he's as healthy as before."

"I cannot doubt the word you tell —
He has a new love to keep him well,
Daughter, O my daughter,
But I am under a poison spell,
Daughter, O my daughter!
He has a new love to keep him well,
But I am under a poison spell."

"What is the woe that you relate,
What is the spell that seals your fate,
Mother, O my mother?"
"My poison is a cup of hate,
Daughter, O my daughter!
My poison is a cup of hate,
And drinking it has sealed my fate."

THIS OLD MAN

Angel Abitua

he is candlelight.

one
night closer to the snuffing-out.
he is candlelight
cast
on the walls of a rented room. one
room closer to the snuffing-out.
he was once (and
this
was a hundred thousand years ago, I
think) a potential prince.
he danced with
Cinderella,
so it seems, but never bothered with
the slipper, and if you don't bother
with the slippers, you become like
this old man:
just candlelight,
cast
on the walls of a rented room. one
room closer to the snuffing-out.

WHITTLING

Hillel Schwartz

You cannot hurry a horse out of wood.
If you do, it will come still-born and stiff
From the shavings, this no matter how good
Your blade. There is a patience to the life
Of animals more akin to wisdom
Than timidity, even if they be made
Of pine or cedarwood. You find they come
At their own pace, feeling out their own way
Through the block. You try to give them some small
Freedoms, let them breathe, shiver, toss their heads.
Often you will notice scars in the grain
Where a particular young rebel
May have tested his hooves, kicking at dead
Branches. If so, then no lacquer or stain

Will hide that wound, a not uncommon birth-
Mark of a colt who winces at your steel.
Take care, then, that what you at last unearth
Is no hunchback stallion you cannot heal
With your artistry. Magicians must know
How to handle splints as well as curses.
Take care, also, that when you set your knife down
And rest, you do not forget that horses
Move more quickly than men, and are easy
To take fright and run. Above all, work slow
And careful, and maybe whistle some
Or sing. Animals tend to shy away
From nervous men. Never pull or push. Show
Your horse a gentle smile. Then he will come.

THE FRENCH DOORS

Hillel Schwartz

Open the French doors
And let the flowers in
Let the morning come for
Breakfast. This house has been
Too often lately dark
And hidden in an unworked

Shawl, fearing what the sun
Might do to dust. Let us turn
This house around to come
Upon a breeze. My words
Have been my souvenirs
So long that now none hear

My songs; they think them gone
The path of other simple things
And pass. And here alone
With you, as loyal as the hinges
On the leaflets of this table,
I sit and touch the fables

That we both remember,
Having set these napkins
Out, day after day, for
Numberless years. Let us begin
Again to touch the flower's bloom.
I will not die inside this room.

A TIME FOR MOVING

Marjorie Allegro

We must be still and still moving
into another intensity. — T. S. ELIOT

I am held fast.
With a great rush of air I swing again,
blood seeking the path of hair — a trail behind.
Up, up to the point of the arc —
an agony of suspension,
a nothingness —
then a quick fall, past my beginning,
farther, farther into irrational necessity.
Another fall — a rise —
another
another.
But in the wise order of being
the arc is narrower
the swing slower
till finally a stillness.
Suspended straight,
stretched, ironically, by gravity,
my hands reach deeper
and deeper
into what surrounds me
and I am held fast by acceptance.

LETTER TO HIS WIFE

Geof Hewitt

Lately I walk without a cane
my legs are stiff but that remains
an old consideration
hardly worth the trouble of your thought.
        I remember once when we were
        young, how we could laugh at older
        couples, their determined optimism:
        polio shots at sixty-five!

I would not have troubled you
so late in life, if you had not been
my wife once and if I didn't feel
a need, some need that cripples
me at times like withered hands:
my cook is good, she makes the broth
for me at midday, the nurse considerate
and as friendly as a volunteer.
        Last spring I had a fall
        (I think it was that cane
        that jinxed me) and since
        I've had to keep a nurse.

I hope you understand: there really
is no reason for my writing you
this way, unless it be that just
once more I like the feeling
of your sullen enmity: perhaps
if you ignore me now, I can be
satisfied again, I'll feel as if
your love for me still turns in you
like hatred stored for years:
the way you severed all your ties
with me, this town, our friends,
was in its way a consolation.
        Some letters came for you last year.
        I opened one inadvertently,
        thinking it for me. After
        so long, one rarely checks the name.

Perhaps you've wondered what would come
of it if you returned. Oh, not for long
— I know your feelings there —
but just for, say, a week,
ten days. I'd give the nurse some time
off, she really only serves to talk
now that I'm walking well again:
I'd light a fire each day you stayed.
There might not be much to talk about,
unless you feel yourself again and want
to bring back those old arguments.
I know I'll never win. That's half the fun.
    Before I close just let me say
    how beautiful this winter is.
    We have a room where you could
    sleep, first floor, no stairs to climb.
    The snow has nearly buried the old shed
    two times this month, and every night is dead
    quiet. Because the dogs are gone,
    I sleep without those ear plugs now.

LE CADEAU

Marianne Confalone

I gift you with
words, music of

a different kind.
Each poem I give

you bridges
another river

between us.
Hand it back

and we will
both drown.

THE GIANT YEARS

Beverly Sopp

Giants were more real
than men. Their golden capes stung
our eyes with light; we
believed. (That year we had slain
forty dragons and could not
wash victory from our hands.)
We did not shudder at strength
but wheeled upon them —
as if they were springing from
dragon's teeth. The clang
of our swords against
their armor stuffed our ears. Young
to blood, we would slip
easily under their legs
invisible because we
closed our eyes. One day we looked
away, then back. Giants shrank
to fire-fly size and
rode the wind. Only we were left;
our legs stilted the grass.

PREGNANT STREET

Tom Wayman

In May, the great trees budded
and the street's day women all
were pregnant. They paced slowly
past each other's lawns, up for
groceries and down, while the
children scooted shouting for
their greater mother.

The van
pulled up late in the warm June
evenings, the man now home to
a beer in the backyard, and
meeting the mother-in-law's
late train, and talking with the
suddenly-lost, suddenly-
lonely children.

In July,
the last July, the great trees
were a green roof on Pregnant
Street. And in the evenings, sounds
of distant traffic, insects
in the flowers, birds hunting,
and all the children playing
war.

THE CAPES OF HORN

Tom Wayman

She is a storm ho! *ho!* a lick and not a kiss.
A rumpling combat with warm writhing flesh.
Who charted me soft comfort drew a mesh
Of easy lies: I anchored there amiss.
Beyond the Capes of Horn, there's no relief from squalls:
I find more wildness there than in the tossed brain's walls.

She is a scratch Good Christ! and her rasp tongue . . .
There's blood! all rapped and rummaging; her arms
Permit no pause from budding, tendrils escalate the farms.
I'm kicked, I'm wriggled and she still pokes at the drum!
Beyond the Capes of Horn, the expected gentle snows
Sizzle in the sheet, the heat, the blows.

She is a bite ha! tickle ho! a jab.
And who could leave the thrashing? Clear the way!
The clock pulled me leg-southward many a day
Past the mere bullet-facing veterans and a sob.
Hovering round the Capes, she arms for my return.
She writes she's learning judo; I, the ways to burn.

Beyond the Capes of Horn by God! she is one war
For me alone, she says she's loose again! the door's ajar.

HAWKWEED AND ASTER

Mary Slowick

Yes, this meadow is worn out.
    See where oats and wheat
        have worked holes through grass,
    the sand-gravel, wash-out scars.

But look at Hawkweed and Asters,
    beaming back at morning sun,
    little suns in their own rite,
And white-thumbed Daisies,
    splotched beneath maroon-rich clover,
And wild vetch and alfalfa,
    blue-green renegades from fenced pastures.

"Growing only where poor soil
    eliminates competition," the Botanical Garden says.

No, wheat and oats won't grow here any more,
But look at Hawkweed and Asters.

CEDAR KEY

Richard Mathews

I

At midnight
the precise and practised stars
stopped time;

like dumb and bandied bundles
the whiskered fisherwomen
mumbled on the dock;

their buckets and sitting boxes
sprouted from the antique boards
in strange square vegetable shapes;

the dock planks
glowed
under buzzing arc-lights,

and if the poised and gleaming rods
danced upon the air,
or if the fine bay vapors
tapped their mists against the wood,
the movement was the same,

the tight strings threading through the air,
the still, cracked hands of the bundled women
gripping and waiting on worn cork handles,
waiting for the sky to break,
for the sea smell
tiding on the violet bay
to split the seams of the
star sewn air in the rich and heavy dark
and to call the gone time back
with the patient nibble of a fish.

And so upon this dock
the fisherwomen wheezed and waited,
counted slowly to themselves,
and the breathing of the old and ragged
ladies mingled with the spellbound air.

II

The tired odor of eternal salt,
the nascent promise of eternal rest,
the fundamental sky was woven with
the simple expectation
of a fisherwoman's catch —
and finally one green cord
jerked darkly at the end of a yellow finger.
The surface of the bay was shattered;
the lady leapt from her vegetable seat.
She threw her rod against the sky
as if in praise, and the sky
dispersed in widening ripples on the bay.
Stars wavered at the edges of the night
and then, released, slipped slowly out of sight.

The ragged woman
labored, reeling fishing cord
in isolated joy.
Her small, drawn eyes
gleamed with the holy light
of reverence,
and just as brilliant
came the sharp, quick
flip of silver
on the water's undulating surface:

a bay fish
cunningly free;
green cord
in useless
collected
profusion.

The woman breathed
and watched the light
with lambent eyes;
her simple face
blushed
with the timeless mission
of embarrassment.
The naked hook
dangled as she counted bait,
replaced a shrimp
precisely
and threw her line into the sea.

III

Upon the rotting planks
another nine shrimp waited,
nudged in a newspaper bundle.
The fisherwomen gripped
their silent lines
more closely
and the vanquished night
resumed.

THREE: TWO PLAYWRIGHTS AND A SCREENWRITER

THE LAST LOST WEEKEND OF MISSIONARY PEALE

Keith Spencer Felton

SCENE ONE

The living room of the home of Ned Peale. It is furnished in a hodge-podge of rattan chairs and a bamboo couch. Between the chairs is a large Congo drum, which serves as a coffee table; this arrangement faces the audience. Behind it, to one side, bamboo shades are drawn over old, incongruous French doors, which serve as the main entry. Near the entry, an old coat rack, with a long black clerical robe hunched on one of its spikes. Upstage, a well-smoked stone fireplace, with a great, fierce-looking brown nubby shield cresting the mantel. The remaining wall provides a door which leads to a kitchen.

The entire room is garnished with the myriad memorabilia of a far-off and long-over jungle safari: on one wall sags a rust-and-blue dyed rattan quilt; pith helmets, walking canes, and spears are seen; machetes legend the corners. Framing the fire are rows of weathered and dusty books, with an old record player and some records sandwiched in on one shelf. A spattered thatched-leaf rug hides the hardwood floor. This tropical pastiche seems ablaze with activity, a gouache of color and light. The kitchen-side wall is a gallery tattooed with faded photos of Ned and assorted Africana — Ned in khaki, greeting the minister of a village; Ned in great flowing beard, spear-jousting playfully with a young boy; Ned smiling a toothy smile, his arms about two bare-breasted black girls; Ned leading an expedition, a rifle proudly shoulder-slung. All these surround, shrine-like a shot of Ned next to an old, proud, bent white-haired man with a thick mustache and smiling eyes. Most of the pictures have bowed to time and temperature, their corners crinkling inward as if to hide their subjects in dated darkness.

Straw mats and decorative beads complete the picture; yet, in spite of the decor, the room does not possess a casual quality. It seems to have wilted in the September heat. It has been swallowed by a sense of suffocation.

Offstage, a deep, resonant voice is singing a Swahilian chant. Suddenly, through the French doors bursts in NED PEALE, the tall, strong man in the photos, who is now several years past forty. He wears khaki shirt and shorts, tennis shoes, and an old, stained pith helmet. He is carrying an armful of groceries.

NED PEALE SPEAKS:

Calling out in a loud voice

POLLY!

No response; he sets down the groceries, hangs the pith helmet on the tip of a spear, then goes swiftly back out through the French doors; a moment later, he returns, carrying a couple of empty cardboard cartons, and dragging a much larger one. He calls out again, louder

POLLLLLYYYYY!

Still no answer. He drops the cartons, goes to the phone, dials, waits a moment

Hello — Phyllis? Hi . . . Ned . . . Say, I was wondering if Polly might be over there . . .

A worried look

Any idea where she is? . . . No, no, it's nothing; I was just going to have to pack up the place by myself if she doesn't come back soon. How about Vanessa? . . .

He chuckles

Ah, well, she's probably off with some young fella . . . No, I don't worry about her; she's a big girl now, she can take care of herself . . . No, no, it's no trouble, really . . . No, thanks anyway; we'll get it all done, somehow . . .

Laughing

Now, I'm sure the church will get along quite well without me! . . .

A pause; sincerely now

Well, we're going to miss you and Harry too, you can bet on it! Yes! Thanks anyway, Phyllis!

Frowning, he hangs up. He sets the grocery bag on the coach, pulls out a bag of potato chips and two six-packs of canned beer. He opens one of the six-packs, then pauses a moment, thinking; suddenly, he goes back to the phone, dials, waits

Hello, Mary Ann? Hi, Ned . . . By any chance is . . .

a chuckle

OK, I'll hold on . . .

A moment

No, that's all right. . . . He did? Well, can you beat that! The little devil! . . . No, just give him some milk and raw eggs and ground-up dried toast, and it'll come right up. . . . Mary Ann, how did he swallow his shoe in the first place? . . . He put his foot in his mouth . . . Wait a minute — have you looked around where he was playing? . . . Now, cool down, Mary Ann. No, I'm sure you're a *fine* mother. . . . I know it's tough . . . Did you ask any of the others? Surely, out of five kids, one of them might have picked up the shoe . . . All right, all right. Never mind. Thanks anyway. Oh — if Polly stops by — please have her call me, OK? Thanks.

Hangs up. He turns his attention back to the potato chips and beer; he rips open the bag of chips, looks for a suitable container; finally takes a native wooden bowl from one of the book-shelves, empties its contents of beads, trinkets, arrowheads onto the Congo table, empties the chips into the bowl, scrapes the trinkets into the potato-chip bag, and puts the bag back where the bowl was on the shelf. As he places the bowl of chips on the table, he gets another idea, goes to the phone, dials, waits

Irene? Ned. Ned Peale . . . Well, it's a pleasure to talk with you. Say, by any chance is . . . What? No, I'm home alone, packing up some of my gear; you know, we're leaving on . . . Alone, that's right. No, Polly's not here; that's why I was calling. . . .

A moment. A bit uncomfortably

Well, gee, that's awfully nice of you, but it's so hot I usually don't eat lunch. . . . Yes, I'll bet your home cooking *is* great! . . . Hate to pass it by . . . Yes, I know, it'll be the last chance I get . . . Naw, thanks, but I have to stay here to interview the new ministerial candidate, and —— what?

He laughs nervously

Well, of course I would rather be in your company than some stuffy old preacher's, but you know how it is. Besides, you're probably in no shape to receive anything —— anyone . . . What?

Another uncomfortable laugh

I know, it would just take a moment to slip into something more . . . No, I —— what will I do when I leave here? Oh — most likely head back to Africa. Yep! Setting up some arrangements now, actually . . . No, I've been planning on it for some time. You know, when you're in the business of teaching people new morality . . . What? No, I meant nothing; just that when you've been a missionary as long as I have, it's kind of hard to do anything else, even . . . if . . . it tempts you sometimes, you know?

A little laugh

Yeah. It sure is kind of hard . . . I say, it's kind of hard . . . No, it's just an expression, Irene. . . . Well . . . If you don't know where Polly is, then we — have nothing to talk about, do we?

He laughs, feeling very foolish

You don't like to talk much anyway? Well, I can certainly underst . . . No, nothing, Irene. Why did I call you if I was looking for Polly? Well — no, I know that you two aren't exactly the best of friends, but . . .

A little chuckle

Oh, no, Irene! Why, that's all over and forgotten! Just a little misunderstanding, that's all. Polly was terribly sorry she'd even *thought* as much . . . Yes, it was a fun Ice Cream Social, wasn't it? Say, now, I meant what I said about paying to have it cleaned. . . . Now, that's nice of you to say that, but even *I* know that raspberry sherbet isn't much good for a blond wig. . .

He laughs patronizingly

Very funny, Irene; raspberry blond. Good! Uh, look, I've got to —— what?

Most awkwardly

Gee, that's too bad, but I'm not much good at repairing worn-out bedroom fixtures. Where's Harvey? Why can't he take care of . . . Oh, you got a letter this week? Well — I'll have to repay you some other way for the wig damage. Yes . . . Good —— yes . . . All right, goodbye —— What?

An apprehensive smile appears

Well, thanks. That's awful nice to hear . . . No, I don't expect many ministers do look like Ramar of the Jungle. But then, I've never seen Ramar of the Jungle; have you — ? No, never mind! Goodbye, Irene!

He hangs up, with relief. He picks up the smaller empty cartons, begins singing the Swahili chant again, heads for the kitchen. A loud knock comes. NED yells over his shoulder

Yeah! Come on in!

Exits into the kitchen, singing. No one is seen to enter, and the knock is not heard again; in a moment, NED returns, carrying another six-pack of beer. He looks up at the audience, which is the position of THE INTERVIEWEE, smiles

Well! Glad you could come. Nice to have a guest on an afternoon like this. Damn, I believe this is the hottest it's been since Lambarene — and that's counting nearly twenty summers! Let's see . . .

He surveys the chairs, potato chips, beer

Hey! Wouldn't you know it! Forgot the opener! If I'm in the kitchen, it's in here. If I'm in here —— oh, what the hell . . . Just go ahead and have a seat — be right there!

He darts back into the kitchen. From offstage

Hope I didn't answer your call too late, but you know how it is —

getting a wife and a teenage kid out of your hair to have a little time to yourself isn't easy! You'd think for something as important as this interview, they'd show a little respect and leave me be! But — what can you do?

He returns

Hell of a day to have to begin moving! Kids threw a going-away party for my daughter here last night — I'm afraid I still haven't recovered! But, I made such a stink about getting out of here as soon as possible; you know, Africa calls! We'll be out of here Sunday evening, the night after my last sermon — thought I'd tell you just in case you're the one who's chosen. Give you sort of a head start! Figured as long as Glenn wants to act so damn fast to get a new man in, well, we'll just get you initiated to the stream of things real quick. Glenn doesn't want the church to lag, of course, not even for a day. I guess my wanting to leave so quick, once I made up my mind, well, it kind of threw him; but I don't want to lose a day that I could be headed back to Lambarene, you understand? Good!

To himself

I'm eager to make up for — lost time, for — a little debt left unpaid. . . .

He straddles one of the wicker chairs; with assumed enthusiasm

Well. What'll it be — beer, or you ready for something stiff? . . .

A pause; an incredulous look

Grape juice? . . . Why? You bring a dog, or something? . . .

Somewhat taken aback, but trying not to show it

Well, well, well . . . Uh, no, I'm sorry, I don't think we have any grape juice . . . No, no apple juice, either. Here in the summer, friend, we drink beer. Beer! That's your first lesson about this church! When things get hot under the old clerical collar ——

He dramatically jerks open one of the cans, drinks

If you change your mind, just holler. Me, I can't live without beer, friend. Too damn hot here. . . . Doesn't it get hot enough where you're from to want a good cold beer? . . . Oh, it never gets that hot in Connecticut. . . .

An awkward pause

Well! As I started to say, this is the house you'll have, if you accept the post, and, of course, if they want you here. Not bad, really — I'll show you through it in a while. . . . Oh? Well, why don't you think you'd like it?

A pause. He glances quickly about the room

Oh, no, no, *these* things don't go with it! They're mine!

He has a good, relieving laugh

Do you mean to tell me you thought all this stuff was part of the parish fixtures!? Oh — boy! That's a good one!

He laughs again; looking at THE INTERVIEWEE, finally the laugh fades

No. No, you see, all this stuff is from my missionary days; it belongs to me. None of it stays. You can have the house, lawn, mice, roaches, all that — but I keep the spears and things. Don't you worry about a thing. . . .

A pause. A bit surprised

What do you mean, you'd prefer an apartment? The minister's supposed to live in the parish house! . . . No, no, I don't always do everything I'm supposed to. But, after all, man, it's just like you work for these people, you know? . . . OK, suit yourself . . . Yeah, there are enough apartments around here. Don't you have a family? . . . Oh. Well, then, try the African Village down the street. A co-op place. But don't let the name fool you: the owner once got a look in my place here, and went out and bought up a whole bunch of cheap imitation crap! Not a genuine piece of goods in the whole business! Imagine, shrunken heads from Japan! Yep!

He downs the beer

You know, my wife, crazy woman, she was on a jag for a while to buy one of those co-op buildings, and run it on the side. That's how the guy got a look in here, the jerk. Be good for our old age, she said. After the kid was grown and gone and all. I told her to forget it! Chances were by then I'd be back in Africa, and she wouldn't feel at all like fighting a bunch of irate tenants, with their leaky faucets and their noisy neighbors, and their sour soup smell, and stealing each other's newspapers at six in the morning, and — you know. I couldn't have stood it, anyway. Most of those places are filled with old fogies at least 110. She finally gave up on me — my wife, that is. Now she's running a kindergarten class down in the basement. Can you beat that? All the parish brats. Place doesn't look bad, actually, all fixed up. Pink water pipes, finger paints and tinker toys. Still smells like a basement, though. Kids will be kids.

He chuckles

Those little guys! Yell and scream, like it was torture to finger paint. Can't get a lick of work done all afternoon. I have my office here, you know. Show you that, too. Be yours, of course, if you decide to stay.

He opens another beer, swigs half of it, then begins taking things off the walls

Yep. Do all my writing here. Do you write, did I hear Glenn say? I'm working on another book, myself. God, must be the third or fourth since I've returned, can't keep track of them. I really come by it easily, I guess, you know? Been to as many exotic places as I have, the books just write themselves! Sure you don't want a beer? . . . What?

He stops cold

Apricot nectar?

Disguising another sour face

Nope. Out of luck, friend . . . But I was telling you about the kids. You wanta know something interesting? You go down to my basement, take a look at those paintings the kids do. Let me tell you: the kindergarten kids of this generation could rule the world. Now! At age five! I mean it. Christ! I went down there the other day, just to observe. They won't be meeting after today, of course, so I figured I'd just see what's going on. Man, did I learn! Now, each kid paints a picture of something, and after he's through, my wife asks him what he had in mind. You know what some of them say? My God! One kid has this huge rocket on the front of his painting, see? Around it are a hundred technicians in a circle, waiting for this big thing in the middle to burn, and they're all looking at their watches. So, Polly — that's my wife — no, she's not here, I told you, she went out. We try to stay . . . anyway, she asks what is all this about, and the kid — all of five years old, mind you, turns to her with the greatest deadpan since Buster Keaton, and says, "This is a master scheme for all future interplanetary space launchings." Christ! I mean, when I was five, I was still struggling to walk! Scares you, doesn't it? . . . No? Well, it scares me! But they're good kids. And my wife loves it. Besides, couldn't be better for me. I mean, gives her something to do. Makes her feel —— you know —— what?

Hastily, as if he had forgotten

Oh, oh, yeah. Sometimes the noise does disturb my writing, I told you that, didn't I? . . . Well, can't have everything, can we?

An awkward pause. NED hides embarrassment. He takes a few more things off the walls. With forced exuberance now

Well! . . . Uh, won't take you long to get the hang of this place. If you decide to come, of course. It's really not all that bad to be here, especially in late summer. The trees explode with the colors of life! No, it's only October I can't stand. Deadness sets in, you see. Deadness and fading colors, when the elm trees shrink back from the sun, and spit away their leaves like shrapnel. Sure a good thing we won't be here!

With a forced apologetic tone

Not trying to discourage you, understand. Not at all. Many great things about this place. But, well, if you've ever known the beauty of Africa, then this place gets to you in Autumn. You feel that you're dying, too, along with all the rest of the suppurating flesh on this wasteland . . .

With mixed feelings now

That's why it's so great just now, avoiding October, I mean, just before . . . we . . . leave.

A moment. Making an effort now to sound matter-of-fact

Of course, there's no chance of my staying; I handed in my notice. The call comes, you gotta go, you know? Africa! Twenty years too late, but Africa! Goddam, I can't wait! Took me so long to get the Board to accept my resignation, but what are you going to do? A good man, and all that. Yep . . . What are you going to do?

He sighs, looks around him. The excitement fades

You'll know this place the day after you arrive. I did.

To himself

And that was twenty years ago. . . .

To THE INTERVIEWEE again

Well. Buck up! Soon, you'll be an old-timer!

The phone rings

Oooop! Excuse a second.

He answers the phone

Hello . . . Who? . . .

With slight irritation

Oh, yeah, you're the kid from the high school group who coughs during the sermons. . . . No? . . . Then you're the one with the motorcycle . . . Yeah, I got it. Well, what is it; I'm a bit busy. . . . No, no thanks, I don't need your motor — that's fine, I'm glad you bought a new side car, but it won't be any use to me. . . . No, there will only be a few boxes today, and my daughter's going to pick them up later on in the day. . . . She's with *you?*

Angrily

Now, look, I've told her not to ride on those things, you can get killed on the back of those damn . . . She's in the side car? Well, what difference does that make? *You* can still get killed, can't you? . . . No, you're not my son, but I do care . . . Because you're a human being, for God's sake, even if you're a stupid one for driving those . . . Well, for crying out loud, if you get killed and my daughter's in the side car — well, what do you expect me to think! . . . You don't expect me to think. Look, sonny, I'm busy now, and I don't have time to listen to your impudence. . . . No, I'm *not* making a value judgment about you! . . . When was the last time you were in church? Last week? Oh; that's why you don't expect me to think . . . No, you're right, it wasn't one of my better sermons, but what does that have to do with my daughter? . . . Well, she's in your side car, isn't she? I think that's got plenty to do with it! You get her out of there! I don't want her in your side car. I don't want her on your motorcycle! I don't want her even associating with —— look, put her on, will you? . . . Why not? . . . Well, when she comes back from buying the root beer. What kind of a gentleman are you, letting her go buy the root beer? Is that all you think of my daughter? Listen, chum, I've changed my mind; when she comes back, don't put her on the phone; hang up, and call her a cab, and put her in the cab, and send her home, and never see her again! . . . Yes, that's final! . . . I don't give a goddam if they don't allow root beer in cabs, that's final! . . . Now look, Junior, I've had about enough; you watch your tone of voice! . . .

Trying desperately to control himself now

Yes, many ministers say goddam! . . . In fact, most ministers say goddam. In fact, more ministers say goddam than anybody else! . . . No, I don't have to prove it, god —— why do they say it? It's their business! Their stock-in-trade! . . . Stock-in-trade, it's an expression . . . No, I will not reconsider about your motorcycle! Vanessa is going to help me in the car! Now, there will be no more said about it; send her home, and go peddle your side car elsewhere!

He slams the phone down; turns back to THE INTERVIEWEE

Boy! What *are* they coming to! . . . Sorry for the interruption. Now — where were we? . . . Ah, yes, Africa! You know, in all the years I've been preaching here, never once has the Board let a year go by without asking me to devote at least one whole sermon to Africa! Begged me, this year! Can you imagine that? Even with all the study programs I've started here, they still want to hear more! Of course, I love to talk about it, it's not that . . . Oh, no, don't get me wrong; I'm not suggesting that just because you haven't travelled to Africa or someplace, that you won't be a valuable preacher here! Quite the contrary! Men have their own special skills, you know. Why, I'll bet you're just as colorful with your little interest, as I am with mine! You bet!

He downs the beer

Uh — what is that interest, by the way?

A pause

Religion. You don't say.

He opens another beer. An awkward moment; then he offers the can

Sure you won't . . . ?

A pause. With a sour face

Kumquat juice?! Not a chance.

Another awkward pause. NED drinks the beer

Well. Uh — how about a little music? Make us forget the heat, eh?

He goes to the record player, puts on a disc; the scratchy strains of a well-worn Bach organ work sift through the room. NED settles back in one of the chairs; his eyes close, his face softens with peaceful rhapsody

Do you like it? . . . Inspiring, isn't it? Nobody plays Bach like the Old Man . . .

A moment. He looks at THE INTERVIEWEE, then, laughing

No, no, not my father! Only in a manner of speaking. I mean the good Doctor.

He points toward the center photo of the old gentleman

He kept me under his wing for many years. I was actually present during some of these recordings; dubbed the tape for one or two. Forgot which ones now. Yep! *There* was a real missionary! Not content to spend fifty years as a tireless worker. Nope! He even took a crummy pile of pipes and a foot bellows bandaged with raw rubber and spit, and turned out the most beautiful music you'll ever want to hear. Put all the money from the recordings into the hospital. He was a saint, the Old Man!

Wistfully, with a shadow of sadness

And do you know why? Because — he stayed there till the end . . .

NED leans back, rocking slowly in the chair, his eyes closed. The somber organ sounds lilt from the machine

You know, the Old Doctor used to talk about Bach. Now, there was a guy you could model yourself on. He really met hardship and opposition; everywhere he went, rigid bastards tried to beat the guy down. But they couldn't. Try as they might, they just couldn't do it. Do you know, he composed a piece after he went totally blind? *When We in Sorest Trouble Are . . .* And then, after he wrote it, damned if his sight didn't come back to him! Shortly before he died, but he saw again. Do you hear that, he saw! Greatness, that's what it is! Why, just listen to this ——

He turns the music up a moment

Lyrical, yet lusty. Solid. Rumbles your bowels! Like a way of life! Like Lambarene itself!

He settles back again

This is all I've got now to remind me of the jungle sounds. . . . Oh, no, I wasn't just in French Equatorial Africa. Only for a few years. Before that, I ran all over the place, like a wild beast lusting for life!

His voice fills with excitement

I followed tiger trails in Tanganyika — fought swamps in the Niger Delta. Those spears there skewered human flesh in the Cameroons, where I found them. The shields I bartered from tribes in the bush lands of the Sahel. Breast plates there from Pygmies in Central Nigeria. Kalahari, Sahara, Congo — exciting places whose names snap off your tongue, and taste still strong after years have mellowed your memory! . . . It's a different world, my friend . . .

Softly, almost with defeat now

It's a dream world now, and I've lost it for so long! . . .

He opens another beer. He becomes a little glazed, a little expansive now, with the brew and the heat. With a sudden laugh

Ah! But you didn't come here to hear all this — why, I'm supposed to interview *you*, see if you're right for us, for this hallowed parish, and all these worshipful people!

He takes a few more things off the walls; the last of these is a long medallion; suddenly, he goes to the French doors, removes his clerical robe from the coat tree; excitedly

You know, when I first came back, they had the damndest time trying to get me to remove Africa from the services. I'd come in wearing this chieftain's medallion over my robes ——

Hastily, he throws the robe over his shoulder, hangs the medallion over his neck

— and have the organist blaring Bach just like the Old Doctor! Why, once I had a sacrifice planned, where the altar would have a Christ statue, painted Bushman black, and spread out like a warrior about to receive the spear of ——

Suddenly, NED's face freezes. He turns toward THE INTERVIEWEE, listens a moment, then goes quickly to the record player, stops the music. Slowly, he removes the robe and medallion, and turns his gaze back to THE INTERVIEWEE. After a moment, hiding deeply hurt feelings

Very well. If that's what you want —— I thought we might get acquainted first, but if I . . . bore . . . you. . . .

He returns to the chair, eats a few potato chips. Quietly

Look, I — I didn't mean to get so far afield, here. It's just that you're such an interesting guy, and I guess I . . . What? . . . You want to know something about the church.

With embarrassed laughter

Well — of course you do! It — it's only natural! Of course! Uh . . . Let's see . . . What can I tell you?

He begins slowly taking the pictures off the gallery wall, inspecting them, then putting them in stacks on the couch or in the box. Somewhat detached

A hundred years ago a handful of missionaries left the cold salt winds of the Atlantic, packing three months supply of lard and turnips and the blessings of the Presbytery, and struck out for the promised land. But when the last of the lard fried the last sour turnip, they settled here, on this very plot of ground, late one magic, pitch-black night. And the next morning, they rose with the sun and looked at one another, and at the red earth of their new home, and their eyes filled with the tears of new devotion!

He takes some more pictures down, but hesitates

before the large one of the Old Man. He leaves it up, goes to another

Things went along smoothly for the good folk, praying to Papa and singing of sin. Smoothly for over a hundred years, in fact. But then, one day into their midst came Ned Peale, a cyclone of a man fresh out of Seminary and ready to tame the world. Well, they sent him across the seas to try to bring their own spiritualism to Africans. But alas, the well-meant plan backfired; when Ned Peale returned, *he* turned out to be the only convert; and he has been trying for twenty years to sell the home office on African spirituality, and——

He turns directly to THE INTERVIEWEE

—damned if those people aren't still hung up on a diet of lard and turnips!

He finished another beer

Anyway, there you have it, my friend: one man in two worlds. But you can't serve two masters, so—I'm going to leave—and go make peace with—with—

He seems caught, about to reveal a deep inner thought, which he holds back. Suddenly, jarred back to THE INTERVIEWEE

——What? With an unpaid debt?

A bit jolted, as if THE INTERVIEWEE had discovered something about him

Yes, I said that, I guess—but that's not all of it . . . Don't pay any attention to that. I didn't mean a thing—let's just say—

He faces the great shield over the fireplace; after a moment of deliberation, he takes it down

I'm giving this place back to the Indians. . . . Now; anything else you want to know?

A long pause

Good! That's settled!

NED sits, frowning with discomfiture. He takes a few swigs of beer. The phone rings

Hang on . . .!

Grateful for the interruption, he gets up, answers it

Hello? . . . Oh, hello, Mrs. Snodgrass, nice to speak to you. . . . Yes, as a matter of fact, I did speak with your son on the phone a little while ago. . . . What? . . .

A little chuckle

Now, really, Mrs. Snodgrass, I can't imagine that our little chat would have sent him home in tears. . . .

More serious

No, of course not, Mrs. Snodgrass, I don't consider it a minister's duty to inflict pain upon his parishioners. . . . Unless it's to act as a purgative, of course . . . A purgative . . . What? No, just a little joke, Mrs.

Snodgrass. . . . No, I do not consider it a laughing matter. . . . Yes, I'm sure he worked very hard to earn the money for that side car. . . . Yes, Mrs. Snodgrass, I certainly do believe in the value of work. . . . It teaches us many things, of course. Work is the center of all things. The saints say so, my good woman. It makes our lives —— what? No, I am not a Marxist; you misunderstood me . . . I merely explained to your son that I did not wish to avail myself of his services today, and that he could go peddle his —— yes, Mrs. Snodgrass, I realize it's a *motor*-cycle; it was just an expression. . . . I *am* aware he's a big boy; that's why he's interested in my daughter, isn't it? . . . No, Ma'am, I did not mean anything lewd by that. Would I make light of my own daughter, dear lady? Of course not . . . Now, wait a moment —— what kind of blasphemy? . . . Please lower your voice, Mrs. Snodgrass, it's hard to hear what you're ——

Irritated now

No, I did not take the Lord's name in vain! No, I —— well, yes, I sort of did say something that could have been taken as —— no, Ma'am, I do not believe that that's the kind of example to set for one's children. But then, I don't let *my* child go around on a motorcycle, Mrs. Snodgrass. . . . No, I'm not dodging the issue, I'm trying to explain to you that sometimes it isn't what a parent says to his kids, but what he lets them do that ——

Impatiently

All right, Mrs. Snodgrass, I'll make a deal with you: I won't use that word in the presence of your youngster again, if you won't let him take my daughter on that death-trap of his! . . . Oh, Jesus, woman! I *know* it's part of his work! —— What? Jesus. Jesus. As in Our Lord. No, I do not mean it in vain, dear lady! I mean it most sincerely!

A pause; mitigatingly now

Now, now, I didn't mean to make you cry, Mrs. Snodgrass. . . . Yes, I realize the boy's the only thing you have left in this world. . . . Yes, he really is a handsome lad. . . . Yes, so smart-looking sitting on the motorcycle. Just don't let him turn it on . . . Oh, you don't turn it on, you kick-start it? Thank you, Mrs. Snodgrass. . . .

He wants to hang up

Yes, you certainly do take an interest in your son's activities, I can see that you're a mother he can surely be proud of. . . . He did? That's wonderful. It's too bad that Vanessa can't grow a beard in my honor. . . . I said —— never mind, Mrs. Snodgrass. I must get off the phone. . . . Yes . . . Yes . . . No, Mrs. Snodgrass, that's one thing, I'm sorry, that I'm absolutely certain of . . . I don't need his services today. I'm sure it's a fine side car, but I just don't need it today. No, not today! . . . NOT TODAY, MRS. SNODGRASS!!!

He slams the phone down, returns to THE INTERVIEWEE

Damned loose-ended parishioners!

He takes a few sips of beer, cools down

You know, if it weren't for people like that, and the fact that I'm dying to get back to missionary work, I'd sort of like to stay here. Yeah, I've made friends here, and it's not all *that* bad a place, but you know how it is. When you've had your mind set on something for so long. . . .

He takes a few books down, begins stacking them by the couch

No, that's the only reason I'm leaving. What's with you? What more reason is there? Besides, I've still got an unfinished book to work on, and I need more information. My work there is very important; you're a scholar, you'd appreciate that . . . What's that? No, I tell you, no other reason. I'm just — itching to get back out into the wild, smell the green African hills, bathe in the good sweat of honest work again! . . .

A moment; then, hastily

No, no, that's not what I meant, I think my work's been very honest here, no one would challenge me on that . . . OK, so I've been a little unusual for this parish. But you can't say it's interfered with my work! I haven't missed a Sunday in years! . . .

His face suddenly registers a bit of surprise

Who in hell told you that! . . . Well, so what? OK, then, I haven't missed a Sunday in months. . . . Well, damn, everybody's got to let off a little steam now and then! What can you do!

He opens another beer; sits, troubled a moment

It was just one of those things . . . I was only gone for six weeks . . . Perfectly understandable; I had a good rest, and — Glenn said that when I got back, there'd be nothing said, and ——

Even more surprised

Now what in hell do you mean by that!?

He slams the beer can down

OK, so what! Yes, it took me that long to dry out! . . .

He gets up, goes over to the record machine, puts on Bach again

Now, I told you once, the only reason I'm leaving is that I want to get back to Africa! That's all I've wanted to do for years! . . . Yes, that was all I wanted to do before I got in the ministry! It's been a lifelong dream, dammit, even when I was a kid!

He stops himself; protectively now, but still shaken

Boy, wait a minute! What is this! The third degree? What nerve! Can you beat that! Guy's over here half an hour, and he's wanting to know your life story! Well, you can forget it? *You* came here to be interviewed by *me,* and that's all there is to it! That's what we're going to do — you just forget me! . . . What do you mean, we haven't really talked about the church at all! What do you think we've been doing —— OK, so I haven't asked about your qualifications; so what?

Angry now

You going to lord some Ph.D. over me? Not a chance! I'm on to that kind of stuff, buddy! . . . Yeah sure, I got my divinity degree. Last thing I ever needed, but I got it —— and you really want to know why?

He removes a spear from the wall, begins waving it at THE INTERVIEWEE; with the force of finality

Because I wanted to teach something to people who really needed to learn something! That's why!

A pause; NED's face contorts

No, I didn't necessarily like living with savages; That's not the point!

Another pause

No, of course I don't think that every missionary is out of his mind! My God, just what do you —— what?

Fuming now

Now that's a damn dirty thing to say! How can you sit there, and tell me because I like Africa, I'm nuts! How about *you,* buddy-boy? You don't like my roaming the bush lands? Well, let me ask you something: what kind of a man stuffs himself in some crummy library, and gets himself a goddam Doctor of Divinity Degree, and then gets farmed out to some rotten churchhouse like this one, and sits up on a pedestal once a week, blathering about spirituality to a bunch of corpses! Mister, you've got a lot to learn, if you're going to be a real preacher! You don't learn it from people here, with their Forums, and their Clubs, and their Book Committees, and their Ladies' Teas, and their What-Do-You-*Really*-Think-About-God horsecrap! You learn it out in the gutland of the world, where it all takes place! Out where it's do or die, and the hell with all that metaphysical rot!

He takes the shield in hand

What do you mean, do I prefer animality! Animal, am I? I was there for spirituality, chum! I tell you, I did nothing I was ashamed of! Nothing! Nothing at all! Boy, it makes my blood boil when I hear people like you call me a savage because I associated with a bunch of illiterates! What's the difference? Who's really the Bushman?

He takes a grass-woven cape affair from a nail on the wall

What makes this stuff any little bit different from your church robes? Huh! Answer me that!

He grabs his pith helmet, shakes it at THE INTERVIEWEE

Wear one of these, mister, and go out in the jungle, and maybe then you'll be a man!

He slams the helmet on his head, then drinks the rest of his open can of beer; quieter, but just as intense now

And let me tell you something else, bud: they don't drink apricot juice in Africa. You want to show you're a man, you mix up a good Nigerian brew — sassafrass root soaked in pig oil, then boiled in rock moss, mushroom mould, bark fibers, lizard tail, turtle dung — and wild dog's toenail! You drink that, fella, and maybe then you'll deserve to have my job!

He opens another beer; with total disgust

Boy, if I'd have known this was the kind of guy they thought was good enough to take my place, I'd have straightened them out long ago! It's an insult to the entire African Continent! And get one thing straight:

He points the spear at THE INTERVIEWEE

If they're going to hire a guy like you to take my place, after all the good work I've done here, carrying the beauty of primitive peoples to this parish, then I might just not quit my pulpit after all!

Threateningly

I might just be tempted to stay on!

He takes a swig of beer, slams the can down emphatically. A long pause. Suddenly, his face blanches of its anger

What —— what do you mean, I can't do that?

Fear takes his features; another pause; he sits slowly, staring at THE INTERVIEWEE

They —— told you . . . ?

He lowers the spear, takes off the helmet, puts the African things down; quietly

Yes . . . it's true. . . .

A long pause; he stares incredulously at THE INTERVIEWEE, his face drained of effect, he speaks in a soft voice of pain and disbelief

Yes . . . they . . . asked me to leave.

Lights fade swiftly to black

SCENE TWO

A short while later. Light warms to find almost all of the African paraphernalia off the walls. The big box is gone, and all that remains are scattered stacks of odd items. In contrast to the beginning of Scene One, the room is now painfully bare and embarrassingly bland.

Empty beer cans now smother the Congo table. NED stands before the gallery wall, taking down one of the last lingering framed objects. All that remain on it now are the picture of NED and the Old Man, and another item, which appears to be a piece of writing. NED adds the piece in his hand to the stack, a sad look in his eyes. Aware of THE INTERVIEWEE again, he attempts to cover his feelings with bravado and insouciance

NED SPEAKS:

And to think this is just *my* stuff! You got *any* idea how much junk a teenage girl and her mother can pull out of a closet?

The phone rings

Jesus! People won't even let you get out of town!

He answers; snapping a bit

Hello! . . .

A pause. Mitigatingly now

Oh, hello, Glenn . . . No, I'm getting it done gradually. . . . You talked to whom? . . . Yes, I know Mrs. Snodgrass. Not intimately, of course —— what? Intimately; it's just an expression, Glenn. . . . Yes, I know she's an old lady. . . .

A feeble laugh

Very good, very good . . . No, never tried any that old. It's against my religion.

He chuckles. The laugh dies

Nothing, Glenn. I meant nothing. . . . Of course, I know a man of God can't go around making jokes about things like that . . . I only thought that since you mentioned . . .

A bit uncomfortable now

Yes, I realize what a position that kind of talk can put you in, Glenn . . . Yes, yes —— and I *appreciate* your telling me this. . . . Not at all. What's the Chairman of the Board for, if it's not to help out his minister?

A long pause; his face begins to twist with pain

No, no, it was not exactly like that, Glenn. . . . Yes, the boy did offer, but I didn't need his help. . . . What? Find something for him to do?

Uncomfortably

Gee, Glenn, I just can't —— hold on a moment, will you?

He sets the phone down, goes through the kitchen; returns, picks up the phone

Too late, Glenn. Vanessa has already come by and picked up most of the stuff with the car; we had it all arranged this morning. . . . No, I didn't see her, but the stuff's gone and . . . Of *course* it was nice of the boy to offer. In fact, it was more than that; it was damned industrious of him!

A pause. Hiding exasperation

Darned industrious, yes, Glenn.

Another long pause; a scowl

Now, Glenn, I don't think that's quite fair. . . . No, I didn't call the boy's mother names to his face. . . . Glenn, please try and keep your temper, it isn't all that . . . Yes, it would have been serious, if it were true, but it's not, and . . . No, I don't think it's at all funny, Glenn. No, I did *not* swear at the woman. . . . I say, I didn't swear at the woman . . . Glenn . . . Glennnn . . . Will you please let me get in a . . .

I said I . . . No, I —— Glenn! —— I DID NOT CALL THE OLD LADY NAMES!

Another pause. He regains his composure

I'm sorry, Glenn. I didn't mean to lose my temper. . . . Yes, he's over here. . . . Thank you, we're not finished yet, and I *would* appreciate it!

Hastily

No, no, I didn't mean that, Glenn, you know I always enjoy talking with you . . .

Totally frustrated, as Glenn resumes the harangue

Yes; the boy's obviously trying to make a few bucks. Probably has to meet payments on that death-trap —— what? Never mind . . . All right, Glenn, I'm sure your point is well taken.

With forced patience

Yes, I understand your position: if we can rehabilitate this one, there will be more, and then think how good the church will look to the community . . . Not a bad idea, Glenn. . . . Well, I'm afraid I already have my last sermon planned; it *is* tomorrow, you know, but it would have been a good idea. . . . Yes, hard work *is* basic to morality, and morality *is* basic to religion . . . What? . . . What does that have to do with anything? No, I didn't ask him what kind of motorcycle it was; but it has a side car, that's how he carries things; now, if you'll excuse . . . What?

His face contorts; quietly now, with effort

Yes, it's an excellent suggestion, Glenn. A great sermon title: CAN GOD FIT IN YOUR SIDE CAR? . . . We could best direct it to the women, I think . . . No, I didn't mean anything dirty by that. I just meant that most women don't know very much about side cars, until they start running around with fellas who know which end of a side car is for which . . . No, Glenn, I'm not being suggestive, for God's sake, I was just continuing your idea of the whole philosophical, allegorical approach to the thing; metaphysics of motorcycling, so to speak. Isn't that what you wanted?

A pause; feeling greatly coerced

Well, if I could get packed up in time, I might be able to write it up by this evening, and deliver it tomorrow morning. . . . Yes, Glenn . . . Yess, Glennnnnn. Yesssssss . . . If there's more than we can handle, I'll call the boy. Right . . . I *know* it's important . . . How *could* I forget the slogan, Glenn: "A happy parish is a happy pastor." . . . Oh, Glenn: as long as things are — the way they are, I mean, about my leaving, let me ask you something: who ever thought up that rotten saying, anyhow?

A pause. His face falls

You did. Well. Good work, Glenn. Yes, we'll be in touch after I leave . . . No, I quite agree. It would be downright silly for two men like us to let things like this get between an old, established association. . . .

Yes, you're right — friendship! . . . Has it been that long? Gosh, eighteen years, eh? Eighteen years . . .

He hesitates now, torn by the need to ask this, and trapped by the presence of THE INTERVIEWEE

Glenn — if you don't mind my asking — was it necessary to relate the — ah, circumstances of my leaving?

A pause; downcast now, defeated

Oh . . . Well . . . Yes, of course. Honesty is my policy, too . . . What? No — that's all I wanted to know . . . Of course I understand, Glenn, of course . . . Right . . . Good, Glenn . . . Yes . . . be talking to you. . . .

Slowly he hangs up the phone. For a moment, he withdraws into thought. Then, suddenly, he becomes aware once more of THE INTERVIEWEE's presence. Offguard

Look — it's not because of what you think! It wasn't that I haven't been competent, or anything like that! I want to make that clear. They — just — didn't like my approach to the pulpit; I mean, lately, they seemed to want just some ordinary kind of preacher. That's nothing against you, understand, but — well, I tried to educate my parish! That's the whole reason I agreed to come here! I even used to think that was why they hired me, because I was a man who had lived with the peoples across the world, and had tried to bring to them some semblance of belief. That's why it was so important that I write my book about them. What good is a quiet missionary? I had to preach the way I did! I had to write that book!

A pause

You look as if you don't believe me. Well, all right ——

He goes to a pile of books, sorts through them, finds a volume, waves it vehemently

There it is, my friend! Ten years of trials and love and sweat! Right here are those savage lands, those black shining faces we want to ignore! It was my obligation to teach more missionaries to go and replace me!

He suddenly jumps away from THE INTERVIEWEE, pulling the book back

Nothing doing! You hear me out first! Do you know how many missionaries there are in Africa right now? A drop in the bucket! And do you know how many schools across the country teach about Africa? A handful! Can you believe that? I wanted to do something about it, that's all!

He pauses a moment, planning his reasoning

Now, obviously, in order to make more people want to do this work, they have to be encouraged about it, don't they? All right, now listen: I have spent five years trying to push through the Board of this almighty church a series of lectures — new lectures — designed to contribute an invaluable dimension to the American theological student's awareness of the African cultural scene. And I am sickened to tell you that for five years in a row, my plan has been ruthlessly rejected! . . . No, there's nothing controversial about it! It's a matter-of-fact, informative discussion of — of certain areas of African mores, that's all! It's an area of great importance to my work, and I told them that if the church was going to benefit from my studies, this discussion program was vital! . . . No, it's a normal part of African life! You'd think they would jump at the chance to hear all about it! . . .

A little more frustrated

Well, what does it matter which areas of mores I was going to deal with? If people are going to be informed, they have to open their minds to every subject of discussion, don't they?

A bit more disturbed

What do you mean, get to the heart of the matter? . . . Well, what in hell does it matter what the title of the lectures was? I — I had no title, really, it was just a discussion program. A series of very honest, frank little chats. Why, they never objected in the past to my Forum in African Dialects, or my Ladies' Club Course in Ethnic Tribal Development, or my Men's Group Meetings in Modern African Governmental Trends. Now, why should they have objected to this discussion for the teenage group?

A pause; then heatedly

All right, I'll tell you the title!

He swigs down the dregs of another beer

A Study of African Sexual Practices as Related to the Lunar Year.

Long pause

Well, no, I *didn't* see anything wrong with it! . . . No, why should I have compromised! That the kind of man you are? That what you're going to do here when someone doesn't like something you say from the pulpit?

A little quieter

Well . . . Yes, I did modify it a bit after they refused . . . No, I left in the sexual practices; I just took out the lunar year. . . . You're wrong! It was a monumental change! It altered my entire approach to the subject! We have our moonlight, they have their lunar year! . . . What did they do then?

Downcast

They told me what I could do with my African Sexual Practices . . . No, then I asked them why they wouldn't let me teach the kids how Africans do the same thing according to the lunar year! . . . No, I'm afraid they weren't exactly pleased. In fact, they threatened that if I so much as described *one* African sexual practice, lunar or otherwise, they'd . . . Oh, the hell with it!

A pause; then, sincerely, with desperation

Do you really want to know why I had to teach that sex study? Not because I don't have enough to do. Not because it's ludicrous every Sunday telling those kids' parents how to save themselves from eternal damnation. But — because that silly sex-by-moonlight bit lets me tell a thousand stories! Lively stories about life in Africa! Not boring morality threats — but delicious little tidbits of humanity! Don't you see? That kind of course is the closest I can come to Africa. And I miss that dirty stretch of bug-bitten earth with a passion you couldn't imagine!

A sudden, sad laugh

Boy! I was such a contrast to the Old Man! I used to belch up stories, limericks, jokes, anything, from dawn to dusk — never stopped! Mealtimes, anytime, any kind of gobbledy-gook, just to pass the time! Except around the Old Man. Isn't that strange? For me, somehow, it was foolish to try and talk to him, even with a simple conversation. You say, "Good morning, Doctor. Boy! The sun sure is hot this morning, isn't it?" And he'd look at you like you were an imbecile! I mean, he'd been there forty years. What good did it do for anybody to tell him that the sun was hot that morning! That's like saying water's wet! Christ! But of course, like a sap, every morning, there'd be old Ned Peale: "Good morning, Herr Doctor. Boy, the sun's sure hot, isn't it?" And there'd be the Old Man, with that patronizing smear of agony on his face. I could always read his thoughts in his old eyes: "What kind of missionary is this?" . . . And to have it all end up — after all those years — like it did.

To himself, with dismay

What kind of missionary *was* that!?

A long pause. NED seems about to cry; then he hides impending tears with forced exuberance

Hey — what's going on here! Some old medicine man boring you again with the darker side of the world's woes? Gosh! Gotta stop me when I get like that!

He opens another beer

Say, you *sure* you won't have one of these? Or anything at all? Sorry about not keeping juice around. . . . Did you know that beer is man's oldest concoction of spirits? Yep! Want to know what the natives drink instead of apple juice, friend? Bwangala! It's half berry juice and half beer. Had it the first day I was there. How can I describe it? It was like water that sits for months inside automobile tires. Of course, you can't insult your chieftain hosts, without losing your stature as a missionary; so, I found the guy in the tribe who made the stuff; turned out he had a thing for the berry juice, so he'd always drink straight juice, and I'd get straight beer!

The story does not amuse THE INTERVIEWEE

Well, no, it wasn't exactly honest, but then, I wasn't just being ——

He stops himself; angered now

Now look, that's a bit unnecessary, don't you think? Just because I doctored up the native brew a little doesn't make me dishonest! You know something, man? You're stuck in the Puritan mire of your life here! Everything is good or evil, black or white, heaven or hell! Well, let me tell you something: a few years as a missionary might knock that stuff out of you! . . . Well, sure, I tried to teach them about being honest; but it just doesn't work the same way there. You gotta learn to give them some latitude! That's what we don't learn over here — too many absolutes, that's what hangs us up! Thou Shalt Not Do This! Thou Shalt Not Do That! Why not — I Promise Not To Do This? Or even — I'll Try Not To Do That? Don't you see? You can't scare people — you've got to enlighten them!

This doesn't seem to sink in

Well, look: take my daughter. If I tell her don't ride on that motorcycle, what's the first thing she'll do? Right! But if I say, "Now, Kitten, why don't you think about it first?" Then, man, the judgment is hers, not mine. She makes sense to herself, not to something I say. It's indirect teaching . . . No, you're still missing the point! Maybe if you had kids, you'd know what I mean. . . . No, I *didn't* mean anything by that ——

A pause. Angry now

Oh, for God's sake! You can stop all this crying about honesty, brother, because I'll set you straight, right now! We're all honest, and we're all dishonest! The only difference is that some of us are honest to others, and dishonest to ourselves, and some of us are honest to ourselves, and dishonest to others. . . . No, one's no better than the other, big shot! We all reek of the same stench. . . . See? There you go again! I don't think you heard a word I said! Nobody ever listens to the truth anymore, goddammit! All right, forget what I said about your going to Africa. You'd make a lousy missionary! Forget it! . . . What? . . .

NED's face falls. He sits with exhaustion

Yes, I know; you're going to stay right here. . . . Right here, in my church. . . .

The phone rings. NED leaps to it

Hello? . . . Yes, goddammit, where have you been? . . . You picked it up already? Well, it would have been nice of you to stop in and say hello! Or are you too sophisticated now to say hello to your old man once in a while? . . . No, I am *not* in a bad mood! And listen, if I ever hear again that you've been riding on a motorcycle, I'll wallop your bottom till it's blue! . . . No, I don't care how old you are!

A pause. He quiets down a bit

All right, I'm sorry. Maybe I wouldn't be such a grouch if your partying hadn't kept me up half the night! . . .

Sardonically

Oh, no, that's all right, Kitten, I was going to stay up all night anyway. . . . What was I doing? Oh — writing my autobiography, doing my income tax, advising the President by phone, recreating the Last Supper on our bedspread with your mother's lipstick, and — designing a better mousetrap. . . . No, Kitten, I'm not serious. . . . No, it's all right. Really; I couldn't sleep anyway. . . . Say, who was the little girl who kept asking me all the questions? . . . No, she was the one with all those wires in her hair; looked like the bride of Frankenstein. . . . All right, pin curlers, I don't care . . . I'm sorry, I did *not* mean to insult your friend. I'm sure she's a perfectly lovely young lady. But why did she give me the third degree? . . . Well, I didn't know where you were, but when I came down about four in the morning for a milk and bourbon, this little thing sprang up to me: "Hello, Mr. Peale," she says. "I've been dying to ask you something for a long time!" "It's four in the morning," I say, "and I did not come down here to answer questions, thank you." "Then, what are you doing down here?" she asks. "I came down," I answer politely, "to try and get drunk so I wouldn't hear the music that you are blaring at top volume." But did that deter her? Not on your life. "Is it really true," she blares ahead, "that African women bare their breasts and that the men put those awful plates in their lips and that they only wear loin cloths and they still use poison darts and blow guns and they split their ear lobes and put things in them, and that some of them even really and truly are still cannibals?!" Well, I forced my way through the flood of flannel nightgowns and carefully avoided the records on the floor, and made it to the kitchen with this little thing that looked like Elsa Lanchester right behind me, and then I poured a glass of milk, and found a bottle of bourbon, and married the two, and drank it, then mixed another and drank that, and then cleared my throat and put the glass down and sat and thought, and then turned to her wide eyes, and said, in my most cultured and educated and ministerial voice, "Yes."

He takes a deep breath

And that was when she leaped back through the living room, stepping on all the records I had carefully avoided, and screamed at the top of her lungs, "Gee, gosh, he's so smart!" And then I belched, and got up, and as I walked back through the streets of the living room they all threw confetti at me and cheered wildly, and I fell into bed and dreamed I was in a ticker-tape parade down Fifth Avenue in New York surrounded by bare-breasted native girls with curlers in their hair. . . .

A moment; a pleasant smile crosses his face

I'm sorry you missed it too, Kitten. No, it was really quite all right. I can't tell you how pleased I am that your friends take an interest in my work. . . . But tell me, why did they insist on playing that one song all night? . . . Which one? *I've Got The We'd-Go-Riding-Baby-But-My-Rolls-Royce-Is-Up-On-Blocks-Cause-I'm-Only-15½ Blues.* . . . What's wrong with it? Kitten, do you know what song I grew up to?

. . . *I'll Be Down To Get You In A Taxi, Honey.* . . . No, I'm not kidding. . . . Oh, sweetheart, I'm not making fun of your friends — I'm just having fun about the party; I'm sure it was a wonderful time, and I'm glad you were able to have it. . . .

The humorous edge disappears now

Yes, it is a shame that it's because we're — leaving. . . .

A pause. Serious now, and paternal

Now, we've talked all about this, Kitten; you know that things just don't allow for us to stay on here. . . . Look, sweetheart, that's all wrong. Daddy's not trying to keep you from your friends at all! . . . Daddy would *love* for you to continue on with high school here. . . . I know it's one of the best around. . . .

Painfully

I *know* how much you've been looking forward to it, but it's just not possible! . . . Because —— look, let's not go into it again, sweetheart. . . . No, it's not that I don't feel like facing it now — I just don't want to discuss it now, do you mind? . . . No, dear, I'm not getting mad at you; I just —— Vanessa, please stop crying. . . . Look, Daddy's worked hard packing, and he's had lots to drink, and he's talked all afternoon with the new man, and he's damned tired, that's all. . . . What? The new man. The fellow who will probably take over the church when we . . . leave. . . . I know it's awful to have to say that, Kitten; it sounds strange to me, too. . . . Kitten, you know no one feels funnier about this than I do. . . .

Hiding despondence

It just has to be this way, sweetheart! Please try and understand! . . . No, we'll probably stay at Grandma's till I know definitely if we're going back over . . .

Trying now to be cheerful

You know, it won't be all bad, Kitten. You'll need special clothes — a whole new wardrobe! . . . I know it doesn't matter to you now, but maybe later, when we've all had time to —— Well, where are you going to be the rest of the afternoon? I may need to reach you. . . . Lunch with whom? Is he the guy with the motorcycle? . . . Vanessa, please don't ride on that thing. No, I'm sure he's a wonderful fella, but I've only got one daughter, and I ——

A moment; his face falls; his voice trails off into a whisper

I don't think you really feel that way, sweetheart, do you? . . . Maybe after we've all had time to get used to leaving here, you'll feel differently. I know I seem like an old ogre, and all that, but —— all right, Kitten. Yes . . . All right . . .

A long pause

Kitten —— what's bothering you? . . . No, I mean it. You're not telling me something. . . . Try not to cry; I can't understand what you're saying. . . .

Suddenly, NED's whole countenance is shadowed with sadness

Now why did she ever tell you that! Christ, it was so long ago! . . . No, I don't care what she said about any "error in my ways." . . . Well, it just wasn't like that. There's not a word of truth in it. . . . Vanessa, you just get that out of your mind! I came back from Africa for one simple reason — to be with you and your mother! Because I *wanted* to! . . . Well, she's wrong, goddammit! She's just taking out things on you that she should be taking out on me!

Softer now; a pause — he regains his temper

Kitten, I meant it; I don't know how many times I've told you all these years that when your mother was pregnant with you she *had* to leave the camp! It was a ruling! Then, I came home when things got too — when you were about to be born. . . . No, dear, I don't for a moment hold anything of the kind against you. . . . Yes, I was working on something that was important, but nothing I was doing — nothing I would *ever* do would be more important than being with my family, and with my Kitten . . . I know, she's said lots of things like that; but don't you listen to your mother, dear. She's just upset today because there's so much to do . . . That's right. No, go let that damn kid with the death-trap buy you another root beer, then you come home. We've got to have a big family pow-wow before tomorrow. The Old Chief's gonna give out the plans for the big exodus. Yep . . . And, Kitten:

Tenderly

Don't you ever again think that I'd put anything before you. I love you, Vanessa, remember that. OK? OK. See you later. . . .

He hangs up slowly; he is dazed; then, aware of THE INTERVIEWEE

Poor, goddam kid . . . Why in hell does she blame herself . . . I only wish I *had* left there because of her . . . That would have been something clean . . . But no, not Old Ned Peale — he had to gum up the works all the way. . . .

Flashing suddenly, in response to THE INTERVIEWEE

Now, how many times do I have to tell you I don't want to talk about it! I — I mean, there's nothing to tell!

A pause; he retreats slightly

For Christ's sake, it was just a damn quirk — a trick of the heat — a — a sudden passionate wind — a —— No, dammit, I won't tell you about it. I won't! I won't!

A long moment's pause. NED sits, opens another beer. Then, softly, slowly, with complete resignation

It was my last weekend there. . . . We'd been working for over a month in broiling swamps, building hospitals for the Old Man. Polly had gone weeks and weeks before, and I was — lonely. . . . Then, that one, last, lost weekend, well — the boredom, and the heat, and the smell of the night just got to be too much, and like a damned idiot, I — went out to find a woman. . . . The first one along was a tribal chief's wife. . . .

He is disgusted with himself, as he has been every time he has thought of it; but he tries to tell it with humor; the result is painful

I began to — teach her some American sex practices. All in the name of religion, of course. Oh, yes. Some missionary, I was. Well, tribal chief comes along just as no-good missionary is hovering over his pupil, about to make his final point. So, tribal chief uses African logic, spares missionary, figuring he knew not what he did. Chief then proceeds to stand wife in front of missionary, and with a spear, tribal chief —— completes the job.

A pause; NED finishes the story with deep reluctance

The next day, I received a present from him. . . . A tiny, black, shrunken head . . . I spent the whole afternoon sitting in the little bamboo chapel I had built for the natives to worship in, sitting and shivering . . . Word finally reached the Old Man, and he —— let me go.

A long pause

I have never been able to forget that. . . . Can you imagine what it's like to destroy almost ten years of service in one night? And to end up no matter how you look at it — with a life on your hands? . . . Now, for the past few years, I have been trying to write it all out of me. . . . Go through the entire time I was there, and make some sense of the wilderness, the heat, the blood smell, the desires . . .

A pause

What? . . . The book? . . . No, that's the last laugh. The biggest joke of all: that book didn't come about. Oh, sure, that's a copy over there. But you can't buy it. Those are the galleys; I had them cut and bound to add to my own personal — memoirs. . . . It was rejected before it went to press, by the League of Decency. . . .

Blurting out, with sudden pain

I wanted so much to write about Africa, and write well! Oh, yes, I've tried to improve the book, to defend it, but it wasn't born to be picked apart, analyzed. . . . Now, I can't write at all. I feel this thing too much, don't you see? I am too violent with this lost love of mine. I rape the page when I try to write. . . .

Suddenly, desperately

Oh, please, don't leave! I'll stop! I promise! I'm sorry to go on like this, but I'm just trying to be honest with you. Please — don't go and cut me off!

He comes closer to THE INTERVIEWEE

Look: you don't understand something, because I haven't said it very well. In fact, I've just been blabbing the whole time, and I haven't said it at all——

Pleading

I don't want to leave here! I can't go back to Africa! I'm nothing there! Don't you see? Here, I'm something! There, I'm a pair of hands — and a rejected pair at that! Please — go somewhere else! Find another position! You can, easily! But this place — this is all I have! This little parish that I can't stand, these idiots who think I'm such a kook — we love each other! I'll straighten up for a while, stop wearing khaki pants to services, stop the drinking — then they'll take me back; they always have. But not as long as you're here! Please! Leave! Get out of town! This is a rotten place for anybody to be — anybody but me!

A pause; desperately

You don't believe me?

He looks about in despair; his eyes fall upon the picture of the Old Man, and the framed piece of writing next to it

Listen to this, then you'll see!

He dashes to the pictures, takes down the piece of writing. After a moment, reading to THE INTERVIEWEE

"My dear Dr. Peale — Yes, it has been many years since you have been here with us at Lambarene. Much has changed, as you could well imagine. The old gray hospital is down, now . . ."

To THE INTERVIEWEE

That's the one I built . . .

Continues reading, but soon his eyes wander back up off the page; he has read it so many times, he knows it by memory

". . . We have held many faces in our hands in these past years. Many little faces, charred with life, eyes ablaze. They live, Dr. Peale, no matter what hunger, what disease! They live! We love these faces here. Sometimes, the Greater Omnipotence gets the better of us, and takes some of the little faces, and douses the light in their eyes. But, as you would have told us, they live on, in the beauty and clarity of memory's perception. . . . Sometimes here in the midst of the life-struggle, faith in oneself turns pallid; indeed, often it seems to overpower one's very capacity to reason. Today, a little boy fell and hit his head on a stone. Such a little thing; but we were too late to help . . . Yes, there is sadness. But that is the time when I move away, out of the crude wooden wards, out of the clinic, out of the swilling sea of little ebonite skins and shining eyes, and flee to my private sanctuary, the only spot which I consecrate as mine alone. Do you remember it? There, in the hollow and darkness of a bamboo shelter, I play my old organ, letting swell the bellows, and listening as the strains of Papa

Bach slip out into the heavy, humid night. I am told it affects everyone for miles, like their own tribal drums; so I do not feel quite as selfish in my escape, for I am sharing the sound. . . . I remember well how intently you would sit, transfixed by the harmony, the old reeds vibrating in perfect rhythm with the palpitations of our hearts. . . . So, I shall go on like this, I suppose. It is not that I don't tire of my work. Quite the opposite; it is that I don't know it well enough. I don't know these twisting hills and tangled jungles well enough, and the charred faces which inhabit them. There is so much yet to learn! After all, I have only been here forty years; and these mountains have been here for — who knows how long! These are the thoughts which excite me; I have so much to look forward to!"

He lets the letter fall. His eyes are wet. A long pause

You see, I can't leave here. I must stay with my savages, just as he stayed with his. So that some day, I can write a letter like this to someone here, who suffered with me. To you, perhaps, because you were here with me today. That one last morning, and this letter — these were the only times he ever really spoke to me, the Doctor. And it means more than all the years I was there.

A pause. Quietly

Don't take this from me. Don't take my Lambarene. It could never be yours! Forget my antics, the stories, all the drinking. They are just more visions of a falling man. Help me — by doing nothing. Just — leave!

A long moment. NED's face looks blank

I — don't convince you?

With quiet desperation

Oh, if you only knew the Old Man, you would know what I mean! He was an incredible man, a man whom no one will really ever understand. Of course, he had gained a reputation of being a bit brutal to some of the natives at times. And I suppose in his aging, he did run out of patience. But like many quiet, efficient men, he was filled with kindness; and behind his brutality was a kind of love. One day, a group of newsmen came into the clinic just after he had severely slapped and tongue-lashed a young mother for ignoring his advice about her baby, delivered by his hand just the week before. The newsmen were aghast, until at last he turned to them, and very quietly said, "You must learn which idols to break, gentlemen, so that the others may remain intact." . . . Before every operation, he would sit and bite his lip with worry, and twist his mustache with the aging fingers until it was unruly. Then, without a word, we would begin the operation; if it was a failure, and we would lose the patient — and we lost many — he would go away, and be alone for hours. But if it was a success — ahh! — he would talk and talk, and laugh with us, and drink lager and joke and be happy. His vivacity would animate his whole face, as he would join in the joking. The bushy eyebrows darted up and down, the eyes would dilate with surprise, then retract with sly cunning. When he would tell stories himself, the mouth twisted, and sent the huge mustache dancing gaily above his lip, to end in a sneer, or a glib cock of satisfaction. And at the end of it all, he would sit there, staring into the fire, far into the night, quiet, his hands locked about a bony knee, and that marvelous patriarchal face smiling with fatigue. . . . I loved him so dearly at those moments. . . . I wanted to forget the cold, calculating physician, and be close with this warm human being. . . . I wanted to reach out, like nascent Adam to God —— and touch fingers. . . .

Suddenly his face falls with despair

But how his greatness reminded me of what I was, a bibulous fool in buffoon's rags. . . . How darkly it comes home to me now, living out this private hell of bucolic dreams and pastoral whimsy. . . . And now, they want me to go somewhere else. . . .

Suddenly, horrified

Why do they want to kill me! Why do they want to strip me of the only thing I have left! Why don't they even try and understand! Must I always help them? Who will stay to help me! Who will keep me from being alone! I can do nothing for them if they don't feel my loneliness — and now, I am frightened —— and so damnably alone!

A long moment; quietly

But now — I have no choice. Get out, is it?

Wildly now

Sure, I'll go somewhere else; but by God, they can't beat me down! A man of my experience can't be stopped, I tell you! So, what if I can't get another church! I will — I will —

He picks up the copy of his book, waves it about

I will rewrite my book, and ten more besides! They can't stop greatness: Just listen to what they say! ——

He fishes a folded piece of paper from the middle of the book, opens it, reads

"Overwhelming flaws remain in this work — great gaps of inexcusable inattention . . . " OK, sure, they had to tell me that, but — "But if so, it is marred by the blindness of love! . . . Its errors are but hasty brushstrokes over the complexion; they have not marred the living rubric of the blood beneath the surface! . . . It is a majestic piece of thought; rich, warm, filled with vitriol and joy, exuberance and tears, with incredible vivacity. Yes, restructure these bones, but fill them with the same marrow . . . Leave its life unscathed!"

He waves the paper at THE INTERVIEWEE

See? See? That's what they say about me, about my work! Rich! Warm! Something you can't kill! Something which must live and live and live on!

Suddenly, he covers his face with the paper, and

slowly collapses into the chair. His head nods as he cries silently; after a long moment

No! No! No! I don't want to finish that book! I don't want to leave! It's just an old, dead dream! It's all a lie! A damn game! But, God, a man needs *some* games to play, doesn't he?

He rests a moment; then, with resignation

I suppose there was just enough of a touch of nobility to being a missionary to make me stay there and sweat as long as I did. And it was such a good feeling, once I got back, to grumble about being here, and not there, in the heartland. . . . It's good to grumble, sometimes, you know? We have to grumble to live! . . . That's the dead dream, now. I can't stay here, and I can't go back there. Man, I don't know where to go just to grumble!

This strikes him as funny; he howls with hysterical laughter for a moment; then, all humor dying, absolutely drained

I'm all washed up, aren't I? I'm all washed up!

After a long moment of staring into space, his face takes on the look of resolution. He stands, goes to the stack of things, removes the long black clerical robe. From the floor, he retrieves the grass-woven cape. He weighs them, one in each hand, for several moments. Then he takes a long look about the room; gradually, a smile of quiet resignation takes over his face. He puts on the clerical robe, and drops the grass cape. He walks to the phone, dials, waits

Hello — listen, Georgia, is Polly there by any chance? Good! No, just let me speak to her. . . .

A moment

Polly? It's me. . . . What do you mean, who? Me! Yes, you too have heard of me. What's that supposed to mean? OK, OK, I know you're angry with me, but forget that. What kept you this afternoon? Where did you hold the kindergarten class? . . . Why at Georgia's? I was home all day; they still could have come over here. . . . Well, I'm glad they had plenty to play with over there, but still —— besides, what?

Sarcastically

No, I don't know what tropical disease they could get from me. . . . Jungle fever; very funny. Now look: I want you to bring back the stuff Vanessa took this afternoon. Polly — we're not going to go!

A pause

What do you mean, *you* are?

Another pause

LEAVE me? But that's absurd! Now, get your head on straight, and listen a minute. . . . Yeah, I know I made an ass of myself in front of the Board this morning, but what's that got to do with —— Are you equating the future of our marriage with whether or not I appeared in a meeting of the Board of my own church in shorts and a pith helmet? . . . Very funny. Oh, that is very, very humorous. . . . Did Vanessa call you? . . . I know; look, I didn't mean to upset her, she just ——

Annoyed

Well, what is it with you women! . . . Who? No, I just called her to find out where you were. . . . Yes, Phyllis too . . . What are you trying to tell me, Polly? . . . OK, so what? Yes, I called Irene, too . . .

Aggravated

For God's sakes, Polly, that is all water under the bridge. . . . Now get off this divorce jag, I've got more important —— Polly . . . If you're going to be like that, I —— stop screaming, Polly. . . . OK, I'll wait.

Long pause. He stands annoyed, but trying not to show it

OK. You through screaming? . . . What do you mean, a woman who's husband has been unfaithful has a right to scream! That's the most ridiculous thing I ever heard. ME! With whom, I ask you! No — I dare you! No, better than that, I *defy* you! I defy you to come up with some one — ah, ha! Thought so! You can't! Nope! Nice try, honey, but Irene won't do for your little accusation at all! . . . What? . . . What do you mean, not even a woman!

Furiously

Polly! What do you take me for ——! Oh, that's not what you meant. . . . Then what in hell did you mean? I've been unfaithful to you with —— what?

A pause. Softly

My obsession with a dead dream.

A moment. He is angry and hurt

All right, all right. I admit it. That's one concession I'll make; you're right. No — more than that — I apologize. Yes, and for all those things I've been saying to you . . . Yes, I know.

With tenderness

Oh, sweetheart, how have all the years come down to this! I know I've been — forgetful. No, that isn't the word — negligent. Yes! And I'm so sorry! But we can have it again, Polly! . . . What? . . .

He smiles sadly, with wistful memory

Yes, we did have some good times together. . . .

He laughs softly

Polly, I haven't thought of that in years! God, do you remember that far back? Yes . . . I was a bit embarrassed to show you how, but we managed, didn't we? . . . What?

His smile fades

Now, Polly, you're letting your temper get the best of you again. . . . OK, all right. Now quiet down, Polly. . . . Why drag out that! It's ancient history! . . . OK. I admit it was a mistake. I admitted it then.

Absolutely. The wrong thing to say. I'm sorry. . . . Oh, Polly, really, I think it's a little foolish now to have to —— all right; if it'll make you feel better: I promise now, I will never again compare your breasts to the buttocks of a Belgian baby. . . . Yes, it *was* rude. . . . Yes. It must have been insulting. . . . What? Why did I ever think of it? Well . . . cleavage is cleavage, Polly . . .

Angered now

But while we're at it — there never has been any excuse for what you said that time when I was interested in tropical vegetables. . . . Yes, you do, you know precisely what I mean! Don't deny it. . . . What? Oh, come on, do I really need to remind you? That oh-so-clever remark about my wearing a gourd around my groin in hopes of breeding a cross between a man and a melon . . . Very funny! . . . OK, I'll wait, you go ahead and have your little laugh.

A long pause. He is hurt but patient

You finished now? Had a good laugh? All right. Listen, I want you to get the box of my African stuff back from Vanessa when you see her . . . It's already there? Good! Now — no, I meant it! We're not going! . . . All right, then *I'm* not going! You can do what you goddam well please! . . . Yes, I'm being serious! Just be sure I get that box of stuff back; bring it over now; some of it's old, and pretty brittle, and —— what do you mean, I'm out of luck?

Angered

All right, goddammit, if you're going to be petty, I'll come get it myself. . . . What? That's not what you meant? . . . Polly, let's not joke around. What *did* you mean?

A pause. He goes ghost-white

Wha . . . Wha . . . Wh . . . You — you didn't! Polly!!

In deepest despair

How could you! Oh, Polly, no, no, no, no, no! I saved it all for years! This is the first time they've been off the walls! I loved each piece like it was my child! What in hell broke them all!? . . .

A pause

You — put them to the best use they've ever had? What —— Polly, what did you do! . . .

With greatest trepidation

What do you mean you've salvaged what you could as toys for your kindergarten class? . . .

Aghast

My Pygmy breastplates! Goddammit, Polly, have you no shame! . . . My shields make good boats! . . . Oh, no, no, no! I can just see the whole class, banging my precious Bwambi tom-toms like dime store drums, and killing each other with the Yoruba knives! A fine teacher you are! They really will kill each other, you watch! And it'll all be your fault! . . . They didn't? . . . A game . . . ? What kind of game?

. . . A spear hole in each picture of me. Very clever. Where did you have them aim — heart or eyes!

A pause. Softly

Heart . . . What? Yes, I heard you! My heart! *Then* you threw it all out? . . . Oh — you tried to give it to the junk man, but he said he wouldn't furnish a cock-fight hall with it.

He collapses with frustration

Oh, Polly, you could at least have given it to some one with taste! All those wonderful beautiful souvenirs! What mementos! What memories for me! . . . What do you mean, it isn't a question of taste! What's wrong with spears at a cock fight? . . . No, no, that's not what I meant . . . Yes, I have been drinking. . . . No, I'm not drunk. . . . What does it matter what I've been drinking? . . . All right, I've been drinking grape juice, apple cider, apricot nectar — and kumquat juice! . . . No, I'm not trying to be funny, Polly. I'm very sad. Very, very sad. I'm really very hurt and upset! . . . Well, if you're going to react that way, then let me tell you something, woman! You just threw out more than a bunch of toys. You just got yourself rid of a husband! . . . What?

Softly, hurt

You're glad I finally realized it. Well, listen here. Do you know what you can do? Do you know just what you can do about the whole mess? In fact, do you know what you *better* do about it?

Suddenly, his whole tone changes. Pleadingly

Polly —— come on home. Yes, yes, you heard me right! I want you to forgive me! . . . Why? Because I mean it, Polly. I spent the afternoon learning all about the guy who was supposed to take my place, but he was so unsure of himself, well, I just could never leave the church in his hands, so I told him to get lost, and I'm staying! *We're* staying! . . . Yes, I promise there will be no more episodes. . . . I'll watch the drinking, yes . . . Yes, I want all forgiveness, and I will forgive all! You see, I wanted you to love me, but I didn't want to love you! And that's how it all started. Because I loved you without *wanting* to love you. You see, after Africa I told myself you never just could love me. You would have to *want* to love me. And that in itself right away would kill every chance you would have of just loving me! . . . What? No, I know you didn't say that, that was me imagining what you were thinking. . . . OK, so it sounded more like what *I* was thinking. . . . Polly, stop crying! I wouldn't have upset you for the world! No, baby, honest! It was just that if you were going to be thinking about what you were probably thinking about, then I had to prepare myself, and begin thinking about what you were likely thinking about, because otherwise I'd be thinking about the wrong things, and your thinking would catch me offguard, and instead of finding out that you loved me, and I didn't love you, I would see that I loved you and you might not love me, and that would just have been too much, because then I would have led your thinking astray and then mine would have done the same, and then —— what? ALL RIGHT, I'LL SHUT UP! But Polly —— COME HOME!

He starts to hang up, then

Oh — Polly . . . Let me tell Vanessa, huh? OK.

He starts again to hang up, then a smile crosses his face

Oh, and guess what? I've thought of a whole new lecture series! It's called "Marriage and the Family In Africa!" Goodbye!

He hangs up; vigorously

Did you hear that? She's coming home! We're all coming home! Home to stay! Friend, I'm going to be a new man! So what if these people don't want to be enlightened! I can stay here and not be a slave to them because I won't be a slave to myself!

Suddenly, he grabs some of the newspaper used to pack with, wads it up, throws it into the fireplace. He takes a match from the mantel, lights it

The hell with it all! The hell with the dead dream! The hell with the book! Burn it, I will!

He begins ripping the pages of his book out and stuffing them into the flame; laughing and crying at once

Burn it to ashes!

More pages are flung into the fire

Burn the world, I say! . . .

More pages

And burn your old ways with it! . . .

More pages

And burn the old me, too, by God! . . .

He throws the rest of the book in, then pivots back around

Come on, friend, let's leap from the ashes and start over again!

Suddenly his face goes blank with surprise

Friend . . . ?

He looks about for THE INTERVIEWEE

Hello! . . . Are you . . . ? . . . He's gone. . . . He's gone!

He stands frozen a moment. Then he rushes to the phone, dials, waits

Glenn . . .?

Very excitedly

Glenn, this is Ned! . . . What? Yes, you bet I'm excited! . . . What for? What do you mean what for! What for . . . Well, you see, I . . . I've been doing some ——

Excitement fades, and is replaced by fear and confusion

Glenn, I — I want to ask a favor —— Glenn, you've got to do something for me! . . . Yes, I — I know you would anyway, it's not like that, I —— no, it's not a matter of moving, or any of that; I —— Glenn, I want to stay!

A long pause

Yes, you heard right. I've got to stay here, Glenn! . . . No, I'm not drunk. I mean it! Look, I know the Board and you and I've had all those disagreements, and all that, but this time I mean it! I'll do a good job. I'll do a damn good job! . . . What? . . . When did he get there?

Suddenly fearful

Yes, he was here for quite a while. . . what did he say? . . . Well, yes, I quite understand your position, bringing him all the way out here. But think it through, Glenn; I mean, is he *really* qualified? He said some pretty strange things while he was here; I just don't think that I would want to trust him with the church, and ——

Suddenly, his face brightens

He did? He said *that!?* . . . No, I don't know what I said to him, exactly, but I sure am happy to hear he thinks I'm the only man for this place!

Beaming

He actually refused to be considered for it as long as I was here, eh? No . . . No, no question of it, he's a man of great charm, Glenn. And intelligence. Intellect — and taste! . . . Yes! . . . Fine . . . Right . . . We'll be talking!

He hangs up. Still beaming, he goes to the record player, turns on the Bach recording. He puts on the pith helmet, and waltzes around the couch, his arms flailing the beat of the music, the clerical robe flying, when suddenly his eyes rest upon the great shield sitting by the fireplace. He stops, stares at it, frozen. Then, after a long moment, the smile reappears, and he takes the great shield from the floor and re-hangs it above the mantel. Then he stretches out on the couch, wraps the clerical robe about him, puts the pith helmet over his face, his hands behind his head, crosses his legs; and as the strains of organ music swell the room,

the light slowly fades to black

CURTAIN

JUST LIKE IN THE MOVIES

Gary Gardner

Early afternoon of an August day. The fifth-floor apartment of a fairly fashionable brownstone in New York City. The stage is split into two levels; the lower and downstage of the two is the living room. There is a couch R.C. in front of which is a marble coffee table. Twin caneback chairs separated by a small occasional table covered with magazines are L.C. The second level surrounds the living area on all three sides, and is higher by three steps; this gives the effect of a sunken living room, which, in essence is what I've been trying to describe. The main entrance is the door R., which leads from the floor corridor. U.R. is the small kitchen area; U.C. is the terrace from which there is a slight view of the city, blocked somewhat by the presence of a fire escape which runs the length of the building. From the hall running from U.L. to D.L. are: the door to Alan's bedroom (extreme U.L.), the door to the bathroom (L.C.), and the door to Joel's bedroom (D.L.).

The apartment is tastefully decorated with marble whatnots and statuettes, potted plants, lavish draperies and toss pillows . . . in other words, a gay bachelor's apartment without the Tiffany lamps. And it is here that Joel Webber has made himself quite at home.

AS THE CURTAIN RISES, TONY *enters from Joel's bedroom, blowing a kiss after him. He is in his early twenties, well built, and presently stripped to the waist. He dances down the steps, retrieves a velour shirt draped over one of the chairs, slips it over his head and on without losing the rhythm, and, still dancing, exits U.C. down the fire escape.*

A few seconds later, the main door R. bursts open and ALAN *enters. He is singing both the soprano and bass parts of Friml's "Indian Love Call," and he is riding a pogo stick. There is a youthful quality about him that belies his twenty-two years; if he drank, bartenders would still be asking for an identification card. Dressed in street clothes, he is what your paperboy might look like a few years from now.*

He discards his pogo stick on the couch, runs to sweep open the drapes U.C., and sings to the skyline. Still humming, he goes to the kitchen area to pour orange juice.

JOEL *enters from his bedroom D.L. in his pajamas. He is in his mid-twenties, and too good-looking in a pretty-boy sort of way. He staggers down the steps and crosses to the door R. to get the milk. Meanwhile,* ALAN *crosses around the upper level, breakfast tray in hand, to Joel's room.* ALAN *has stopped singing, and the two are unaware of each other's presence.* JOEL *starts back into the living room and ALAN, noticing him for the first time, begins serenading him.*

ALAN *(singing):*

"Miss Otis regrets she's unable to lunch today,
Madam,
Miss Otis regrets she's unable to lunch today . . ."

JOEL: For God's sake, Alan, not so loud. Do you realize what time it is?

ALAN: Yeah, it's almost one o'clock in the afternoon.

JOEL: Well, tone it down. You'll wake up the neighbors.

ALAN *(placing the tray beside him, kisses his forehead):* I forgot I'm a New Yorker now. Your breakfast.

JOEL: Where are my cigarettes?

ALAN: Oh, I'll get them. *(Going to bureau)* One fag, coming up.

JOEL: Baby, you've got to quit calling them that.

ALAN: But that's what Rita Tushingham calls them.

JOEL: Rita Tushingham is English, and the English have always been fifty years behind the times on these matters.

ALAN *(very Uta Hagen):* All right, George. Have a ciggipoo. (ALAN *sticks the cigarette in* JOEL*'s mouth and lights it)* There. Is that more Manhattan?

JOEL *(spotting the pogo stick):* What in God's name is that?

ALAN: Well, what does it look like? Never mind, it's a pogo stick. You ride it.

JOEL: But not in public?

ALAN: You can if you want to. I rode it down 42nd Street this morning.

JOEL: Are you pulling my leg?

ALAN: Don't be silly. I can't even reach your leg from here. Oh, of course I got a lot of funny looks. But you know how people are. I probably would have got arrested for it back home in Peoria. People there are even worse. But what the hell, it was fun.

JOEL: Why?

ALAN: Why not? Look, I'm on vacation, aren't I? The first real vacation of my life. And aren't vacations supposed to be fun? I didn't scandalize you in any way. Don't worry. Not one pedestrian pointed and shouted, "Look. There goes that friend of Joel Webber's on a pogo stick!" No one threw stones at me, no one told me to get out of town by sunup, and no one took my picture for the *Times*. And anyway, what if they had? I've never had my picture in the *Times*.

JOEL: What did you do on *43rd* Street? Cartwheels?

ALAN *(almost regretting he hadn't thought of it):* No. But I did have fun today. I went and sat in the audience of a quiz show. It was great.

JOEL: Please, God, don't let it have been "I've Got a Secret."

ALAN: No, it was one of those daytime giveaway programs. I can't remember the name of it. It's where they give you the answers and you have to supply the questions.

JOEL: Sounds like the detention room of Precinct 5 to me.

ALAN: Now don't be sarcastic. Anyway, this man with a ton of makeup comes out before the show and starts and warms up the audience by playing the game with them, and I won five dollars.

JOEL: You won five dollars playing a game with a man in a ton of makeup? What game?

ALAN: The quiz game. He'd give us answers and we'd raise our hands if we knew the questions. Anyway, do you know that I was the only one in the whole audience who knew that Allan Jones, not Nelson Eddy, was Jeanette MacDonald's leading man in *The Firefly?*

JOEL: So what?

ALAN: And I knew all the others, too. Like Cinderella's stepsisters' names, and that Johnny Green wrote the score for *Raintree County,* and that Robert Stack, *not* John Wayne, was the pilot in *The High and the Mighty.* But the man with the makeup wouldn't call on me after I'd won once.

JOEL: But it *was* John Wayne.

ALAN: No, it was Robert Stack. John Wayne was the co-pilot. You remember. And Laraine Day and John Howard were getting a divorce, and Phil Harris was the man with the crying towel, and Jan Sterling wore those fake eyelashes, and —

JOEL: Okay, okay. I believe you. So what else did you do today?

ALAN: I had coffee with this very nice schoolteacher from Nebraska. But let me finish the other story first, because they're connected.

JOEL: Male or female schoolteacher?

ALAN: Male, of course. Who ever heard of a woman coaching football? Anyway, after the show, they asked the audience if any of us would like to be contestants on the show, and I thought that sounded like fun, so I raised my hand and about ten of us went up to this office where we took a test. You know—name recognition like knowing that Doris Kappelhoff is Doris Day's real name, and all. It was really easy except for Gregor Pedestri. Have you ever heard of Gregor Pedestri?

JOEL: Was that the football coach's name?

ALAN: No, his name was Smith. John Smith. Well, I never heard of Gregor Pedestri either, so I left that one blank. But that was the only one. And then they gave us more answers and we had to go around the circle — they had us seated in a circle — and each give a different question to an answer. Well, I was the last one, and sometimes it was hard thinking of responses.

JOEL: John Smith? Sounds like a phony name to me.

ALAN: No, it's not. Well, he's from Nebraska. Anyway, are you listening?

JOEL: I'm listening.

ALAN: Well, they gave us answers like "two cups." Well, of course, the first lady said, "How many cups in a pint?" and another said, "What's the proper place setting when having tea for two?" which I thought was kinda cute, and the other questions all were similar. Some of them couldn't think of anything. What would you have said?

JOEL: I wasn't a contestant. What did you say?

ALAN: I said, "What's in a brassiere?"

JOEL: Oh, God.

ALAN: It got a lot of laughs. And another answer was "break the glass." Well, the first people said things like how do you punch a fire alarm and what's the old French custom after proposing a toast, and all. So I said, "How would you destroy Cinderella's slipper?" And Mr. Smith said that was by far the most original answer.

JOEL: So when do you go on the show?

ALAN: I don't know. *They* call *you*. But Mr. Smith said maybe I wouldn't get called on because I had questions for all the answers and that might hurt my chances. He said that in television they don't like you to know too much.

JOEL: What else did Mr. Smith have to say?

ALAN: Oh, lots of things. He was really interesting. First we talked a lot about the quiz show, and how the contestants today weren't really very bright except for this one dumpy old housewife whose husband was an invalid. She knew quite a bit about horticulture. In fact, she was today's champion. She won eight hundred dollars. Boy, the world sure has a lot of money to give away to stupid people.

JOEL: Maybe when you get on the show, you'll win enough money to open a nightclub I can sing in.

ALAN: Oh. Things went bad with Radzman last night, huh?

JOEL: Well, after cutting four demonstration discs, an agent's suggestion of a fifth isn't the best news in the world.

ALAN: Now don't get depressed. Eighteen publishers turned down *Peyton Place* before Grace Metalious finally sold it.

JOEL: Was that meant to be a comparison?

ALAN: No, silly. I just mean that you shouldn't get discouraged this early in the game. I feel uncomfortable when people are depressed. Like poor Mr. Smith.

JOEL: Don't tell me. Let me guess. He's tired of being stereotyped as a football coach in Nebraska. No one really understands him. He has a lot of outside interests like books and the theatre, but his friends are the type who only want to argue about the World Series.

ALAN: Exactly! You know a lot more about people than you let on, you know that? He thought I was the most interesting person he'd met in New York just because I knew a lot about art and old movies. He even invited me up to his suite to talk.

JOEL: I've got the picture. He liked *Walden* and Judy Garland, too, and he could probably learn a lot from you.

ALAN *(wary):* Something like that, yes.

JOEL: Alan, baby, don't you see that that's the oldest line in the world? This guy was some repressed old queer from Nebraska on vacation trying to pick up a few tricks in New York, and you looked like a good thing.

ALAN: I don't believe that, Joel. He was a lonely out-of-towner, just like Geraldine Page in *Dear Heart,* who only wanted someone to talk to.

JOEL: In his hotel room.

ALAN: What's wrong with that? How many people do you see dissecting Emily Dickinson in Sardi's?

JOEL: Did you go with him?

ALAN: No, I came home to fix lunch for you.

JOEL: Thank God. Rita Tushingham has nothing on you. You could have gotten into a lot of trouble with that old pervert.

ALAN: Pervert? You're completely off base. Why, why, he's a football coach!

JOEL: Don't tell me about football coaches. Football coaches, schmootball coaches. I know all about football coaches. Always patting their players on the butt and lifting them onto their shoulders. Perverts, all of them. They're no different from us. What do you think they do in those huddles, anyway?

ALAN: All right, be cynical. You wouldn't be you if you weren't. That's part of your charm. But I prefer to think of him as a lonely old man who liked Willy Loman.

JOEL: You silly little optimist. You're cute. *(Moves toward him)*

ALAN *(edging away):* Good Lord, you're frisky for the middle of the afternoon.

JOEL: This is New York. Not Peoria.

ALAN: You sure slept late enough. What time did you get in last night?

JOEL: Oh, it was pretty late.

ALAN: I stayed up till 2:30 watching the Late Late Show with Elvira. It was Charles Laughton in *The Isle of Lost Souls.*

JOEL: Well, I didn't get away from Radzman's until about two or so, and then I just walked around for awhile. You know.

ALAN: Yeah, whenever I want to think or something, I do the very same thing. I just like to wander all over and not see anybody. Just think.

JOEL: You know, I honestly think you mean that.

ALAN: Of course I do. I just hum show tunes to myself, or think about a book I've read, or . . . oh, Lord. I just remembered. I gave him our number. I told him he could call me and talk some evening.

JOEL: Oh, boy.

ALAN: Well, if he calls I can just tell him that I'm busy and can't see him. That way I won't shatter any illusions.

JOEL: Was he cute?

ALAN: What difference does that make?

JOEL: Maybe you'd have fun shattering some of those illusions.

ALAN: That's not my type of joke. *(Kidding)* And anyway, I'm a one-man man. *(Starting toward kitchen)* How does a bologna sandwich sound?

JOEL: You imbecile. I love you.

ALAN: With cheese?

JOEL: Yeah, but hurry. I promised Radzie I'd meet him at two.

ALAN: Well you can't become Caruso on just bologna. I'll fry you a couple of eggs too.

JOEL: Scrambled.

ALAN: Okay. *(Puttering in the kitchen)* Is Radzman coming here?

JOEL: Yeah, why?

ALAN: Oh, nothing. He just makes me nervous, that's all. He acts like he owns the place, and I'm always afraid he'll find dust under the sofa or something.

JOEL: Radzie *does* own the place, and we can't ever forget that. Not every struggling young singer lives like I do, and for that we must always be nice to Radzie. Okay, cherub?

ALAN: How nice?

JOEL: Ho-ho-ho. Now who's sounding cynical? Radzie is the great white father who's *letting* us live here. Don't ever forget that.

ALAN: I'll kneel down and say three "Allahs" when he arrives.

JOEL *(jovial):* Shut up and scramble the eggs.

ALAN: Really, Joel, sometimes I feel like I'm being kept. And I don't like it.

JOEL: *You're* not being kept. *We're* being provided for.

ALAN: But with provisions.

JOEL: Are you trying to shame me? It's not easy. I'm a big boy now and I know what I want. And Radzie's helping me get it, that's all. For a very small price — gratitude. That's all the rent I pay. Comprehend?

ALAN *(not in the mood to argue):* Comprehend. Hurry up and shower.

JOEL *(with a huge leap toward the bathroom):* I am off!

ALAN: Only don't sing "My Heart Belongs to Daddy." I have a very jealous nature. Okay?

JOEL: Okay. Now shut up and scramble.

Suddenly, a shoe hits the U.C. terrace from above. Then another shoe. Then two very skinny legs come into view.

JOEL: Guess who's coming.

ALAN: Couldn't be the postman. He always rings twice.

ELVIRA *enters from the fire escape. She looks like something out of a Jules Feiffer cartoon. Everything about her is misshaped — long, bony legs, a huge pot belly, the neck of a swan, and the face of an ugly duckling. The Bronx Jew, she is extremely flat-chested although at this moment her breasts are bulging.*

JOEL: Elvira, you're a vision.

ELVIRA: You really think? *(She turns around and examines her body)* Yeah? Well, I did wash my hair last night. *(She removes two cans from her breast)* Anybody want some kosher pickles? I stole four jars from the delicatessen this morning. *(Whiffs the air as she comes in)* Ummm. What smells so good?

JOEL: Bologna.

ELVIRA *(swallows whole slice):* Ummmmm.

ALAN: It wasn't blessed.

ELVIRA: So? I'm company, and it would be impolite for me to expect you to observe my customs.

ALAN: Hi.

ELVIRA: Hi, Al. Hit me again. *(Swallows another slice; to* JOEL*)* You look dreadful. Does that mean you're a star yet?

JOEL: Hi, Elvira.

ELVIRA: Gee, a body never gets any conversation around here. Never a kind word. So what's new?

JOEL: Alan met a tall, dark stranger today named Smith.

ELVIRA: Yeah? Is he going to keep you?

ALAN: I, uh, no!

ELVIRA: Pity. *(To* JOEL) You're Scorpio, aren't you? You're going to meet a stranger today, too. That's what the *Post* astrology guide predicted, anyway.

JOEL: Is he going to keep me?

ELVIRA: I don't know. The horoscope didn't say.

ALAN: What's going to happen to you today, Elvira?

ELVIRA: I'm going to enter into financial matters with great hesitancy. Which means my new roommate will probably be broke, too. If she ever gets here. She was supposed to arrive early this morning. Do you know what I dreamed about last night? Claire Trevor. Whatever happened to her? She was riding a palomino in my dream. Do you think that means anything? Rode that goddam horse right into a big, long tunnel. That's the first time I've dreamed about Claire Trevor in an age. *(To* JOEL) So when do you find out anything from the recording company?

ALAN: He's going to cut a record.

ELVIRA: Yeah? That's nice.

ALAN: And the record company's going to love it. And a couple of local D.J.'s will pick it up and play it night and day.

ELVIRA: Yeah? That's —

JOEL: All the high school Harrys in all the hamburger heavens all over New York will start whistling it.

ELVIRA: Yeah?

ALAN: And they'll start playing it on jukeboxes and raving about the new singing sensation.

JOEL: And suddenly *Variety* will headline "Joel New Juke Joker," and their charts will show my steady climb to number one disc in the country.

ALAN: And fan clubs will spring up.

JOEL: And little children in the streets will cry, "We want Joel. We want Joel."

ALAN: And —

JOEL: And —

ELVIRA: And the eggs are ruined.

ALAN: Spoil-sport.

JOEL: Bitch, bitch, bitch.

ELVIRA: I hate to see good food go to waste unless it's on me. Hit me again. I'm famished. I think Claire Trevor took everything I had out of me. . . . There she was on this palomino. And she was saying, "Elvira. Elvira."

JOEL *(tasting the eggs):* They are ruined.

ELVIRA: Only this and nothing more. "Elvira. Elvira."

The telephone rings.

ALAN: Oh, God, that may be Nebraska.

JOEL: Better let me get it.

ELVIRA *(in trance):* "Elvira. Elvira."

ALAN: Or maybe I got accepted for the TV show. After all, I hadn't heard of Gregor Pedestri.

JOEL *(on phone):* Hello. Joel Webber speaking. *(Then)* Oh, you nasty old man.

ALAN: Now how could he tell so fast? I was with him all morning and I thought he was perfectly normal.

JOEL: But I just got *out* of bed.

ALAN: That *couldn't* be John Smith.

ELVIRA: When Joel coos like that, it's a sure sign that it ain't Pocohontas, either.

JOEL: Of course I can.

ELVIRA: That's the understatement of the year.

JOEL: Well, you said two o'clock. That still gives me forty-five minutes.

ALAN *(relieved):* Oh, it's only Radzman.

ELVIRA: I don't like that man. He looks like the mask of Fu Manchu.

ALAN: Elvira! He'll hear you.

ELVIRA: And he walks like Mary Astor.

ALAN: Sshh!

JOEL: Me to you. Bye-bye. *(He hangs up, runs over and kisses* ELVIRA) Mwah. I love you.

ELVIRA: Yeah? That's nice.

JOEL: Your stars didn't lie. I'm going to meet Mr. Parkay today. And you know what *that* means.

ELVIRA: No.

ALAN: Oh, Joel, that's wonderful.

ELVIRA: You got any more eggs? These are ruined. I'll trade you two jars of pickles for —

JOEL *(grabbing her):* Listen, Elvira, listen. Do you hear them? There are children out there shouting in the streets. "We want Joel Webber. We want Joel Webber." Don't you hear them?

ELVIRA *(listening):* No.

JOEL: Well, you will. You will. The whole world will. Now, Alan, fix this lovely woman an egg. After all, she predicted I'd meet a stranger today. And that stranger is going to be Harrison Parkay. *(Kisses her on the head)* Mwah. My God, Elvira, you need to wash your hair. Eggs, Alan, eggs for everyone. I am off. *(Joel exits up the steps, into the bathroom)*

ELVIRA: Alan? Alan, I don't hear anything in the streets.

ALAN *(smiling warmly):* Neither does he . . . yet. But it's part of a dream. And his dream is going to come true. It really is. He's got it. Talent in his little finger. So keep listening, Elvira. Keep listening. There *will* be shouting.

ELVIRA: Alan?

ALAN: Hmmm?

ELVIRA: You like Joel, don't you?

ALAN: I like him a whole lot.

ELVIRA: Hmm. How long you known him?

ALAN: We were fraternity brothers together back at the University of Illinois. Joel was my pledge father.

ELVIRA: Yeah? That must've been one helluva ritual.

ALAN: Elvira! We did the craziest things. We were always like two kids at recess. One day when I was still rushing — that's when you go around to all the different houses before you pledge one — I got into a conversation with Joel at Lambda Chi.

ELVIRA: What?

ALAN: Lambda Chi. That was the name of the house.

ELVIRA: Sounds Greek to me.

ALAN: Elvira! Anyway, we got into this conversation about theatre. I guess we were both trying to impress the other or something. Anyway, Joel said something about Beckett. Well, I thought he meant the play *Becket,* and I said in my best name-dropping tone, "Oh, you mean the thing with Olivier." And Joel replied, "No, I don't think Olivia deHavilland has ever been in anything by Beckett." Then we both realized and started laughing at ourselves. It was great. And we've been the closest of friends ever since.

ELVIRA *(who hasn't followed any of this):* Yeah?

ALAN: Don't you see? He thought I meant Olivia deHavilland when I said Olivier. Laurence Olivier.

ELVIRA *(still unimpressed):* Oh, yeah.

ALAN: And he really meant the author, Samuel Beckett, but I thought —

ELVIRA: Are my eggs ready?

ALAN: Well, anyway, it was funny. *(Hands her a plate)* Here.

ELVIRA: So you've known him for a long time then, huh? *(Gobbling eggs)* Ummmmmmm.

ALAN: It was like we grew up together. He taught me practically everything I know about books, music, theatre, everything. I was a complete dolt before I met Joel.

ELVIRA: But I thought you were a Phi Beta Kappa.

ALAN: Sure, in school work involving Byron, Keats, Shelley, and all phases of speech education and therapy. But not in common sense or the things that matter.

ELVIRA: What are the things that matter? My mother always said that the things that mattered were cooking, sewing, and finding a man. So I guess I still haven't got any smarts in those departments, either. But I was school champion in Trivia. I beat every other kid at Steinmetz High. Really. I could quote every film that Richard Arlen ever made. I'm still single, though. Hey, will you teach me how to cook an egg, someday?

ALAN: Someday, yes.

ELVIRA: You cook good eggs. The guy that lived with Joel before you couldn't cook a goddam thing. Except yogurt. And, God, did I hate that. All he did was eat yogurt and chin himself on the fire escape. Had a nice body, if you like that sort of thing. But you, you're different. You're a real person. You cook eggs.

ALAN: Yeah.

ELVIRA: God, I hated yogurt. When do you have to go back to Illinois?

ALAN: I wish never. No, I start teaching the day after Labor Day.

ELVIRA: High school?

ALAN: Yeah.

ELVIRA: Labor Day. That's in September, isn't it? I was never much on holidays. Except Halloween. It was the one day in the year I could really express myself. All the kids in our neighborhood used to get together and scare the pants off each other. Sort of exciting. Oh, the Hershey bars I collected in those days. Do you think you'll like that?

ALAN: Like what?

ELVIRA: Speech therapy. Working with all those cleft palates, and the like. Stutterers, you know.

ALAN: Somebody has to. My degree says that somebody should be me. And so does my draft board.

ELVIRA: Yeah? They don't draft teachers, huh?

ALAN: Not so far. But they're beginning to. All except the math and science teachers. They're the ones who can teach future generations all the practical things, so they're necessary. But the teachers of speech and English will soon be expendable. They only fill kids' heads with dreams.

ELVIRA: God, I'd hate to be a guy and have to go to war and get my guts blown out. Bam. Bam. Bam . . . and I'd never be able to dig a foxhole.

ALAN: Be thankful you're a woman.

ELVIRA: Yeah, women got it easy. Except child-bearing. God, I'd hate that. I saw Jennifer Jones die from it once in a movie. Ugh. So when I was eleven I took a vow never to get into a situation which might result in child-bearing. And so far, goddammit, I've stuck to it. Oh, the things we say unthinkingly as children! How does Joel stay out of the service?

ALAN: He knows this doctor back in Chicago. You let him pinch you, and he certifies that you have a bad back or something.

ELVIRA: Why don't you do that?

ALAN: Because 1) it would be a lie . . . I don't have a bad back; 2) I can be deferred by teaching, and 3) I wouldn't want some old man pinching me.

ELVIRA: But if it's okay for Joel to —

ALAN: Joel's different. They don't defer singers. If he has to fib a little to get what he deserves, well, well . . . What could he do in the Army anyway?

ELVIRA: I shudder to think of it.

The telephone rings.

ALAN *(answering it):* I got it. *(Into phone)* Hello? — I mean, Joel Webber's residence. Alan Reynolds speaking. Oh, how nice. *(To* ELVIRA) Oh, God, it's him.

ELVIRA: Who?

ALAN *(into phone):* You are? *(To* ELVIRA) My dark stranger. *(Into phone)* Well, really, I was uh, I was, uh . . . no, I *wasn't* doing *that.* "Is it all right if you . . ." *(To* ELVIRA) What do I say?

ELVIRA: What did you say before?

ALAN: What? Yes, I adore Marlene Dietrich, but —

ELVIRA: Ask him if he's got anything to eat. I'm famished.

ALAN *(into phone):* Well, yes. I'll see you then in a . . . yes, in "a few little while." heh-heh. *(Hanging up; to* ELVIRA) Oh, God, Elvira, he's on his way up.

ELVIRA: Who?

ALAN: John Smith of Nebraska. How do I get rid of him?

ELVIRA: Who is he?

ALAN: This man I was nice to this morning.

ELVIRA: And he's back this early in the afternoon? Now that's what I call stamina.

ALAN: No, no, it's nothing like that. Well, *he* thinks it is, but really . . .

ELVIRA *(shoving him U.C.):* I like you. Now run along upstairs, and I'll convince him he's got the wrong apartment.

ALAN: But I — great! Great. Mwah. *(Blows her a kiss)*

ELVIRA: I'll convince him he's in the Twilight Zone or something.

ALAN *(ascending the fire escape):* Great! You're a love.

ELVIRA: I'm a real Bette Davis when you come right down to it.

ALAN *is just disappearing from sight as* JOEL *enters from the bathroom with his robe around him, and stares out after* ALAN.

JOEL: Where's he going now?

ELVIRA: To practice his chin-ups.

JOEL: What the devil — ?

He stands completely bewildered.

ELVIRA: Sshhh. *(Shouting)* And if you ever speak like that to my mother again, I'll leave you forever. *(She stuffs the can of pickles under her jersey)* I'll jump down the stairs and kill the baby, that's what I'll do. I'll kill the child you conceived in lust, you, you masher, you. *(Going to door R.C.)* I'm off to kill our baby. *(She is now in the corridor talking to Mr. Smith, who is never seen or heard by the audience)* Don't stop me, mister. Let me jump. I don't want to carry his child. He made me what I am today. Let me jump. Watch out or you'll burst the pickles, you knuckle-head. I don't know who you're looking for, but this isn't the place. Nope. Nobody here but me and my common-law husband whose baby I'm going to kill if you'll just turn around and go home and clear the stairs, and — hey, where are you going? Why are you going upstairs? Hey, listen. But, but. . . . *(Running back onstage)* Oh, damn. He said he must've had the wrong floor. Now he's going up to my place. Hell, hell, hell. *(She heads for the terrace and starts up the fire escape)*

JOEL *(befuddled):* Elvira, what the — *(She swings loosely on the fire escape)* Elvira, don't jump. No matter whose baby it is, don't don't. . . . *(she's out of sight)* What the hell is going on up there? That wasn't Mr. Radzman, was it? Elvira, if that was Radzie, and you — (ALAN *is seen descending the fire escape)* Alan, what's happening? What are you . . . did you get Elvira pregnant? I had no idea you even —

ALAN *(now in full view):* Heavens, no. We're thwarting John Smith. He's in the building trying to find me.

JOEL *(interested):* Oh? What does he look like?

ALAN: Oh, Joel. Go brush your teeth. *(He shoves* JOEL *back into the bathroom)*

ELVIRA *(from above, in her room;* ALAN *stands with his back to the audience listening up on the terrace):* Agh! Aaagh! Get out of my apartment before I call the police. You, you fiend. Yeah, I'll *bet* you got the wrong apartment. I'll just . . . No! No, it's not downstairs. No, it's — wait, stay. Let's talk. I — I *love* Marlene Dietrich, do you? Yeah? Really? Well, whaddaya know. Sit down. Make yourself at home. I'll fix you some pickles.

While ALAN *has been U.C. listening,* CYNTHIA QUINN *has entered through the door R., not seeing him. She scans the room, puts some bags down, takes off her hat and starts to fan herself. She is twenty-three, very pretty, all smile with a warm glow that shows through even now as she starts to sit down and sits on the pogo stick.*

CYNTHIA: Aaaah!

ALAN *(startled by the sound, he is audibly surprised):* Whaa? *(He totters on the edge of the terrace)*

CYNTHIA *(startled by his cry):* Oh! *(Turns to see him trying to steady his weight on the terrace)* Don't jump. Whoever you are, don't jump. *(Madly improvising to prevent what she misinterprets as a suicide attempt)* There's everything to live for. There's the whole future ahead. Sure, some days look gray and hopeless. We all know despair. But you musn't end your young life now. Please, don't jump. Please, please don't jump. Now say it. Say it after me. Say, "I won't jump." Now repeat it. Say, "I — won't — jump."

ALAN *(confused, but amused):* I won't jump.

CYNTHIA *(sighing relief):* Oh, thank goodness. Thank goodness. Now just come in here and calm yourself down. *(He moves into living room area)* Now, sit. Sit down and relax. Just relax. Sit, sit. *(He does so)* There, that's better. Are you comfortable?

ALAN: Yes, thank you.

CYNTHIA: Good, good.

There is a long silence. He stares at her, and she smiles reassuringly.

ALAN: Hi.

CYNTHIA *(plays along with him): Hi.*

There is another long, awkward silence during which she smiles forcefully.

ALAN: It's a nice day, don't you think?

CYNTHIA: Yes, yes, a lovely day. A lovely day. The world is beautiful. "God's in His Heaven, all's right with the world," as they say. Everything to live for. A lovely day. Browning. It was Browning.

ALAN: I beg your pardon?

CYNTHIA: Browning. It was Robert Browning who said, "God's in His Heaven, all's right with the world."

ALAN: Yes, I know. "Pippa Passes."

CYNTHIA: I beg your pardon?

ALAN: "Pippa Passes." That was the name of the poem. The Browning poem. The one you quoted from.

CYNTHIA: Oh, yes. Yes, of course. "Pippa . . . Passes."

ALAN: Do you believe in God?

CYNTHIA *(hesitant):* Yes.

ALAN: Good. So do I.

CYNTHIA: Oh, good. Good.

There is another long silence.

ALAN: Are you comfortable?

CYNTHIA: Yes. Yes, thank you.

ALAN: Good. *(Pause)* Could I get you a drink?

CYNTHIA: Uh, uh, no. No, thank you.

ALAN: Oh, I'm sorry. I'll bet you don't drink.

CYNTHIA: No, I — well, yes, I do sometimes. Just a little. But not right now. I mean, *I* don't *need* a drink right now.

ALAN: Oh.

CYNTHIA: Could I get *you* one?

ALAN: No, thank you. I don't drink either.

CYNTHIA: Oh.

ALAN: Well, what I mean is, I can't drink. I get morbid when I drink. Very somber and mean. Some people, you know, they *need* a drink every once in a while to loosen themselves up. To break down their inhibitions so they can have fun. For those people — if that's the only way they can do it — I recommend a drink. With me it's just the opposite, though. I'm naturally very uninhibited, and I'm always happy. So alcohol has a sort of reverse effect on me. I get grouchy and sit off in a corner — or I become the essence of truth and proceed to tell everybody exactly what's wrong with them. It's really embarrassing. I tell them all sorts of secrets about themselves that they don't want to hear. Then they get angry. And I don't really blame them, do you? What right has anybody got to tell other people things that will upset them? I mean, really. I'd much rather stay sober and have people think well of themselves, you know what I mean? So I don't drink.

CYNTHIA: Oh. So you're, uh, you're naturally very happy.

ALAN: Yes, all the time. Aren't you?

CYNTHIA: Well, yes. Yes, I'm very happy.

ALAN: Good. But you do look hot and thirsty. Let me get you a Coke.

CYNTHIA: No, thank you. I mean —

ALAN: Wouldn't you like a Coke?

CYNTHIA: Well, yes, I would, but —

ALAN: Good. Me too. I'll get you one. It's no bother.

He goes up to the kitchen area.

CYNTHIA: Uh, you seem to know this apartment pretty well.

ALAN: Well, I should. I live here.

CYNTHIA: You . . . ? *(To add to her puzzlement,* JOEL *crosses from the bathroom door to his bedroom, singing at the top of his lungs, oblivious to the two of them;* CYNTHIA *watches him intensely as he exits into his bedroom)* Who was that?

ALAN: Joel. We're rooming together — temporarily. *(He hands her a Coke)* Here.

CYNTHIA: Oh, thank you.

ALAN: You're welcome.

CYNTHIA: Thank you. *(Pauses to reflect)* I always thought Elvira was a girl's name.

ALAN: I beg your pardon?

CYNTHIA: Elvira. The name Elvira. I always thought it was a girl's name. Of course, I've never really known anyone named Elvira . . . except for the first wife in *Blithe Spirit.* Her name was Elvira. And I just naturally thought that anyone named Elvira would be a girl. You know, the name ending in "a," and all. In Latin — I had four years of Latin in high school — in Latin, only feminine words end in "a," so, well, I naturally thought Elvira was a girl's name. I mean, there aren't many men's names ending in "a," now, are there. So you see, it was a natural mistake on my part. Oh, except for Ira, of course. Ira ends in "a," and that's a man's name, isn't it? Like Ira Gershwin. Yes, yes of course. I didn't think of that. So I guess Elvira is all right, too. Well, naturally if I'd known you were a man, I'd never have accepted. I mean, well, I'm not that type of girl. I mean, well I do need to save all the money I can, and you're offer sounded like the best bet . . . just the thing I wanted, but of course you *do* see that I just can't. I'm afraid the deal is off.

ALAN *(very obviously confused):* I beg your pardon? I think —

But ALAN *is interrupted by a very low, husky voice from above.*

ELVIRA *(offstage; very Marlene Dietrich):* "Falling in lohve again, Never wanted to . . ."

CYNTHIA *(amazed):* Does Marlene Dietrich live in this building?

ALAN: No, that's only Elvira. *(It suddenly hits him)* Elvira! You're looking for Elvira.

CYNTHIA: You mean there's another —

ALAN: No, no, no. *(Beginning to laugh)* There is only *one* Elvira. She lives upstairs right above us. In *6*-A.

CYNTHIA: In. . . . ? Oh, I'm sorry. I thought this was — . Oh, I'm sorry. I mean, well it seemed like six flights of stairs, and I . . . oh, I'm sorry. I —

They both begin giggling — like kids at recess. Finally realizing how silly their conversation has been, their laughter grows and grows before ceasing.

ALAN *(after a long pause):* Hi.

CYNTHIA: Hi.

ALAN: I'm Alan. Alan Reynolds.

CYNTHIA: I'm Cynthia. Cynthia Quinn.

ALAN: Cynthia Quinn? You must be an actress with a name like that.

CYNTHIA: No really. Well, I — yes, yes, I guess I am an actress in a way. But it's my real name. I mean, I didn't change it or anything. I mean, well, I was born with it . . . Cynthia Quinn.

ALAN: Cynthia Quinn. That's great.

CYNTHIA: Thank you.

ELVIRA *(her Marlene Dietrich voice again starts its moaning from offstage above):* "Underneath the lantern
By the barrack gate . . ."

CYNTHIA: Does she always — ?

ALAN: Oh, no. No. In fact, I think she secretly despises Marlene Dietrich. I mean, well, Elvira's Jewish, you know, and Marlene Dietrich . . .

CYNTHIA: Thank you for the Coke, Alan. I — I won't trouble you any longer. *(Rising)* I'll just get these things upstairs, and —

ALAN *(hastily):* Oh, no, you can't go up there right now. Elvira's not herself now. I mean, she's very busy.

CYNTHIA: Well she was expecting me early this morning, and I'd better let her know —

ALAN: But she's entertaining now, and can't be disturbed. You see, she has a man in her room.

CYNTHIA: Oh, but —. Does she often have men in?

ALAN: Oh, no. Very seldom. In fact she *never* has men in.

CYNTHIA: But then, why is she — ?

ALAN: Well, you see, he's a friend of mine, and Elvira is sort of helping out.

CYNTHIA: Well, then, why are you — ?

ALAN: Well, you see, it's someone I'm trying to avoid. It's this man. Mr. Smith. I mean, really he's a very nice old man, but Joel warned me to be careful because he was a repressed football coach, you see, and so Elvira is singing to him upstairs in order to . . . *(Stops to think)* Does this make any sense to you?

CYNTHIA: No.

ALAN: Me either, now that I stop to think about it. Here is this lonely old man from Nebraska, and I'm the one person he's able to talk to, and I try to pawn him off on . . .

During the above speech, ELVIRA *is seen descending the fire escape.*

ELVIRA *(running into the room, grabs a toss pillow and stuffs it under her jersey):* Damn. Damn. Damn. *(Noticing Cynthia)* Hello. *(Hurries to the door R. and exits, closes it behind her, and begins hammering on it from the outside)* Please open up, Harry. I love you. I want to have your baby. Do you hear me, Harry? I'm proud to be carrying your infant.

CYNTHIA: But I thought your name was Alan.

ALAN: It is. I'll clear this thing up in a minute. *(He starts toward the door, stops when he hears* ELVIRA*'s voice from beyond)*

ELVIRA *(still offstage; now conversing with Mr. Smith):* No, no, I didn't kill the baby. I love the baby. Harry loves the baby. Everybody loves babies. What right have we to kill them? Bye bye now. Oh, you met my sister upstairs? Wonderful kid, isn't she? She loves babies, too. She's gonna be my baby's godmother. Isn't that swell? Well, now, run along. I'm just going inside to have my baby and live happily ever after. Yeah. And it was nice meeting you, too. (ALAN *opens the door at just the wrong moment, for* ELVIRA *falls through it to the floor; she quickly hollers offstage to Mr. Smith)* No, no, that's okay. It's a tough kid. It'll be all right. Bye bye. *(Quickly she closes the door behind her, panting as she leans against it, then checks a look through the keyhole; satisfied, she starts back into the room)* He's gone. Boy, is that a relief. I couldn't remember the words to "Lili Marlene." You were all wrong about him, Alan. He's very nice. We're going to discuss Oscar Wilde the next time he's in town. *(Notices* CYNTHIA) Hello.

ALAN: Cynthia, Elvira. Elvira, Cynthia.

ELVIRA: Oh, you're here. I was expecting you this morning. Hi. You look like a size nine — that'll work out swell.

CYNTHIA *(immediately sensing she's going to like Elvira):* Hi. Don't tell me — you're an actress.

ELVIRA: Of sorts. I do commercials.

ALAN: Last month she told Mrs. Kirby all about new Fab with Borax, and before that she had unruly hair.

ELVIRA: They always cast me as the "before," never the "after." I did triumph once, though. My prep school had 76 per cent fewer cavities. Did you catch that one by any chance? And if my agent ever comes through, Hertz is going to put me in the driver's seat sometime in September.

CYNTHIA: And just doing commercials can keep you alive in New York?

ELVIRA: Heavens, no. My aunt in Ithaca pays for my place. She wanted to be an actress herself once. But she married my uncle, the white slaver. Anyway, I thought by sharing the place I could save money. Are you rich?

CYNTHIA: Afraid not. But I do have enough for a couple months' rent.

ELVIRA: Super. Then you can move in. Alan'll help us get the stuff upstairs. God knows, he owes me a favor. Oh, have you met Alan?

ALAN: Yes. Cynthia saved my life. She talked me out of a suicide.

ELVIRA: Yeah? That's nice. Have you met Joel?

CYNTHIA *(slowly):* Well, he really wasn't dressed.

ELVIRA: You've met Joel. *(Starting off and up the fire escape)* I'll run upstairs and pick up my dirty underwear first, alrighty? The place is really a mess. I dreamed about Claire Trevor last night, you know? *(She is out of sight)*

ALAN: Why don't I help you with your stuff, okay?

CYNTHIA: Okay. I . . . hi.

ALAN: Hi. So you're going to be an actress, huh?

CYNTHIA: I don't know. Not really. But that's what I tell people. Really, I'm just on vacation. A vacation from secretarial duties, Minneapolis, time clocks, and everything else that hints of responsibility. I'm running away, is what it is.

ALAN: You mean I'm harboring a fugitive? Great. Did you rob a bank and get the cops after you?

CYNTHIA: Afraid not. Can I tell you a secret?

ALAN: I won't tell a soul but Louella.

CYNTHIA: I just allotted myself a few months to get away from everything. Back in Minneapolis I came to the point where I could no longer play efficient young typist and .community theatre devotee. Dinner and movies every Saturday night, bowling league once a week, singing alto in the Presbyterian choir, and sitting out on the porch swing with the boy next door eating fudge till 2 a.m. Then all of a sudden, the boy next door proposed. Believe me, that's the scariest moment in a girl's life — the proposal from the very nice, very respectable boy next door. If she says "no" she may wind up all alone on the porch swing for the rest of her days. If she says "yes" . . . so I ran. In a way I am an actress, you see. Running until I decide the role I want.

ALAN: And the boy next door?

CYNTHIA: He'll wait for me to come back. I hope I don't go, but I may. But until then — vacation.

ALAN *(sincerely):* I like you. And so will Joel. You're different.

CYNTHIA: No, I'm not. But I try hard to be. I'm afraid I'll find out in the end that I'm just hopelessly, Midwestern old me.

ALAN: You'll love Joel. He's a singer. And he's really going places, too. I have all the faith in the world in him.

MR. RADZMAN: Perhaps you should be his agent instead of me, Alan. Forgive me, the door was open. I didn't know my guests had guests of their own.

ARNOLD RADZMAN *enters the room from the door R.; he is nearly fifty, polished, attractive in carriage, and cold. He* could *resemble the mask of Fu Manchu, and he* does *walk like Mary Astor.*

ALAN: Oh, Mr. Radzman. This is Cynthia. Cynthia Quinn. Cynthia, Joel's agent, Arnold Radzman. Cynthia's an actress.

RADZMAN: Sorry, I don't handle women. Are you planning on moving into this menagerie, also, Miss Quinn?

ALAN: Cynthia lives upstairs, Mr. Radzman. She's just arrived.

RADZMAN *(to* ALAN): Will you tell Joel I'm waiting?

ALAN: What? Oh, yes. Yes, of course.

CYNTHIA *(uncomfortable):* Alan, I'll just take these things upstairs. *(She moves toward her bags)*

ALAN: All right. I'll be up to help you in a minute.

CYNTHIA: Fine. It was nice meeting you, Mr. Radzman.

RADZMAN: Miss Quinn. *(He dismisses her by the tone of his voice, and she exits through the door R.)*

ALAN *(staring after her):* Isn't she beautiful?

RADZMAN: Rather striking, yes. A very pretty face. She has her qualities.

ALAN: She's so fresh, and alive, and —

RADZMAN *(impatient):* Will you tell Joel I'm here, please?

ALAN: Oh, yes. I'm sorry. *(He makes a move toward* JOEL's *room)*

RADZMAN: On second thought, Alan, wait. I'd like to talk to you for a moment.

ALAN *(sitting down as if ordered to do so):* Okay.

RADZMAN: Well . . . how are you enjoying New York?

ALAN: I love it. I wish I could stay here forever.

RADZMAN *(grimacing):* Oh. But you will be going back to the Midwest soon? I mean, you do have to go teach and all.

ALAN: Yes. And all.

RADZMAN: When does school start back there? Isn't it around Labor Day or something? What is that — three weeks? Four?

ALAN: Nearly four, Mr. Radzman.

RADZMAN: Yes, yes. I lose track of the holidays, it seems. They slip right up on us. You know, "time and tide," as they say. Only four weeks till Labor Day. That doesn't give you much time to get back and settled, does it?

ALAN: I'll be leaving in exactly three weeks, Mr. Radzman, pogo stick and all. And before I go, I'll wash the windows, vacuum the carpet, and polish up the handle on the big front door. *(He stops himself)* I'm sorry.

RADZMAN *(studying him):* Alan, you resent me, don't you. Why?

ALAN: I don't trust you, Mr. Radzman. I feel very uncomfortable when you're around . . . for both myself and Joel. I realize you pay Joel's bills here, and I know how very much he needs your assistance. I'm very appreciative. But at the same time, I can't help feeling uncomfortable. *(Pause)* Again, I'm sorry.

RADZMAN: Don't be, Alan. Honesty is a very admirable trait . . . in some. But it would be the downfall of many great men I know. In a few of us, it's just unnatural. Alan, what — what are your feelings toward Joel?

ALAN: That's a strange question, Mr. Radzman. I'm not quite sure how to answer it.

RADZMAN: But you'll answer honestly. That's the important thing.

ALAN: All right, then. Honestly . . . I love Joel. He has been the kindest, warmest person I've ever known. And also one of the most talented. I've never had any brothers of my own. Only a sister. An older sister. So much older that the only thing we were ever able to discuss together was not duplicating Christmas presents for the folks. Joel, I suppose, is my "brother substitute," if you want to get Freudian about it. And more, of course. You're wise enough to see that.

RADZMAN *(simply):* Yes.

ALAN: And I'm really devoted to him. Yes, really. I want more than anything else for him to have what *he* wants, get what *he* deserves in this world, which is so much. And I'm not sure that he knows himself what it is he needs. I'm a child in many ways — he often tells me that — naive and unsuspecting. Maybe it's true. But I have the vision to at least see what it is he needs. And I want to help him get it, in some way.

RADZMAN: Alan, the shepherd. Leading the lost sheep back to the fold.

ALAN: That's one way to think of it, I suppose. But Joel isn't lost yet. Although he could be, very easily.

RADZMAN: And you think I'm the evil, magnetic force pulling him out into that world which he shouldn't know about?

ALAN: Yes, sometimes. And no. That's what causes the uncomfortable feeling, Mr. Radzman. You're helping Joel; I realize that. But I'm not sure of your reasons. That scares me. I'd kick, bite, maul, and maim anybody who tried to hurt him. And yet you're hurting him so gently that I can't paint you completely black and label you "the bad guy." I'd far rather you were an *overt* bastard. Subtlety confuses me.

RADZMAN: I'm afraid, Alan, that at your tender age many things confuse you, more so than you care to admit. Suppose I told you that I loved Joel, too?

ALAN: I'd want to believe you. But I wouldn't. You can't love someone and want to possess them, too.

RADZMAN: Take that advice yourself, Alan. Before it's too late and hurts both you and Joel. We can't play gods. We have to let people run their own lives, you know.

ALAN: I know. Perhaps that's why I want so much to teach. To help students run their lives the right way.

RADZMAN: And you're sure your way is right?

ALAN: No, I'm not *sure* of anything. But I do think my way is honest. That's a term you used yourself.

RADZMAN: Yes, but loosely.

ALAN: "Honesty is the best policy," as they say.

RADZMAN: Not compared to double indemnity.

ALAN: Now you're talking in riddles again. But it's my turn to ask the question. What do *you* feel for Joel?

RADZMAN *(his reserve down, he is trying to speak as honestly as he can):* It's an *ersatz* feeling, I suppose, Alan. But I call it love. If one tries hard enough, it's possible to fit almost anything under that category. I guess if there is such an emotion as "the real thing," I felt it only once, many years ago, with my wife. But that was many years ago — a mirage in a desert of dreadful ambiguities. I'm too old now to go searching for "love." But I treasure very highly a comfortable relationship.

ALAN *(sincerely):* I'm sorry.

RADZMAN: Don't be. I'm very satisfied that my way is the right way. For me and Joel. Perhaps if I were young again, and a student in your classroom, you could influence me otherwise. I'm not a villain, Alan. But I do have interests to protect. I won't hurt your friend. And I can help him very much.

ALAN: I'll be running interference the whole time.

RADZMAN: No, Alan, you won't be much longer. You'll have other lives to mold in less than a month. And Joel has a mind of his own. Give him the privilege of using it. You have other lives to mold. And your own as well. *(Pause)* Will you tell Joel I'm waiting?

ALAN *(shouting):* Joel . . . you got company. Excuse me, Mr. Radzman. I'm expected upstairs. (ALAN *exits via the fire escape)*

RADZMAN *inspects the apartment briefly, pausing only long enough to frown at the pogo stick.* JOEL *enters from his bedroom, dressed at last, but with a boa thrown over his shoulders.*

JOEL *(a la Garland):* Dahlings. Thank you. Thank you. It's so good to be back here at Carnegie Hall. Or is this the Palladium? Oh, well. My little daughter couldn't come with me tonight which is really just as well because she sings flat. But I'm here, and as the other loudmouth belter always says "Who could ask for anything more?"

(Singing — or wailing, rather)

"If happy little bluebirds fly
Beyond the rainbow . . ."
Hiya.

RADZMAN *(who has not been amused; seriously):* I got a letter from Margaret today. She's arriving back in town next week.

JOEL *(upset):* Well, that's a hell of a how-do-you-do. *(He lights a cigarette)*

RADZMAN: Joel, please try to understand. *(His is the voice of a placating, old man)*

JOEL *(flippantly suppressing his feelings):* What made wifey-dear decide to cut her European vacation short? Does she miss her hubby-wubby so terribly much, or can't she make it with the bullfighters in the old Brett Ashley fashion?

RADZMAN: That isn't funny, Joel.

JOEL: No, I don't think it is, either. And of course she'll want her apartment back.

RADZMAN: Of course.

JOEL: Well, that's very nice. After a full year abroad she gives us a week's notice. What fun. Do you intend for Maggie and I to be roommates? Hmm? I'll butter her toast, she'll shine my shoes, we can share the bathroom and swap anecdotes. I can't wait.

RADZMAN: Joel, I know you're upset, but it will all be better this way. You should have moved in with me a long time ago. We've discussed it dozens of times. Margaret's coming back just makes it a necessity.

JOEL: Yes, I suppose so, but —

RADZMAN: No "buts" about it. Under the same roof we can work twice as fast. Your career needs planning. It's not going a mile a minute, you know.

JOEL *(firm):* Radzie, I don't want to move in with you.

RADZMAN: Would you rather walk the streets?

JOEL: I've done it before.

RADZMAN: With little success.

JOEL: I — well, I —

RADZMAN: Are you worried about Alan? Where would Alan go? What would Alan say?

JOEL: Oh, Alan Schmalan. Alan is the furthest thing from my mind.

RADZMAN: I'm sure he'd be happy to hear that.

JOEL: Anyway, he'll be going home in about —

RADZMAN: Three weeks. That's a long time.

JOEL: Alan can manage for himself. I'm not responsible for him. It's just that —

RADZMAN: Just that what?

JOEL *(blurting it out):* I just don't want to feel like I'm being kept.

RADZMAN: But you are being kept, Joel. I'm keeping you. In shirts, in ties, in frozen meats, in wall-to-wall carpeting, and demonstration discs.

JOEL: You phrase it quite well.

RADZMAN: I phrase it accurately.

JOEL: All right. All right. You own me. But that doesn't mean we have to be open about it.

RADZMAN: You don't think this accommodation is open? Everyone knows that this is my wife's apartment. Everyone knows that you've been staying here for eleven months. And everyone knows how to add two and two.

JOEL: Yes, but . . .

RADZMAN: What are you worried about, Joel? Afraid I'll keep watch on you twenty-four hours a day? Well, I probably will. It will mean an end to your inviting every stray fraternity brother and weight-lifter over for "a couple of days." But that's all it will mean an end to. It will mean many more beginnings.

JOEL: Radzie. Are you trying to be romantic?

RADZMAN: No, practical. Alan will have to leave here within the week. How you tell him is your problem, not mine. And then you'll move in with me. If you decide, however, that sleeping around with old fraternity brothers and whatnot is more important than your career . . . well, that's your decision, too. But I think you should weigh it over carefully. I understand that Alan and you are very close. I accept that. But he'll be leaving New York in a very short time — one week or three. His vacation is over. Yours doesn't have to be . . . ever.

JOEL: Radzie, I actually think you're jealous.

RADZMAN: I am, Joel. I am. It's a flaw in the characters of several old men I know.

JOEL *(evasively; kissing his forehead):* Let's discuss all this some other time, okay? We should be getting to work now. What about Parkay?

RADZMAN: Mr. Parkay cannot meet with us today, after all. We've postponed the audition until the day after tomorrow.

JOEL: But I thought that —

RADZMAN: You can't rush these things, Joel. Trust me.

JOEL: I have to. What else is there to do? *(Pause)* She's coming back next week, huh? What day?

RADZMAN: Tuesday. That doesn't give you much time. And it gives Alan even less.

JOEL: Don't worry, Radzie, I'll take care of it. Joel will take care of everything.

RADZMAN: I hope so. For your sake. And for mine. *(He goes to get his hat)*

JOEL: Don't be melodramatic. Where are you off to now?

RADZMAN: I've got a ton of things to do at the office. I *am* a businessman, you know.

JOEL: A businessman. Yes. Yes, I know.

RADZMAN: I'll call you first thing in the . . . afternoon.

JOEL *(not really looking at him):* Bye, Radzie.

RADZMAN: Joel —

JOEL: I know. And I love you, too. Just as much. In my own funny selfish way . . . but just as much.

RADZMAN *(exiting):* Goodbye.

> JOEL *weakly waves after him, then grabs another cigarette, slouches onto the sofa, placing the feather boa and the pogo stick off where he won't have to look at them. He sighs, props his feet on the coffee table, and closes his eyes.*

> CYNTHIA *enters from the U.C., having come via the fire escape. She approaches* JOEL *with the warmest of loving smiles, and places her hands over his eyes.*

CYNTHIA *(reciting softly):*

Still sits the schoolhouse by the road,
A ragged beggar sleeping.
Around it still the sumacs grow,
And blackberry vines are creeping.

JOEL *(without looking up, but a happy-sad smile on his lips as he recites):*

"I'm sorry that I spelt the word,
I hate to go above you.
Because, you see" — the brown eyes fell,

"Because, you see, I love you."
(Unbelieving certainty): Cynthia?

CYNTHIA *(uncovering his eyes):* You haven't forgotten John Greenleaf Whittier. And I hoped you hadn't forgotten me.

JOEL *(rising; out of his trance):* Good Lord, Cynthia! What in the world —

CYNTHIA: I'm your new neighbor. Upstairs.

JOEL: I — I — it's amazing.

CYNTHIA: You passed me as you left the shower not ten minutes ago, singing at the top of your lungs just like you used to do back home in Lincoln Park. My heart jumped for a moment, then I continued the small-talk with your roommate — whom I actually did think was committing suicide when I came in. He's really very nice. A bit kooky, but —

JOEL: Cynthia Quinn. You're like something from another world.

CYNTHIA *(the pace of her explanation gets increasingly faster):* You see, I really did get the wrong apartment at first, and —

JOEL: What in the world are you doing in New York?

CYNTHIA: And then I met Elvira, although at first I thought Alan was Elvira, and —

JOEL: What made you decide to —

CYNTHIA: I'd never heard of a man named Elvira, but I told myself, well, this *is* New York, and I was all confused and —

JOEL: I can't really believe that you're —

CYNTHIA: Oh, Joel. Shut up and kiss me. *(They embrace for a very long time. Again, she recites after he slowly breaks the kiss)*
"He'll come to learn in later years,
How few who pass above him.
Lament their winning and his loss,
Like her — because they love him."

JOEL: Whittier's *School Days.* It was always sort of "our poem." *(He surveys her)* You've grown up.

CYNTHIA: Girls generally do between seventeen and twenty-two.

JOEL: Sit down, and tell me everything. I just can't believe you're here.

CYNTHIA: Me either. I should be getting married—tomorrow as a matter of fact. And I just ran out. I decided to take a vacation. Right in the middle of the Ed Sullivan Show, I just jumped off the davenport, kissed Mama on the forehead, asked her to pray for me, and took off.

JOEL: But why?

CYNTHIA: I'm still a romantic. Keats, Shelley, and yours truly. I've been in the city three days . . . at the YWCA — it's horrible. I was afraid to call you. I walked by this place four times a day, scared to come up. And then when I noticed Elvira's sign of

"Roommate Wanted," I — kiss me again. *(He obliges; another long one)* Hi.

JOEL: Hi.

CYNTHIA: You remember me?

JOEL: I could forget you? You were the girl I proposed to three times a week during lunch periods at high school.

CYNTHIA *(reflecting):* Why didn't I ever say yes?

JOEL: *I* could never figure it out.

CYNTHIA: When we moved that summer after graduation, I completely lost all track of you. Sometimes I'd buy *The New York Times* to see if I could find your name somewhere in the cast lists, and the last time I went back to Chicago, I'd heard you were downstate at the University of Illinois, starring in every play they did there . . . and at least a dozen times I'd start to write letters, but never finished them, and —

JOEL: Shut up and kiss me. *(She does; they do)* You're the nicest surprise I've had in five years. The times I've thought about you — does she still dig Katharine Hepburn, does she still inhale when she laughs that crazy cackle of hers, has she gotten fat, married, pimples, pregnant? And now all of a sudden you're here. But . . . why?

CYNTHIA *(with a meaningful shrug):* I'm trying to recapture the past, I guess. Mama calls it "evaluating the behind before rushing into the what's up front that counts." I jilted the nicest young businessman in Coldwater, Minnesota.

JOEL: But, I still don't —

CYNTHIA: Keats, Shelley, and me. He proposed, I said yes, and then I started thinking. He was average, Joel. He was normal, healthy, All-American. It scared the daylights out of me. I've always expected a white knight, with an Ipana smile and the greaseless look. You were the closest thing that ever came near that ideal. Don't be frightened . . . I don't expect you to keep that proposal open for five years, but I had to see you again, had to have fun, had to get away, before I made any decisions. And so, here I am.

JOEL *(stopping to think):* A lot happens in five years, doesn't it?

CYNTHIA: Not really. Not in Minneapolis.

JOEL: I don't know if I'm the same fellow you knew back then.

CYNTHIA *(joking):* Are you trying to get rid of me?

JOEL: It's all so sudden, I —

CYNTHIA: We were always impulsive.

JOEL: If only I could . . . Cynthia, let's try it.

CYNTHIA: What?

JOEL: Painting the town. Coney Island, Broadway shows, every night club that's open — just the two of us. Laughing, singing, spouting Whittier, the whole routine. We were always children. We can make it work again. Kiddo, you're on a holiday and we're gonna make the most of it. *(Very gallant)* How about a date tonight?

CYNTHIA *(beaming):* Sir Galahad, you haven't changed at all.

JOEL: We'll go to one of those all-night movie houses where they show nothing but Katharine Hepburn, chew popcorn, giggle, neck, have an ice cream soda, and sing *The Pirates of Penzance* all the way home. Okay?

CYNTHIA: Okay. It's a date.

JOEL *(suddenly serious):* Cynthia, I need you. Very much.

CYNTHIA *(baiting him):* Oh, I didn't think budding young stars needed anything but big breaks.

JOEL: No, there's more. Much more.

CYNTHIA: I hope so. I'll be your crutch if you'll be mine.

JOEL: Agreed. Now, shut up and kiss me.

They are doing exactly that as ELVIRA *enters from the fire escape, bedecked in a frilly pink frock.*

ELVIRA: It fits. It fits. Oh, don't I look lovely in pink? I feel so Jane Wyman. *(Sees them)* Oh my goodness. I see you've met Joel.

CYNTHIA *(her eyes never leaving him):* Yes. Yes, I've met Joel.

ELVIRA: How very nice. Joel, you never cease to amaze me. *(Flippantly throwing it off)* I've just decided to have the electricity in my apartment rewired. I can't tell which circuits are AC and which are DC.

JOEL *(although Cynthia hasn't understood):* Elvira!

ELVIRA: Don't shush me. From now on I'm Jane Wyman and I play only deaf mutes like Johnny Belinda. And it's a new color for me . . . pink.

CYNTHIA: You look ravishing.

ELVIRA: Yeah? I hope you're a prophet. I haven't been ravished in an age. Oh, I almost forgot. I'm throwing a party tomorrow night. Alan and I are going from door to door, inviting the whole apartment building. I'm even going to call John Smith. It's sort of a "Cynthia's here" party. You're coming of course.

JOEL: We wouldn't miss it for anything in the world. Cynthia's here. But tonight she's mine and nobody else's.

ELVIRA: Fine, as long as she doesn't want to wear the pink.

CYNTHIA: Tonight, Elvira, the pink is yours. But I had better go finish unpacking and get ready.

JOEL *(bowing):* I'll call for you at seven.

CYNTHIA: Okay, but Mama wants me home by . . . November.

JOEL: Mama may be disappointed.

CYNTHIA: I hope so. Come on, Elvira. We've got work to do. Why, you're gonna go ape. I haven't even unpacked the puce, yet.

ELVIRA: Puce? Oh, goody. That'll make me feel so Cathleen Nesbitt.

CYNTHIA *(starting upstage)*: See you at seven.

JOEL: It's a date. Oh, and Cynthia?

CYNTHIA: Yeah?

JOEL: Hi.

CYNTHIA: Hi.

She exits

ELVIRA: Joel?

JOEL: Yeah?

ELVIRA: Oh, nothing. *(Imitating him)* Hi. *(She scurries up the fire escape and out of sight)*

JOEL *has scarcely had time to turn around before* ALAN *comes bounding through the door R., panting.*

ALAN: Hi. *(Rattling it off)* You are most cordially invited to a gala party in Apartment 6-A at eightish tomorrow. It's in honor of—

JOEL *(smiling to himself)*: Cynthia.

ALAN: Yes. Cynthia Quinn. Have you met her?

JOEL: I most certainly have.

ALAN: Isn't she marvellous? It's the first time I've been instantly in love since I saw Diane Varsi in *Peyton Place.*

JOEL: Me, too.

ALAN: See? You do have good taste. These next three weeks are going to be absolutely great, huh?

JOEL: Three weeks?

ALAN: Parties every day. A "Cynthia" party every day for the next three weeks.

JOEL *(suddenly remembering)*: Oh, Alan. Radzman was here today.

ALAN: Yes, I know. Damned depressing, that man. What did he have to say?

JOEL *(putting it off)*: Nothing, really. Nothing. We'll talk about it later. *(An afterthought)* We've got a lot to talk about later.

ALAN: Okay, 'cause right now I've still got to invite the Morgans, the Murphys, and that wop model in 3-A. *(He starts toward the door, sees the boa)* What's this? Are you wearing your boa?

JOEL: No, Alan. Not tonight.

ALAN: Good. I wouldn't want Cynthia to get the wrong impression. *(Singing giddily)* A party, a party, we're gonna have a party. *(He exits and then comes right back)* You know, I think I'm in love. I feel great! Hi!! *(He exits singing)*

JOEL *(a note of melancholy)*: Hi. *(He picks up the boa and starts toward his room)*

THE CURTAIN FALLS ON ACT I

ACT II

SCENE ONE

The scene is the same as Act I; it is early afternoon of the following day. As THE CURTAIN RISES, CYNTHIA *is asleep on the couch.* ALAN *enters, dressed, from his room. He carries a blanket which he puts gently over* CYNTHIA; *he stares down at her for a moment, smiling, then goes U.R. into the kitchen area to check the coffee.* CYNTHIA *stirs, notices the blanket, rises sleepily, and tosses the blanket around herself. She notices* ALAN, *and stretches.*

CYNTHIA *(imitating Katharine Hepburn):* Oh, I feel fine this morning. I feel so fine. Do you feel fine? I feel fine.

ALAN *(smiling):* Hi.

CYNTHIA *(directly from* The Philadelphia Story*):* Good morning, Dexter. Aren't the magnolias lovely this morning?

ALAN *(attempting a Cary Grant):* You look very yar, Tracy. Very yar indeed. Coffee coming up.

CYNTHIA *(herself):* Those marvelous old movies! . . . We missed the first part of *Alice Adams,* but *Philadelphia Story* is better anyway. I love Cary Grant, don't you? Don't you just love Cary Grant? *(Sips the coffee he's handed her)* Umm. Hi, Alan.

ALAN: Hi. You look rested.

CYNTHIA: I passed out on the couch, I guess. Is Joel up yet?

ALAN: Up and off. Do you realize it's after noon? Radzman called early this morning. They had to meet to go over some arrangements before they get together with this Parkay fellow who's opening a nightclub.

CYNTHIA: And Joel didn't wake me up to say good morning? That wasn't very romantic of him.

ALAN: Oh, it's always more romantic just to gaze down on Sleeping Beauty without disturbing her.

CYNTHIA *(delighted):* Oh, did he do that?

ALAN: I'm sure he must've. If he didn't, he's a damn fool.

CYNTHIA: The Handsome Prince gazed down whilst I slumbered. Oh, that's pretty. I love New York. It's just like in the movies.

ALAN: Drink your coffee.

CYNTHIA: Ummm. You make good coffee. *(Toddling drunkenly and acting Hepburn)* "I was born on the side of a hill." *(Returning his smile)* Are you going to commit suicide again today. I do hope so; it was all such fun.

ALAN: No, not today. Today's no day for suicide. Today I feel like singing in the streets. How about you?

CYNTHIA: Marvelous idea.

ALAN: When I was a kid back home, and I had my paper route, each day while delivering I'd whistle selections from a different Broadway musical. Generally flops, because they always had the best music. The Alan Reynolds Overture Hour, I'd call it. And I'd always hope that someone would stop me and say . . . "Hey, that's from the *Golden Apple,* isn't it?" or "I know that song, sonny; it's from *Goldilocks.*" But the only time anyone realized what I was whistling was when Mrs. Halperin recognized "I Could Have Danced All Night." Her husband had one of those Adults-Only record albums that played the tune with a different set of lyrics, and she thought it was quite naughty of me to whistle such risqué songs on Franklin Street. So I deliberately left the comic section out of their newspaper the next Sunday.

CYNTHIA *(impulsively):* What's your favorite song?

ALAN: It varies from day to day. Each day I proclaim that such-and-such is my favorite song ever written. Today I guess it's the one I was humming in the shower . . . "So Long, Oo-Long, How Long You Gonna Be Gone?"

CYNTHIA *(ecstatic):* My God, I was singing that on the train coming out here.

ALAN: I didn't think anyone else remembered it. Joel swears that I made it up.

CYNTHIA: I remember it. I love it!

ALAN: Shall we?

The two of them wildly sing the old Bert Kalamar-Harry Ruby number and improvise a vaudeville dance and harmony as they go along. At the end they dance right off, out the door R., returning as if for an encore with the tag ending of the song. When they finally, after much ado, stop, they are convulsed with laughter.

CYNTHIA: But we were supposed to sing it in the streets to wake up New York.

ALAN: You know what I've always wanted to do? Plant people all around like they do in the movies, and start a song on a busy corner. First a bald old tenor with shaving lather all over his face leans out of his third-floor window and starts "Oh, What a Beautiful Mornin' "—then the apple vendor below joins him, and the policeman directing traffic—all planted—and passers-by and the shoeshine boy and everybody, until there are about forty of them singing. Then the regular people just walking along would feel duty-bound to join them, and spontaneously the whole block would be singing just like in the movies. I really think it would work. Someday we've just got to try it.

CYNTHIA *(sharing his enthusiasm):* Wouldn't that be great? Everybody singing and taxis honking out the beat.

ALAN: That's the way it should be. But people probably wouldn't go along with it. They'd all be too embarrassed by the thought of having fun.

CYNTHIA: But we ought to try it. Just once. Come on. *(She leads him onto the terrace, and looks down)* What'll we sing? Something they'd all know.

ALAN: Uh, how about "Wait Till the Sun Shines, Nellie"?

CYNTHIA: Fine. Hit it.

ALAN AND CYNTHIA *(singing loudly to sidewalk below):*

"Wait till the sun shines, Nellie,
And the clouds go drifting by.
We will be happy, Nellie,
Don't . . . you . . . cry."

(Their song dies out.)

CYNTHIA: Maybe if we had twenty more people.

ALAN: No wonder Joel was madly in love with you and proposed all through high school. You're fun.

CYNTHIA: Really? I've always wanted to be, but in Minneapolis it was hard. Once I did a soft shoe routine on the garbage cans just like Gene Kelly in *Singin' in the Rain.* You know, just for the hell of it. Not only did the neighbors call my mother and tell her that her daughter was a wanton kook, but I caught the damnedest cold you've ever seen. Nose ran for two weeks. Terrible.

ALAN: But worth it, huh?

CYNTHIA: Yeah, it was the only good rainstorm of the year.

ALAN: What's your favorite movie?

CYNTHIA: Today it's *The Philadelphia Story.* But I'm also a sap for *Mary Poppins, Funny Face,* and *Ziegfeld Girl* with Lana Turner. What's yours?

ALAN *(with a flourish):* The Reynolds Award for the best all-time movie is: . . . oh, wait. First the nominations. The nominees are: —oh, this isn't going to be alphabetical . . . uh, the nominees are: *Friendly Persuasion,—*

CYNTHIA: Oh, I loved that.

ALAN: Sshh. The nominees are: *Friendly Persuasion, Mr. Deeds Goes to Town, State of the Union, The Wizard of Oz,* and *Peyton Place.*

CYNTHIA: *The Wizard of Oz?*

ALAN: Correct.

CYNTHIA *(hugging him):* Oh, I love you. Every Christmas I watch it and cry like a baby.

ALAN *(quoting):* "Oh, Auntie Em, Auntie Em, there's no place like home."

CYNTHIA *(as low as she can get for Frank Morgan):* "Remember, a true heart is not judged by how much you love, but by how much you are loved by others."

ALAN: Cue: "Lions, and tigers, and bears."

CYNTHIA *(picking it up):* "Oh, my!"

ALAN *(singing):* "We're . . ." Are you ready? "We're . . ."

ALAN AND CYNTHIA *(singing and skipping about like kids at recess):*

"... off to see the wizard,
The wonderful wizard of Oz . . ."

Their skipping carries them all over the apartment, uncontained in their gaiety; when they finally finish, they fall over each other in a heap on the couch.

CYNTHIA: Hi.

ALAN: Hi. I wish you'd have gone to my high school.

CYNTHIA: Why?

ALAN: I'd have forced you to say "yes."

CYNTHIA: No wonder you're Joel's best friend. He was just like you when he was in high school. Crazy and wonderful and uninhibited and unpredictable. And you know what? All the school snips were jealous and called him queer, just because he knew how to have fun and be himself and they never did.

ALAN *(hesitant; stopped by her use of "queer"):* Cynthia, I —

CYNTHIA *(remembering merrily):* Did he ever tell you about Senior Recital where he was supposed to play Chopin nocturnes and instead he played a fifteen-minute series of modulated Chopsticks?

ALAN: Yeah, he told me how the audience roared.

CYNTHIA: Audience? There were only four or five of us. It was just a rehearsal.

ALAN: Oh, I thought he said it was the final night of performance.

CYNTHIA: No, no. *(Almost regretfully)* Only in rehearsal. Joel has his limit. He always wants people to think the right thing of him. Wild as he was, he's too conservative to ever do it in public.

ALAN: Yeah, I guess I know what you mean. *(Covering Joel's lie)* It must've been me who misunderstood and thought he said it was in performance. You're in love with him, huh?

CYNTHIA: A little bit, I think so. Yes.

ALAN: You're great, you know that? Exactly what he needs.

CYNTHIA: I'm not so sure anymore. I'd like to think so, but lately he seems . . . I don't know.

ALAN *(smiling):* Don't argue with me. I have superb judgment, and I'm never wrong. With you at his side, he'd play Chopsticks if he felt like it, and to hell with everybody else.

CYNTHIA: Oh, that's what I'd want the man I marry to do. The Chopsticks Concerto, come hell or high water. Back home when I'd say my prayers, I'd actually pray that Richard — that was his name, my fiance, not Rick or Rich or even Dick, but

Richard — I used to pray that Richard would once, just once, do something wildly unconventional. You know — belch, fart, anything. Really, I used to say, "God bless Mama and Papa, bring peace to Viet Nam, and please, God, please, make Richard goof up. Once, Just once." Negative. He even used to wear a coat and vest to the drive-in!

ALAN: But a person can't go too far out. Sometimes — in performance — he has to do the sensible thing.

CYNTHIA: Only if he's doing it because *he* thinks it's right. Not for Joe or Fred or Ethel or anybody else. Not if it's sensible by *their* rules. Only if it's what *he* feels like at the moment. *His* rules. I don't want Joel to be a kook, just someone who'll love me, treat *me* as an individual, and be an individual himself.

ALAN: Then you've got your man. Don't let him slip by you. He needs you just as much as you need him.

CYNTHIA: I don't know. Five years change people. Last night, for instance, he fell asleep in the middle of Hepburn's swimming pool scene.

ALAN: A guy gets tired.

CYNTHIA: But at a moment like that? Oh, I know it's crazy, but the old Joel would never have done that. Not to Hepburn. Nobody could be that tired.

ALAN: But he has a career ahead of him, too. He, uh, he has to be fresh for rehearsals.

CYNTHIA: Yeah, I suppose so. Wouldn't it be my luck to fall for an actor.

ALAN: There are worse things.

CYNTHIA: Like for instance?

ALAN: Oh, I don't know — businessmen. Nine-to-fivers. Guys who never think of anything but making money, who balk at the idea of a vacation until they're too old for a holiday.

CYNTHIA: You're funny. And what do you want to be when you grow up?

ALAN: I don't ever want to grow up.

CYNTHIA: That's a wise answer. But an evasive one.

ALAN: What do I want to be when I grow up? I really don't know. Happy, I guess. Happy. That's what I want to be. And I'm not sure what that means anymore.

CYNTHIA *(studying him):* A teacher. You should be a teacher. Kids would adore you. I'd love to sit in on your classrooms.

ALAN: You're invited. I begin teaching in four weeks in La Grange, Illinois.

CYNTHIA: You're kidding.

ALAN: Nope. Honest Injun. Mr. Reynolds of the English department.

CYNTHIA: That's great. Lucky kids.

ALAN: I hope so. It's something I really want to do. I hope I can restrain myself and still keep learning fun and creative for them. And I pray that the school board will allow me to improvise Chopsticks every now and then without demanding Chopin. Not all the time, mind you. Just every now and then. *(Suddenly)* Do you like kids?

CYNTHIA: Love them. I want seven hundred at least. Really. I'd make a great Catholic.

ALAN: Me too. Not seven hundred — but five, maybe.

CYNTHIA: Make it six. An even number.

ALAN: Four?

CYNTHIA: Six. And what are you gonna name them?

ALAN: Well, I imagine my wife will have some say in it, but I'm gonna push for Tracy and Spencer.

CYNTHIA: I want a Tracy, too. I guess it's the Katharine Hepburn influence. But *Spencer?* What an awful trick to pull on a little kid.

ALAN: Joel loves kids, too, you know. He jokes around and says he doesn't but deep down he adores them.

CYNTHIA: You're quite the matchmaker, you know that?

ALAN: It's my favorite fault. I want the people I love to love each other. To get together and not waste themselves on anything but the best.

CYNTHIA: Do you think Joel's wasting himself right now?

ALAN: Oh, I don't know. But he might if he stays around here too long. Minneapolis, Chicago, Peoria — they may sound awfully stuffy, but it's the kind of atmosphere that's necessary for marriage, for kids, for happily ever after. It's hard to breathe too long in the City. If you take too big a breath, you can get carried away. *(Inspired)* Hey, I know what let's do. When Joel comes home, let's all go to Central Park. We can play hide-and-go-seek or something.

CYNTHIA *(her cup of tea):* And roll down the hills on our bellies. And make believe we're spies, and enemy agents are after us. *(Whispering)* Here. You guard the emeralds.

ALAN: The park is great for that. We can swing and play leapfrog, and —

CYNTHIA: And make mud pies. I'm the best mud-pie maker in Minneapolis, Minnesota.

ALAN *(overwhelmed with fun):* Great. Oh, I love you. *(Impulsively he kisses her; the kiss becomes longer than either anticipated)* I — I'm sorry.

CYNTHIA *(not stopping to admit she enjoyed it):* Oh, I can't wait. Let's go. Why doesn't he come?

ALAN: He'll be here pretty soon. I promise. Ooh, and we can wade in the streams, too.

CYNTHIA: Oh, are there any guppies in the bottom?

ALAN: Sure.

(Singing)

"Down in the bottom of an iddy-biddy poo . . ."

ALAN AND CYNTHIA:

". . . phwam thwee liddle phiddies and a Momma Phiddy, too.

'Phwim,' sed the Momma Phiddy. . . ."

ELVIRA *enters while they sing their silly song and stares at them.*

ELVIRA: My God, are you auditioning for a kiddy show?

ALAN: Elvira, you're not just getting up?

ELVIRA: You bet your sweet ass I am. I refused to open my eyes before I finished my dream. Boy, was it a weirdo.

ALAN: Not Claire Trevor again?

ELVIRA: Nope. Huntley and Brinkley. They were duelling over me with long, pointed swords — really long, really pointed — and Chet wounded Dave and I cried like a baby. Do you think that means anything?

CYNTHIA: Sounds phallic to me.

ELVIRA: Anyway, between the two of them, I'm worn out. And famished. Got any bologna?

ALAN *(heading toward kitchen):* Coming up. And more coffee.

ELVIRA: What I'd really love is a cherry Coke. Wonder why. I just have this awful craving for a cherry Coke. Duelling. Over me. And Chet kept fondling the locket around his neck with my graduation picture from Steinmetz Grammar School in it. Golly, that was sweet of him. *(To Cynthia; matter-of-factly)* Did you sleep with Joel last night?

CYNTHIA *(shocked):* Elvira! No, I slept on the couch.

ELVIRA: Oh. Oh, well, it figures. *(Pause)* Oooh, what time is it? I gotta get all the stuff for the party tonight. Alan, you'll have to come with me. I'll pick it out, you pay for it.

ALAN *(re-entering with sandwich):* Okay. I can't stay long, though. I have a date to go to Central Park.

ELVIRA: Not with John Smith from Nebraska?

CYNTHIA: No, silly. With me.

ELVIRA: Yeah? That's nice. Strange, but nice.

ALAN: Don't worry. Joel's coming along to chaperone us.

ELVIRA: Pity. Is Mary Astor going too?

CYNTHIA: Who?

ALAN: Nothing. Just one of Elvira's dream sequences. *(He stuffs bologna into* ELVIRA'S *mouth)* So who finally won you? Chet or Dave?

ELVIRA: Neither. It had a happy ending. They shared me.

CYNTHIA: Oh?

JOEL *enters from the door R. He does not look joyful.*

ALAN and CYNTHIA *(singing):*

"Good morning, good morning,
The best to you each morning,
K-E-double L-O-double good,
Kellogg's best to you."

JOEL, *without a word has crossed the room and exited into his bedroom, slamming the door behind him.*

ELVIRA: Something there is that doesn't love a song.

CYNTHIA: What do you think's the matter?

ELVIRA: Maybe he stayed too long with the fair.

ALAN: Probably a bad rehearsal. You'll get used to it. Go in and talk to him. He'll cheer up for you.

CYNTHIA: Maybe I shouldn't —

ALAN: This is when he needs you most. When Chopsticks goes sour. Don't argue. March in there. Come on, Elvira, let's go shoplifting.

ELVIRA: Great. I'll get my big, baggy purse and my dark glasses and we're off. *(She starts up the fire escape)*

CYNTHIA: Alan? Hurry back. We have a date in Central Park. I mean . . . the three of us.

ALAN: You think I'd miss a good mud pie? Not on your life. Now go to it. *(He goes up the fire escape)*

CYNTHIA *(knocking on Joel's door):* Anybody home? *(No response)* Guess not. I thought an old beau of mine was in there. *(Katharine Hepburn)* Hello. My name is Tracy Lord. Are you home, Dexter? *(Low voice)* This is your Fuller Brush Man. I have a special on this week for a toilet bowl cleaner that can wipe out the dismallest mess. Hello? Hello? *(She goes back into living room area)*

JOEL *(entering):* Hello, Tracy. This is Dexter. Dexter Flop.

CYNTHIA *(trying to be gay):* Dexter Flop? Why yes, I knew your mother. Won't you come in, sit down, have some tea, and tell Aunt Cynthia your life story?

JOEL: Very funny. Scoot over.

CYNTHIA: Hi.

JOEL: Knock it off. I'm in no mood to play games.

CYNTHIA: Well, tell Mother all about it. Bad day at the office?

JOEL: Very funny.

CYNTHIA *(mocking him):* Very funny.

JOEL: Cynthia, I can't come to the party tonight. I'm sorry.

CYNTHIA: Me, too. But is that all that's bothering you? What is it — business or another woman?

JOEL: You know there's no other woman.

CYNTHIA: No, I didn't. But I'm glad to hear it. Business, then?

JOEL: Radzman wants me to meet this fellow who's opening a nightclub. Thinks it could mean something big. You know I'd rather be at the party, but . . .

CYNTHIA *(warmly):* You lovable imbecile. Of course you'll go meet this nightclub owner. What's a silly party when your future's at stake?

JOEL: That's what Radzman said, too, but . . .

CYNTHIA: Better yet, couldn't you maybe invite them to the party, too, and then —

JOEL *(quickly):* No, no I couldn't do that. I wouldn't do that. Business is business, and you . . . are you. A party's no place for . . . planning recording sessions.

CYNTHIA: Joel, let me tell you a story.

JOEL: Oh, Cynthia, not now.

CYNTHIA: No it's a very familiar story. You'll like it, I think. Once upon a time there was a high school girl — very pretty, really — crooked teeth and frayed bobby sox, but huge dimples and no acne — who had a crush, a very big crush, on a high school boy — very handsome, Ipana smile, the whole bit — who was born to be a performer. Oh, he liked her too, sort of, and proposed to her regularly during lunch periods — "I'll give you my apple and my ham salad if you'll marry me." She would have said yes right away — she loved him and ham salad — except she knew that he had another love with which she couldn't compete, so she held him off knowing that he'd never be worth a hoot and a holler to her, or she to him, until he'd conquered the other love first. Well, five years later, when our hero is about to master his other love, our heroine certainly isn't going to take any chances and pull a switch. So she kisses him on the forehead, laughs at his simplicity, and sends him off to a business meeting. End of story.

JOEL: I love you.

CYNTHIA: Good.

JOEL: You're not angry?

CYNTHIA: Of course not. Do you think there can't be a party without you? Vain, vain, vain. Alan will be there. He'll substitute. He's very much like you in many ways.

JOEL: Don't say that.

CYNTHIA: Why? What's the matter? It was a compliment. To both of you.

JOEL: Oh, nothing. Alan is very mixed up, that's all. And very young. He's little more than a child.

CYNTHIA: But a delightful child.

JOEL: He's having problems, now. I'm trying to help him. You shouldn't let yourself get mixed up in any of this. You shouldn't have to bother yourself with Alan.

CYNTHIA: Joel, Alan's no bother. I like him. Very much. And

whatever his problems are, he hides them very well. He'll cheer me up immensely at the party tonight. We'll probably sing old movie themes the whole time.

JOEL: Alan won't be coming to the party tonight, either.

CYNTHIA *(hiding the hurt; doubtful):* What's this? My two favorite beaus both deserting me? He didn't say anything just now about not coming. In fact, he and Elvira are out shopping for the food. It's a game to them.

JOEL: Like everything else. Everything's a game to Alan. A silly, childish game. I almost wish he'd never come to New York.

CYNTHIA: Joel, that's cruel. Alan adores you.

JOEL *(snapping):* I know that. Don't you think I know that?

CYNTHIA: Joel, what are you trying to say?

JOEL *(purposely; to make her ask for more):* Nothing, Cynthia, forget it.

CYNTHIA: No, no, I want to know.

JOEL: Well, it's hard to explain. I'd rather not . .

CYNTHIA: I like Alan. I'd rather.

JOEL *(as if it pains him):* Cynthia, Alan's . . . Alan's . . . queer.

CYNTHIA *(immediately):* Joel! I don't believe such a thing. Why —

JOEL: That's why this evening is going to be such a mess. I can't believe he hasn't told you yet.

CYNTHIA: Joel, for heaven's sake, pull all these loose ends together. Told me what?

JOEL *(slowly):* The only reason I got this interview tonight is because my agent, Mr. Radzman, is interested in Alan.

CYNTHIA: You're joking.

JOEL: No I'm not. That's why Radzman does me all these favors. Because of Alan. Alan has taken me on in his Offspring-of-the-Month Plan. Radzman helps me, and Alan pays him what he wants.

CYNTHIA: Oh, Joel, what an awful thing to say.

JOEL: I didn't want to say it.

CYNTHIA: But why should —

JOEL: Alan has always seen me as more than a friend. He wants to mother me. He'll do anything to further my chances as a singer, and that's exactly what he's doing tonight.

CYNTHIA: It's ugly. It's all so ugly.

JOEL: You think I don't know that? Radzman wouldn't get me an audition at the stockyards, though, if Alan didn't ask him.

CYNTHIA: But when they were here yesterday, they seemed almost hostile toward each other. I just can't believe that —

JOEL: Haven't you ever heard of appearances? Stay around Alan long enough and you'll learn a lot about appearances. Oh, I hate to knock the kid. He does it all for me, but —

CYNTHIA *(rational for what she's just heard):* Joel, be sensible. You can't afford to pass up a chance like this, even if —

JOEL: I know. Alan will be leaving soon, and then Radzman's interest in me will be all shot to hell. I've got to make something out of this appointment tonight. It may be my last chance.

CYNTHIA: How strange. You'll find few people as devoted as that.

JOEL: Devoted, maybe. But put yourself in my place.

CYNTHIA: He did talk a lot about all the things he wanted for you. But very unselfishly, I thought. He even included me among the things you needed.

JOEL: Well, there he was right. You are. And that's why I feel like such a heel about the party tonight. If I had my way, you know I'd be there.

CYNTHIA: Joel, nothing should stop you from getting the things you deserve. If Alan really is foolish enough to let himself be used for those means, well, *you* can't go around blaming yourself.

JOEL: Oh, Cynthia. Hey, why the glum look from you?

CYNTHIA: Oh, nothing. I just feel sorry for Alan. I really liked him.

JOEL: He's an irresistible child.

CYNTHIA: The child playing Chopsticks.

JOEL: What?

CYNTHIA: Oh, nothing. Nothing at all. Kiss me, Joel. *(Theirs is a brief kiss)* Now you get some rest before the appointment tonight. And I'll go straighten up the apartment. You can tell me all about your success tomorrow. We'll go to Central Park and celebrate. *(Trying to revive the fun that it* had *sounded)* Swing in the swings, wade in the pool . . . make mud pies. But for now, get some sleep, okay? I'll see you in the morning.

JOEL: Cynthia?

CYNTHIA: Yes?

JOEL: Did I ever tell you I loved you?

CYNTHIA: Many years ago, yes.

JOEL: Well, I still do. Even more.

CYNTHIA *(smiling again):* Gee whiz, maybe I'll get a proposal soon, huh?

JOEL: Just might be. From a very famous star.

CYNTHIA: I can't wait. But I will. Till tomorrow. Now, sleep. That's an order. *(She starts up fire escape, but slowly)*

JOEL: Cynthia? Hi.

CYNTHIA: Hi. *(She exits)*

JOEL *(as soon as he is sure she's gone, he runs to the telephone and dials a number):* Hi. Everything's fine. But it took some doing. No, I haven't talked to Alan yet, but I will. Don't worry. I *know* Mr. Parkay insists on having a date. Alan will oblige. *(Chuckling)* He never says no to me, you know that. I just gave one of the best performances of my career, and there'll be another coming up shortly. I feel like a first-class heel, but an effective one. Never mind. Yes. Don't worry. Everything will work out fine. I know I haven't much time. Okay. Me too you. Bye bye. (JOEL *hangs up the receiver, lights a cigarette, and just starts to sit down as* ALAN *comes in the door R.)*

ALAN *(bubbling spirits):* Hiya. In a better mood now, you old grouch? I had to leave the supermarket. God, was I embarrassed. Elvira was stuffing food into that bag like Noah stuffing the Ark. Except she took *ten* of everything, I swear. Why on earth she wanted so many prunes, I'll never know. Maybe somebody's constipated. Where's Cynthia?

JOEL: She went upstairs to lie down. She wasn't feeling well.

ALAN *(disappointed):* Oh, no. We were all gonna play spies in Central Park. Gosh, I hope she's better by tonight. You know, if you don't marry that girl immediately, I'm gonna turn you over my knee. Really. She's marvelous.

JOEL: I know. But I have a lot of messes to clear up first.

ALAN *(sincere):* Joel, if it's me you're worried about, I know when to butt out. If I ever found a girl like Cynthia, well I'd . . .

JOEL: Alan, I need your help desperately.

ALAN: Sure, Joel, Anything.

JOEL: Tonight's the big night.

ALAN *(delighted):* You mean you're gonna propose tonight? At the party?

JOEL: No, no, not yet.

ALAN: But soon.

JOEL: Yes . . . of course.

ALAN: Well, then, what's tonight?

JOEL: I'm meeting Parkay.

ALAN: You're kidding. Parkay? Tonight?

JOEL: Yes. Just listen will you?

ALAN: Give me a cigarette. I'm so excited, I need a cigarette.

JOEL: Alan, you don't smoke.

ALAN: I'm excited.

JOEL: Alan, you don't smoke.

ALAN: I'm nervous.

JOEL: Alan, you don't smoke.

ALAN: Well, I can pretend, can't I?

JOEL: Here. But you'll get sick.

ALAN: Go on. Go on.

JOEL: Today at rehearsal Radzie told me. Just like that, he springs it on me. Parkay got in town today. Called Radzie up and wants to meet me immediately.

ALAN: It can't wait till tomorrow? After the party?

JOEL: Parkay has to leave town early tomorrow morning.

ALAN: Are the cops after him?

JOEL: We're all going out to dinner, and Radzie's footing the bill. I'm gonna sing for him tonight. If he likes me, I'm signed.

ALAN: Joel, that's marvelous. But what about the party? Cynthia will feel awful.

JOEL: I've already explained and she understands.

ALAN: Only she would. She loves you, you know.

JOEL: Yes, I know. And that's where I need your help. You know how Radzie is about me. You're not blind.

ALAN: Sometimes I try to be.

JOEL: This deal with Parkay could mean the end of Radzman. If I can get this job, I can swing clear of Radzman in no time.

ALAN: You're finally talking sense. You've got to get away from Radzman. To help you do that, I'd do anything. Name it.

JOEL: Well, Parkay, it seems, has his eccentricities that way, too.

ALAN: Oh, no. The frying pan into the fire.

JOEL: You see, Parkay won't meet us tonight unless there's someone for him to escort, too. He's lonely, out of town, you know.

ALAN: Like John Smith of Nebraska. I know.

JOEL: And, anyway, well it would help so much if you'd come along, too.

ALAN *(almost laughing):* Me? Oh, wait a minute, Joel. Are you trying to "fix me up"?

JOEL: No, silly. Don't say it that way.

ALAN: Is there another way to say it?

JOEL: It's just that we have to have a fourth.

ALAN: Are you auditioning or playing bridge?

JOEL: Now, dammit, don't get flip.

ALAN: Joel, I am *not* going out with some old man tonight. That's final.

JOEL: Alan, please, I need you.

ALAN: Why me? Why not Cynthia? Or Elvira?

JOEL: Parkay wouldn't want them to come. And do you think I'd subject Cynthia to —

ALAN: Well, at least you have some decency. You do think of her.

JOEL: I'm thinking only of her. Believe me.

ALAN: Then why get mixed up with this Parkay at all? Can't you see he's just another Radzman except with a Park Avenue pinch?

JOEL: Because I need him, Alan. Once I have the chance to be seen, I won't have to be mixed up with any of their kind. No more Radzies. Just as soon as someone gets a chance to see me —

ALAN: See you with Parkay? That's gonna help?

JOEL: Yes! I'd be seen with the devil himself if it would boost my career.

ALAN *(sadly):* Yes, I believe you would. Joel, every sentence you've just uttered has begun with "I" and ended with "me." Where does Cynthia fit into these plans?

JOEL: Well, I, I want to marry Cynthia, Alan. I want to turn back time to five years ago and be the person I was then before I can think of asking her to accept me. I have to erase Radzie, you, everything.

ALAN: And you think tonight will do it? My playing gigolo to some old man? Joel, that's not me.

JOEL: Do you think it's *me?*

ALAN: I don't know. I hope not. Joel, I just can't do something like that. I — all right — I've stayed here with you this summer. I've, we've . . . it wasn't right, I know that. But it was a part of you, and so it became a part of me. You know how scared I was at first, I . . . but I *loved* you, Joel. So I told myself it was all right. But I didn't give a good goddamn about anyone else, and especially someone who's —

JOEL: Alan, I'm not asking you to go to bed with him. Merely let him escort you for a night on the town. Parkay is a gentleman.

ALAN *(firmly):* So am I! That's why it won't work out.

JOEL: Alan, you have to go. For me. For Cynthia.

ALAN *(his idol is falling; slowly):* Do you really want me to go, Joel? Tell me. Tell me that *you* really want me to go.

JOEL: You know if there were any other way . . . yes! Yes, Alan, I really want you to go.

ALAN *(staring at him sadly):* Okay. *(Moves U.C.)* I'd better tell Cynthia I won't be coming tonight.

JOEL *(quickly):* She's asleep. Really pooped. She'll understand. We'll explain it all in the morning when we have a contract in our hands. Don't worry. She'll understand.

ALAN: I hope so. Better than I do.

JOEL: Now don't be melodramatic. *(Starts to kiss him)*

ALAN *(shrinking away):* Don't, Joel.

JOEL: What's the matter?

ALAN *(moving away):* Just don't.

JOEL: Oh, don't worry. You'll have a good time.

ALAN *(falsely flippant):* Of course I will. Some friendly conversation, a few drinks. Nothing like it. *(Pause)* Should I wear the boa?

JOEL: No, silly. But you should be getting into a suit. We're starting with early cocktails at Radzie's.

ALAN *(spiteful):* Early cocktails. To sort of get us in the mood. What fun.

JOEL: But, Alan, go light on the liquor, huh? You know how you are when you start drinking, and —

ALAN *(shouting):* Joel, I am twenty-two years old. *(Subdued)* True, maybe sometimes I don't act it, but I am capable of taking care of myself. Like you, Joel, I'm much too old for mothering. Okay?

JOEL: Okay. Come on. Let's get ready. Are you all right?

ALAN: Yes, yes of course. It's just the cigarette. You were right — it made me a little sick. *(Perking up)* Come on. Last one dressed is . . . is the last one dressed. Let's shower together, shall we? For Auld Lang Syne. You scrub my back and I'll scrub yours. *(Alan exits into his room)*

JOEL: Sure. I'll even give you a head start. *(Dials phone)* Hi. Me again. We'll be ready in forty-five minutes. Of course I said "we." Me too you. Bye bye.

He lights a cigarette and smiles to himself as

THE CURTAIN FALLS

ACT II

SCENE TWO

The scene is the same apartment, later the same evening. AS THE CURTAIN RISES, party noises are heard from above, but no one is on stage. It is about 11 p.m., that time of the evening when businessmen start getting tired.

Noises are heard off right, and JOEL *enters with* ARNOLD RADZMAN *behind him, followed by* HARRISON PARKAY, *a very distinguished "gentleman" who is carrying his pet, a skunk named Hermione.*

JOEL: Well, here we are.

PARKAY: Oh, it's really quite lovely.

RADZMAN: Come on in, Harrison. Make yourself at home. Let me say again that it's really quite a treat to have you and Hermione with us. Here, I'll put Hermione in the bathroom.

JOEL: I really can't get over it. How unusual to have a pet skunk.

PARKAY: Hermione goes with me wherever I go. I'd really be lost without her.

JOEL: Where's Alan? He's not still trying to prove he's sober enough to slide down the bannister, is he?

RADZMAN: No, he'll be along. He's still playing leapfrog with his imaginary friend.

PARKAY: Oh, that climb's enough to tire anyone. I could use a drink.

JOEL: Excellent idea. Let me get you one. What'll it be?

PARKAY: Bourbon and water, I guess.

RADZMAN: And put on some coffee for Alan.

PARKAY: Quite a live wire, that boy. A real individual. Genuine, to say the least.

RADZMAN: He did rather come out of his shell tonight, didn't he? Surprised me.

JOEL *(calling from kitchen area):* Radzie, what are you drinking?

RADZMAN: Whatever you're drinking is fine. Well, Harrison, what do you think?

PARKAY: Your boy's got talent all right, Arnie. He may be just the man I need.

ALAN *enters from the door R. Though at first he acts drunk, we become more aware that everything he's doing is an act that he's seen somewhere else, and not himself at all.*

ALAN: Hello, everybody. My name's Baby Alan. What's yours? *(Singing)*

"Wait till your son turns Nellie . . ."

PARKAY: Alan, baby, come join the party. We thought we'd lost you.

ALAN: Oh, goody. I love parties. I'm really feeling my oats. Hiya Radzie. Wanna feel my oats?

JOEL *(returning with drinks):* Alan, uh, coffee will be ready in a minute.

ALAN: Coffee, schmoffee. Where's the booze? Drink time. *(He snatches* RADZMAN'S *drink)*

RADZMAN: Oh-uh-uh. That's a no-no.

ALAN: Don't be silly. It's a bourbon.

PARKAY: But Alan, baby, you have Mr. Radzman's drinkiepoo. Naughty, naughty.

JOEL: I'm afraid Alan's not feeling himself tonight.

ALAN: You're damn right I'm not feeling myself. But I'm feeling everybody else. *(Moves toward Radzman)* Tickle tickle. Gitchy gitchy goo. *(The drink spills down the front of Radzman)* Oh, I'm sorry. Alan did a no-no on Radzie-Radzie's pants. Wipe. Wipe. Wipe.

RADZMAN *(annoyed):* Alan —

ALAN: Don't worry. I'll get you another. *(He moves U.R. to find bourbon bottle)*

PARKAY *(chuckling):* Quite a live wire, that boy. Genuine, to say the least.

RADZMAN *(pushing):* But we've got another boy to talk about now, Harrison. No less genuine in his own way, if you know what I mean. A real talent.

JOEL: Radzie, please. I'll get embarrassed.

PARKAY: No need for embarrassment, Joel. When a person's got what you've got he should be proud.

JOEL: Thank you . . . Harrison.

RADZMAN: I'll drink to that. *(Searches for his drink)*

PARKAY: Bottoms up.

ALAN *(returning with drinks):* Well, if you wish, but I prefer facing

. . . (JOEL *almost spits out his drink with shock)*

RADZMAN *(recovering toast):* To Joel.

ALAN: Long may he wave.

JOEL: Alan, I really don't think we need you anymore.

PARKAY: Oh, let him go ahead. He's having fun.

RADZMAN *(watching Alan pour himself a straight drink):* Alan, that's straight bourbon; don't you think it needs some water?

ALAN: Water? Water? Terrible stuff. Never drink water. Fish muck in it, you know. *(again,* JOEL *gags)* A toast.

RADZMAN *(in there pitching):* To Joel.

ALAN: And Cynthia.

PARKAY: Who is Cynthia?

ALAN: A marvelous girl . . . she sings, and dances, and plays leapfrog.

RADZMAN: Just one of Alan's imaginary friends.

ALAN: Love your tie, Radzie. It has a certain *savoir fairy.*

ELVIRA'S *unmistakable legs are seen coming down into the room.*

PARKAY *(jumping):* My God, someone's coming down the fire escape. Is it a photographer?

ALAN *(delighted):* Hell, no. It's Elvira.

JOEL: Oh, God. Elvira.

ALAN *(runs to her):* Elvira, darling.

RADZMAN: Harrison, I don't think we'll get much talking done with Alan around.

PARKAY: But he's delightful. A real live wire.

RADZMAN: Yes, but we do have to go over the contracts sometime tonight.

PARKAY: Later, later.

ALAN: Everybody, this is Elvira. She came down to pee. Elvira, everybody.

ELVIRA: Hello, everybody. Excuse me. I got locked out of my bathroom. That wop model ate too many prunes. Mind if I use yours?

PARKAY *(entertained):* Not at all.

RADZMAN *(furious):* Be our guest.

PARKAY *(moving to her):* I'm Harrison Parkay.

ELVIRA: Charmed, I'm sure. I'm Elvira Gluck. And I really do have to go. Excuse me.

ALAN *(walking her to bathroom door):* Elvira, stick by me. I need you.

PARKAY: Strange quality, that girl. Ethereal, to say the least.

JOEL: She studies astrology. In fact, she predicted I'd meet you.

PARKAY: How very unusual.

RADZMAN: Joel's quite a man with the ladies, too. Built-in box-office appeal, I call it.

ELVIRA *(running onstage horrified):* Aaagh! Aaaaghh! There's something in there. And it's alive.

ALAN: Oh, God. The skunk.

PARKAY: Oh, that's my pet, Hermione. She won't hurt you.

JOEL: Go back in, Elvira. It's all right. Hermione's deodorized. Are you?

ELVIRA: But the goddam thing keeps running around me. A skunk!

PARKAY: It's a pet.

ALAN: Her name's Hermione. Cute, huh?

PARKAY: It's all right. She won't hurt you.

ELVIRA: But she makes me nervous. I clutch up if anybody's watching.

JOEL: She isn't an anybody; she's an anything.

PARKAY: Although she's very human in her mannerisms.

RADZMAN: Elvira, if we let her out, she may piddle on the carpet.

ALAN: And if you don't, Elvira may.

JOEL: Elvira, we're very busy. Couldn't you use your own bathroom for once?

ELVIRA: Oh, what the hell.

ALAN: Elvira, please stay. I need you.

ELVIRA: Alan, I can't really. I'll be lucky if I make it upstairs. Nice meeting you all. Come on up to my place if you get bored. John Smith's doing Melina Mercouri imitations. Bye bye. Catch you all later. *(She exits)*

RADZMAN: Does she do that often?

ALAN: Three or four times a day, I imagine. Depends on her liquid intake. How about another drink? You look too solemn.

JOEL; Alan, for Heaven's sake, stop —

ALAN *(spilling drink down Radzman):* Oops. There I go again. I'm awfully sorry.

RADZMAN: I'm soaked.

JOEL: Come on in the bedroom. You can change there.

PARKAY: Sneaky, sneaky.

RADZMAN: We really shouldn't leave Harrison.

PARKAY: Don't worry; take your time. Alan will entertain me.

ALAN: Sure. I haven't even begun my backrubbing bit yet. Joel adores it. It loosens your tensions.

RADZMAN: Alan! We won't be a minute.

JOEL: Come on, Radzie, I have to talk to you anyway. (JOEL *leads* RADZMAN *into the bedroom)*

ALAN *(nervous):* Where did everybody go?

PARKAY: They're changing pants.

ALAN: This early in the evening? How about that.

PARKAY: Sit down, Alan. We haven't had a chance to talk.

ALAN: But where did —

PARKAY: They'll be back. Don't worry. Come on. Sit down. I

won't bite. Unless, of course, you want me to.

ALAN: Later, tiger, later. What are they —

PARKAY: I think Joel's going to chastise Arnie for putting the hard sell on me. And, of course, Joel wants to find out from his agent exactly where he stands with me. That's all.

ALAN: Exactly where does he stand with you?

PARKAY: In pretty good stead. Don't worry. I'll probably sign him before I leave. That's a talented boy in there.

ALAN: You don't know the half of it.

PARKAY: My bar is going to be a special kind of club. For a select clientele, if you know what I mean. Joel will be just the kind of drawing power needed to get it on its feet.

ALAN: Select clientele? Does that mean what I think it does?

PARKAY: Come on, Alan, you're a big boy, now. Don't play naive with Daddy Harrison.

ALAN: Don't worry, Daddy Harrison. If I had any naivete when I came to New York, it's all gone now.

PARKAY: Now that's what I wanted to hear. Come on, sit down.

ALAN *(pacing nervously):* I'm too loose to sit. I feel like moving around. All around. I'm a free spirit.

PARKAY *(rising):* Fine, then we'll dance. I feel rather limber myself. Shall you lead or shall I?

ALAN *(moving away):* Knock it off, will you? You're old enough to be my aunt.

PARKAY *(grabbing him):* Oh — uh-uh. Playing hard to get huh? Come on. Tra, la, la . . .

ALAN *(squirming to free himself):* I forgot to tell you about my crotch rot. Stop it, please. Please, I — I . . . Cynthia!

Indeed, CYNTHIA *is standing at the door R., having observed the last minute or so. She and* ALAN *stare at each other.* PARKAY *moves slightly, releasing* ALAN.

CYNTHIA: Excuse me, Alan. I didn't know you had company.

ALAN *(regaining composure):* Oh, Cynthia, this is Harrison Parkay. Mr. Parkay, Cynthia Quinn.

PARKAY *(so suave):* My pleasure.

CYNTHIA: How do you do. *(To Alan)* Is Joel in?

PARKAY: Why, yes, he's —

ALAN: No. No, he's not. *(Covering as best he can)* No, he's still out making some plans with Mr. Radzman, Cynthia. He probably won't be in until much later.

CYNTHIA: Oh. Well, I'm glad to see he's doing something by himself, without your eagle eye watching him. I'm glad to see he's at last getting out from underneath your protective grasp.

ALAN: Cynthia, what are you talking about?

CYNTHIA *(mounting hurt and fury):* Alan, I've had enough of your games. Don't talk your way around it. I listened to you this afternoon with all the inspiration and awe of a bobby-soxer. You're quite spellbinding with your routine, you know that? For a while I was actually a little bit in love with you.

ALAN: Cynthia, I —

PARKAY: I think I'll make myself some coffee. Will you excuse me? *(He retreats U.R. into the kitchen area)*

CYNTHIA: When I first got here, I knew something had changed Joel. But I didn't know what it was. Five years, I told myself. Five years make for a lot of changes. But now I see that it was you. And your friends. Joel takes you in for a summer, he tries to be nice to you, and you have to take charge, mother him to death, try to mold his life around yours. Well, it won't work, Alan. Joel's too good for you.

ALAN: Cynthia, you don't understand.

CYNTHIA: Oh, but I do. Everything. I'm sorry Joel ever got connected with you, in any way. You're the last thing in the world he needs. If you think you're helping him, well, baby, you've got it completely wrong. Joel's too good for the likes of you. All your fancy talk and career intrigues will never alter him. So give up. For a minute this afternoon, I mistook you for a human being. And that's what a woman needs. A man she can call hers . . . one who needs and loves just her . . . one she can devote her whole life to loving. We're simple creatures, really, Alan, but we do need that. I love Joel for what he is . . . when he is with me, not what he is when he's with you. You cheapen him.

ALAN: Cynthia, why do you think I'm here right now? *(Near tears)* Why do you think —

CYNTHIA: Don't preach me nobility. I've heard your mother routine. Two faces look very silly on a man who hasn't even *one* mind. I'm sorry for you, Alan. I pity you all the more because I liked you so much. Goodbye. *(She turns to go)*

ALAN: Cynthia, you can't leave.

CYNTHIA: I've got to, Alan. I'm a little sick at my stomach. Excuse me again . . . for interrupting. *(Turns; very hard)* Oh, and Alan, when Joel comes home, tell him I'll be waiting. Goodnight. *(She exits through the door R.;* ALAN *stands motionless for a minute)*

PARKAY *(coming back into the living room):* That's quite a woman who just walked out the door. In love with Joel, is she? Does she know him well?

ALAN *(quietly):* Maybe she doesn't know him, but she seems to have me pegged, doesn't she?

PARKAY: Why, Alan, I actually think you care. That's touching. I cared once about what a woman thought . . . many years ago.

I remember actually wanting to marry her. A wonderful girl in every other way, except she couldn't accept . . . me. What I was. I felt very bad for a time. Then I got Hermione. And what the hell? It's all very much the same.

ALAN *(bitter):* Is it? How very nice for you.

PARKAY *(moving toward him):* Oh, come on now.

ALAN *(suddenly):* Mr. Parkay, will you promise me one thing?

PARKAY: Of course, Alan. What?

ALAN: Will you promise that you'll sign Joel to that contract?

PARKAY: Of course, Alan. It's as good as done.

ALAN: I want someone to get what they want out of this mess. And that job *is* what Joel wants.

PARKAY: Don't worry. I'll take care of it.

ALAN: You won't go back on your word?

PARKAY: I promise. And I am a gentleman.

ALAN *(ironically):* Yes, yes, that you are.

PARKAY *(moving in):* Now, have a dance with Daddy Harrison, and we'll forget about it.

ALAN *(removing his hand):* Please go away. *(Harrison makes another attempt)* I — I — stop it. *(Parkay draws* ALAN *to him;* ALAN *whirls and slaps him across the face)* Damn it, take your hands off me. I'm sorry, Mr. Parkay, but I'm not in a playful mood. Not at all. I'm sorry if I gave you the wrong impression, but . . . but I'm tired. That's all. Please leave, please.

PARKAY *(angry):* Now wait a minute, you goddam little tease —

ALAN: Please, please, just go.

PARKAY: Now just what the hell —

ALAN *(screaming):* Goddammit, get out of here before I kick you out. And take that bitch of a skunk with you.

JOEL *and* RADZMAN *come running out of the bedroom.*

RADZMAN: What the hell is going on out here?

ALAN *(cold):* Party's over. Guests can go home. Don't worry, Joel, you got your job.

RADZMAN: Harrison, let me explain.

PARKAY: I don't need any explanations, thank you. *(Gathering his things)* I think I'd better be leaving.

JOEL *(furious):* Alan, just what the hell are —

ALAN: Have no fear, Joel. Mr. Parkay *is* a gentleman.

PARKAY: Where's my hat?

ALAN: Don't forget your goddam skunk.

RADZMAN *(growing red with anger):* Listen, Alan, I've had just about enough of you.

ALAN: And I've had more than enough of you. Here's your hat. Thank you for stopping by, and don't come again.

JOEL: He's drunk . . . really, Radzie.

RADZMAN: I don't care what he is, he's sober enough to hear this.

Listen, you flippant little punk. Nobody orders me out of *my* apartment. Who do you think pays for this place, huh? You'll be out of here by Tuesday, but that's not soon enough.

ALAN *(ceremoniously):* Hail, Allah. Hail, Allah. Hail . . . (RADZMAN *slaps him very hard across the face;* ALAN *slaps him right back)*

RADZMAN: I thought Joel would have told you by now, but I guess he didn't have the heart. Your vacation is over, sonny. If you're not out of here by Tuesday, I'll have you evicted. *(Starting after* PARKAY, *who has exited)* Harrison, Harrison, wait.

JOEL: Radzie, catch him.

ALAN *(pleading):* Don't leave, Joel. Please don't go. Please don't go with them.

JOEL: Shut up. Radzie, get Harrison over to your place. Calm him down. Don't let him go. I'll be over as soon as I can. Fifteen minutes. Give me fifteen minutes. We'll work this out. Please Radzie, please.

RADZMAN: All right, but get this bastard out of here and fast. *(Exiting)* Harrison, Harrison, wait.

JOEL *(coming to* ALAN): All right, goddammit, why? Why? You, I thought I could trust.

ALAN: Tuesday, huh? Is that what you were always going to tell me "later"? That you were trying to kick me out gently by Tuesday? All right, Joel. Go ahead, I don't care any more. But if you have any feeling at all for Cynthia, don't go with them.

JOEL: Cynthia, Cynthia! Between the two of you, I could go crazy. You may have just botched up everything I've been working two years for. A pretty pair, you two. Everything that really matters to me —

ALAN: Everything, Joel? Is that all you want — to sing for a bunch of fairies?

JOEL: That's only the beginning, baby.

ALAN: No, Joel, it's the end. I give up on you.

JOEL: *You* give up on *me?* That's damn generous of you.

ALAN: Joel, don't talk like that?

JOEL: You think I wanted you here all summer? Hopping around on pogo sticks, quoting old movies, trying to create a make-believe world for me? Play your own games on your own time. In your own place!

ALAN: But you said you —

JOEL: Needed you? Loved you? I need and love anybody I can use.

ALAN *(incredulous):* You really mean that, don't you? And Cynthia?

JOEL: Cynthia came here at a very bad time. She's young, she's mixed up, and she's looking for something that she lost five years ago. And me? For a minute the past looked attractive. It always does — for a minute. But then we — no, not *we* —

some of us realize that there's a real world. Real situations we're up against. Real people. Real places. Not Katharine Hepburn and a backstage movie lot. Maybe I'm not proud of what I am, but at least I'm something. At least I'm real. And that's more than I can say for you.

ALAN: Cynthia was here tonight. While you were in the bedroom. She told me to get away from you, to let you be your own man. That you were strong enough to stand by yourself. That nobody could touch you.

JOEL: Are you trying to shame me? Well, forget it. It won't work. Not you, or Cynthia. For her, I'm sorry I can't be what she wants me to be. For you, I'm sorry I can't be what you want me to be. But I'm not sorry I'm me. What she said was right. Leave me alone; let me be my own man. Get off my back! You have until Tuesday.

ALAN: That's damn generous of you.

JOEL: Alan, for God's sake, wise up.

ALAN: Joel, I went along with you tonight. Because I believed you. What you said about you and Cynthia. I let that old slob pinch me, I cuddled his skunk, and I poured a fortune in liquor into that potted palm when you weren't looking. I tried to play the role for you, and I couldn't. I just couldn't.

JOEL: Don't kid yourself, Nellie. You *wanted* everything that happened tonight to take place or you wouldn't have done it. You *wanted* to hop into bed with me all summer or you wouldn't have come to New York. Don't kid yourself, at least. I tried to keep you happy! I let you play the romantic, but frankly, sweetheart, you bored me silly. There's no doubt about your sexual preferences, but you've got a lot to learn before you go very far. Just calling it "love" doesn't make it very good in bed! (ALAN *slaps him)* Truth hurts, huh? Goodnight.

ALAN: Joel, don't go after them. Think of Cynthia, please.

JOEL: If you're so concerned about Cynthia, take care of her yourself. But you'll have to prove you're a man, first.

ALAN: Joel . . .

JOEL: Sleep tight . . . Nellie. *(He exits, slamming door after him)*

ALAN *sits exhausted on the sofa, head in hands. Suddenly he reaches for the bourbon bottle.* ELVIRA *has meanwhile descended the fire escape, and entered.*

ELVIRA: Is the coast clear? How was *your* party?

ALAN: Swell.

ELVIRA: Ours is still going strong. John Smith is putting the make on the delivery boy from the delicatessen, and Mrs. Murphy is washing out the carpet where her husband puked. Great fun. Except for Cynthia. She went to bed crying like a baby. What gives around here? Everybody's too sober to enjoy themselves.

ALAN: Not me, Elvira, not me. I've just decided to give up sobriety. *(He pours from the bottle)*

ELVIRA: Yeah? That's nice. Me too. So share.

ALAN: Cynthia was cryin', huh?

ELVIRA: Yeah. Midwestern kook. At her own party.

ALAN *(toasting):* Cynthia's here.

ELVIRA *(raising her glass):* Cynthia's here. *(They drink)* How did things go for Joel?

ALAN: He'll work them out. He always does. He's his own man, you know.

ELVIRA: He sure didn't get much. Poor Cynthia. I think she still thinks that the two of them can —

ALAN: Elvira, Cynthia's nice. You know that?

ELVIRA: I'll drink to that.

ALAN: She's warm, cultured, and unspoiled.

ELVIRA: And a size nine.

ALAN: I'll drink to that.

ELVIRA: She'll make some man a perfect wife. She'll probably even bear children painlessly. It's disgusting.

ALAN: All seven hundred. Did you know that she wants to have seven hundred children?

ELVIRA: That I won't drink to.

ALAN: Elvira, you're nice.

ELVIRA: True.

ALAN: And warm.

ELVIRA: Exceptionally.

ALAN: And compatible.

ELVIRA: You're damn right I am.

ALAN: And feminine as hell.

ELVIRA: Well, yeah, sort of.

ALAN: A man could really go for you.

ELVIRA: So find me one.

ALAN: What's wrong with me?

ELVIRA: Alan, you're a swell kid, but —

ALAN: So what's wrong with me?

ELVIRA: Well, . . . you're not in love with me. I guess that's reason enough.

ALAN: Love, schmove. Other than that, what's wrong with me?

ELVIRA: Well, nothing.

ALAN: I'll drink to that. Elvira, I desire you.

ELVIRA: Yeah? That's nice.

ALAN: I mean — really — desire you.

ELVIRA: Alan, are you making fun? I don't find that very amusing. *(He kisses her)* Now why did you want to go and do that?

ALAN: Because I wanted to.

ELVIRA: But you might spoil a nice friendship that way.

ALAN: Friendship, schmiendship. It's fun, isn't it? *(She kisses him)*

ELVIRA: I'll drink to that. (ALAN *knocks the drink from her hand, and begins caressing her; the lights are dimming slowly)* Alan? Alan, what are you doing? Alan? Al-an? Al. . . .

ALAN: Just shut up, Elvira. It'll all be over in a minute. Relax. Just settle back and enjoy yourself. 'Cause that's exactly what I'm gonna do.

THE CURTAIN FALLS

ACT III

The following morning, about 11 a.m. ELVIRA'S *ankles are visible behind the sofa as THE CURTAIN RISES. After a moment of silence, there is a soft knock at the door R.;* ELVIRA'S *head pops up, then the rest of her rises, and, with a smile goes to the kitchen area and starts examining the coffee pot. The knock on the door is heard again, and* TONY, *Joel's friend from Act I, enters in his velour shirt.*

TONY *(noticing Elvira):* Is Joel home?

ELVIRA: No, he went to a slumber party last night.

TONY: Oh, really? Do you know when he'll be back?

ELVIRA: No, I really haven't the vaguest — Oh, damn. Do you know how to make coffee?

TONY: I beg your pardon?

ELVIRA: It's my first fling at being domestic. Come here and see if I'm on the right track.

TONY: Everything seems okay. Did you put water in?

ELVIRA: Yeah, and then the grounds.

TONY: And you've got it plugged in? *(She nods)* Then you're all set.

ELVIRA: Honest? Hell, that was easy.

TONY: You've never made coffee before?

ELVIRA: Huh-uh. I don't drink it myself. It goes right through me. It's for Alan. I've got a feeling he'll be needing a lot of it this morning. It does come out black, doesn't it?

TONY: Sure. Who's Alan?

ELVIRA: Joel's roommate.

TONY: His roommate? But that's what I came to see Joel about. He invited me to move in with him.

ELVIRA: Yeah? *(She looks him over)* When was this?

TONY: A couple of nights ago. We met while I was walking my poodle, Ingrid.

ELVIRA: How long does it take to bubble?

TONY: Five minutes or so. Joel said he got the place rent free, and that it would be a groovy idea if I moved in for a while. He said there'd be plenty of room to practice my ballet. There wasn't anybody else when I stayed here the other night. *(Pause)* Well, I'll stop back later then. This sure would be an ideal place to practice my body movements. *(He turns)*

ELVIRA: You're leaving already?

TONY: I've got to take Ingrid to the vet this morning. She's getting so fat, I'm afraid she may have been indiscreet.

ELVIRA: Give her my congratulations. But what about the coffee? Will it be okay?

TONY: When it starts to perc in the bubble on the top, it's ready. Oh, and tell Joel I stopped by, okay? The name's Tony. He'll remember me.

ELVIRA: Is that Tony with a "y" or Toni with an "i"?

TONY: With a "y."

ELVIRA: Yeah? That's nice. You can't be sure nowadays. Nice to have met you. My name's Elvira Gluck. *(Offers her hand)*

TONY: Elvira. Do you live here too?

ELVIRA: No, I live in the apartment right above. But I slept here last night. Alan raped me.

TONY *(he's picked it up already)*: Yeah? That's nice.

ELVIRA: Yeah, I sorta thought so. It was a first for both of us. Say, I'll be looking for a roommate myself soon. I can't cook, but I'm a lovely person in every other way. So if Joel finks out, give me a ring. My apartment's just as big — plenty of room to move your body around.

TONY: Well, thank you, Elvira. I'll, uh, keep the offer in mind. Goodbye.

ELVIRA *(calling after him)*: Bye. And I love poodles. Even indiscreet ones. I'd make Ingrid a wonderful mother. Oh, well. Oooh, it's starting to bubble.

ALAN *enters from his room, dressed, carrying two bags. He walks to the couch, smiles down at the scene of the crime.* ELVIRA *approaches cheerfully from behind him.*

ELVIRA: Good morning. Good morning. Here's your coffee. Your paper. Have a good night's rest? Mwah. *(Kisses him on forehead)* There, was that domestic?

ALAN: Elvira. Uh, good morning.

ELVIRA: Drink. Go ahead, drink. It's good for you. It's coffee. I made it myself. With my own two hands.

ALAN: Oh, my God, Elvira. I'm just beginning to remember last night.

ELVIRA: And you groan? *I'm* the one who's supposed to be remorseful. Drink.

ALAN: But Elvira, what we did last night —

ELVIRA: You didn't enjoy it?

ALAN: What has that got to do with it? I feel like a heel.

ELVIRA: You didn't enjoy it?

ALAN: Well, uh, well yes, of course I did.

ELVIRA: Me too. Now drink your coffee. This is the first chance I've ever had to play housewife. So drink, smoke, read the morning paper, and grunt inaudibly whenever I ask you a question. I want this to be just like I've always imagined. Okay? You want I should get you some eggs?

ALAN: Elvira, you don't know how to fry eggs.

ELVIRA: Quit breaking the illusion. I'll get you some bologna and Alka-Seltzer. *(Sees suitcases)* Alan, those are yours. Are you skipping town?

ALAN: Elvira, sit.

ELVIRA: But the coffee pot; it's still plugged in.

ALAN: It's supposed to be. Sit.

ELVIRA: But your bologna —

ALAN: Sit.

ELVIRA: Sit, sit. He treats me like a dog. I feel so domestic. Good morning.

ALAN: Good morning. Yes, those are my bags. Today's moving day.

ELVIRA: What is this strange effect I have on man?

ALAN: Elvira, dear sweet Elvira. I'm not leaving because of you. It's because of me. I'm being evicted. No, that's not the reason. I want to go. It's time for me to go, and I've got to get out of here.

ELVIRA: Just because you finally saw through Joel?

ALAN: Well, that's a big part of it, I guess. But it's more than just Joel.

ELVIRA: Well, that leaves only the obvious. *(Telling him)* You're leaving because you're in love with Cynthia.

ALAN: Who said that?

ELVIRA: Who said summer follows spring?

ALAN: What?

ELVIRA: Never mind. I was getting poetic. Did I tell you what I dreamed last night.

ALAN: Elvira —

ELVIRA: I dreamed about Judy Garland and Bert Lahr. Oh, don't worry, it wasn't dirty. At their age it could be dirty? No, it was a very pretty dream. In Metrocolor. They were running down this yellow brick road, see. Just like in the movies. She was looking for a way to get back to Kansas and he was looking for courage. And they were laughing and singing the whole damn way, having one helluva good time. And at each turn they made, they'd stop and weigh the pros and cons before going ahead. Then all of a sudden they came to a place with three turnoffs: one read "Return Trips to Kansas," the second read "Courage," and the third was labelled "Pot of Gold." And those damn fools separated! She took the first road and he took the second. I tried to call out and stop them, but on they went, she her way and he his. But pretty soon after they'd each gone away, they each realized that they weren't happy traveling alone. It was dark in the forests, and witches were after them. And all of a sudden they realized how important their companionship was. If they'd taken the third road, they could have been laughing and singing and dancing the whole way. She could have given him all the courage he needed, and he could have given her more love than she ever dreamed existed in Kansas. So they ran and ran to get back to where the road forked . . . and then I woke up. I don't know if they ever got together on the third road or not. And they should have. They really should have. They needed each other. Do you think that means anything?

ALAN *(understanding):* Elvira, God made a lovely person when he made you.

ELVIRA: You really think? That's nice.

ALAN: Elvira, about last night —

ELVIRA: Alan, shut up, please. Last night was beautiful. It made me feel for the first time in my life that I was a woman. Really, I was beginning to have my doubts. And if you say one word to spoil it, I'll . . . I'll never make you coffee again. It was all so perfect. I was wearing pink; you were wearing blue. I think that's the way God intended things, you know?

ALAN *(smiling):* Elvira, where the hell's my bologna?

ELVIRA *(kissing him on forehead):* Coming right up. It'll be ready in a jiffy.

ALAN *returns to his room to pack;* CYNTHIA *enters; from the fire escape.*

CYNTHIA: Hello? Anybody home?

ELVIRA: Cynthia, you're just in time for some of my home-brewed coffee.

CYNTHIA: Is Joel back yet?

ELVIRA: No, no he didn't come home at all last night.

CYNTHIA: You were here all night?

ELVIRA: Yeah. Isn't that a lovely couch to sleep on?

CYNTHIA: Elvira, you're grinning like a Cheshire cat.

ELVIRA: No, Cynthia. Like a poodle. A poodle named Ingrid. Care for some bologna?

CYNTHIA: No. I wonder where Joel is. We have so much to talk about.

ELVIRA: Really? Did I tell you what I dreamed about last night? Bert Lahr. And Judy Garland.

CYNTHIA: Are these Joel's bags? He's not moving, is he?

ELVIRA: No, those are Alan's. He's finally wised up and is leaving

New York. I think last night made a new man of him.

CYNTHIA: Elvira, what are you hinting at?

ELVIRA: You don't tell me your secrets. I should tell you mine?

CYNTHIA *(melancholic):* Alan's leaving. That's a shame.

ELVIRA: Last night you were saying you hoped he left for good. Sometimes, dear roommate, I don't think you know your own mind.

CYNTHIA: Joel must've asked him to go.

ELVIRA: He may have. But Alan's leaving of his own choice. I think he knows what's right and wrong much better than any of us. We should all have such high moral convictions. It would make America a better place to live. Better for our children . . . whether we have seven . . . or seven hundred.

CYNTHIA: Elvira, you know something you're not telling me.

ELVIRA: You're damn tootin'. You're old enough to learn things for yourself, Cynthia. Oh, if you're waiting for Joel, mind the coffee, will you? All that bubbling terrifies me. I think I'll go upstairs and lie down for awhile. God knows I didn't get much sleep last night. Ta-ta. *(She exits up the fire escape)*

CYNTHIA: Elvira? Elvira?

ALAN *enters from his room with another suitcase. The two exchange glances.*

ALAN: Good morning, Cynthia.

CYNTHIA: Good morning. I was just waiting for Joel.

ALAN: Fine. Care for some coffee?

CYNTHIA: Uh, no, no, thank you. *(Pause)*

ALAN: I think I'll have some. *(He starts to kitchen)*

CYNTHIA: Yes, do. Elvira recommends it highly.

ALAN: Yes, yes I know.

CYNTHIA: Oh. *(Pause)*

ALAN: Elvira's gone back upstairs?

CYNTHIA: Yes, she said she needed . . . some rest.

ALAN: Oh, I see.

CYNTHIA: Yes. *(Pause)* I was just, uh, just waiting here for Joel.

ALAN: Yes, you said that.

CYNTHIA: Yes, I guess I did.

ALAN: Yes. *(Pause)* It's good coffee.

CYNTHIA: Yes, Elvira recommended it . . . highly.

ALAN: Yes, yes she did.

CYNTHIA: Yes. *(Pause)*

ALAN: Are you sure you don't care for some?

CYNTHIA: No, no really.

ALAN: A Coke, maybe?

CYNTHIA: Well — no, no, thank you. *(Pause)*

ALAN *(rises):* I'll get you a Coke.

CYNTHIA: Yes, please. If it's no trouble.

ALAN: It's no trouble.
CYNTHIA: Thank you. *(Pause)* Are these your bags?
ALAN: Yes.
CYNTHIA: You're leaving?
ALAN: Yes. You want a glass?
CYNTHIA: No, don't bother.
ALAN: I'll get you a glass.
CYNTHIA: Thank you. Going back to Illinois?
ALAN: Yes.
CYNTHIA: Oh.
ALAN: We don't have any clean glasses. I guess we dirtied them all last . . . night.
CYNTHIA: Oh, the bottle's fine. I don't mind. I really don't mind. It's fine.
ALAN: I'll wash one out.
CYNTHIA: Thank you. Alan?
ALAN: Yes?
CYNTHIA: Nothing.
ALAN: Oh. *(Pause)*
CYNTHIA: You'll be starting school soon, huh?
ALAN: Yes. Here you are.
CYNTHIA: Thank you.
ALAN: Cheers.
CYNTHIA: Cheers. *(A pause; they drink)*
ALAN: Cynthia . . .
CYNTHIA: Alan . . .
ALAN: Go ahead.
CYNTHIA: No, you.
ALAN: Ladies first.
CYNTHIA: No, really. You. *(Pause)*
ALAN: Cynthia . . .
CYNTHIA: Alan . . .

They laugh at each other — and themselves.

CYNTHIA: Hi.
ALAN: Hi. *(An enormous pause; then very fast)* Joel should be back any time.
CYNTHIA: Good. I — I — want to talk to him.
ALAN: Yes, of course.
CYNTHIA: We've got a lot to discuss.
ALAN: Yes.
CYNTHIA: About his future. About our future. And . . . all.
ALAN: Yes.
CYNTHIA: Yes. This is a good Coke.
ALAN: Cynthia, I'm sorry for —
CYNTHIA: Alan, about last night —
ALAN: No, I understand exactly what you —

CYNTHIA: I didn't mean what —
ALAN: I know how it must have looked, —
CYNTHIA: I barged in like a mad bull in a —
ALAN: If there is any way to explain, I'd —
CYNTHIA: Shouting about nothing, really, because —
ALAN: I guess I was so flustered, because —
TOGETHER: I really like you. *(Pause)*
ALAN: Cynthia, about Joel, I —
CYNTHIA: You don't have to explain anything, Alan. Joel is a very easy person to fall in love with. *(Correcting herself)* With which to fall in love. Well, either way, you know what I mean. I'm really glad he had someone like you to help him along.
ALAN: But you don't understand.
CYNTHIA: Yes, I do. We're not all so naive in Minneapolis. Childish, perhaps. But not naive.
ALAN: I mean about —
CYNTHIA: I understand all I want to. Or need to. When we start asking ourselves too many questions about too many things, well, we get a lot of answers but we forfeit half the fun and mystery of life.
ALAN: You mean you'd love Joel even if he and I . . .
CYNTHIA: Yes, I think so. It's something that you can't answer just like that. But when you love someone — when all of a sudden those bells they talk about start ringing like crazy . . . well, they drown out all the sour noises before, and you just thank your lucky star that at last you've caught the melody. *(A blushing apology)* That's probably very corny and very Whittier, but that's the way I feel.
ALAN *(taking her chin with his hand, and kissing her):* God bless you.

Their kiss is interrupted by the arrival of JOEL *at the door R.; he stares at them a moment and then walks into the room.*

JOEL: Well, well, well. Don't let me disturb you. This is the day for everybody to be kissing everybody. Break out the champagne. *(With a flourish; proudly)* La contract. Signed and ready to go.
CYNTHIA *(running to him):* Oh, darling.
JOEL: I open in three weeks. Oh, and how do you like this — my stage name: Joel-Joel.
CYNTHIA *(repeating it):* Joel-Joel.
ALAN: Sort of like Hari-Kari.
JOEL *(ignoring that remark):* Alan, you're not celebrating. Everybody must be happy.
ALAN: I'm very happy for you, Joel. I know how much it means to you. Congratulations.

CYNTHIA *(starting a move toward him):* Alan —

ALAN *(turning away nervously):* Excuse me, Cynthia. I have some things to gather up. And I know you two have a lot to discuss.

JOEL: Are you leaving already?

ALAN: It's an old stage maxim: always exit on a happy note. *(He goes into his room)*

JOEL: What's he so sullen about? Oh, well, jealous I suppose that I made it on my own. Let's celebrate, shall we? I feel like throwing an enormous party. How about you?

CYNTHIA: Oh, I had enough of parties last night. How about a long walk in Central Park? We could go wading, and make mud pies, and —

JOEL: Sure, Cynthia, we'll get around to all that later. But first we have to have fun. A lot of people. A lot of laughs. You know, a real party.

CYNTHIA *(dully):* Like the one last night. Joel, when are we going to talk about us?

JOEL: Cynthia, we'll have plenty of time to discuss all that —

CYNTHIA: Between parties and rehearsals, we may never get a chance to be alone, and —

JOEL: Of course we'll be alone. We'll start going out, be seen in all the clubs, maybe take in a couple of shows —

CYNTHIA *(raising her voice):* Joel, I was supposed to get married yesterday. I didn't walk out on the most serious relationship of my life to take in a couple of shows.

JOEL *(tired):* All right, Cynthia, what did you walk out for? To come haunting me with old times? To try to relive a past that was built on adolescent fantasies? Whittier and Katharine Hepburn and *The Pirates of Penzance* are all very fun. They were then and they still have their place. But this is here and now. I've got a future ahead, a career to work toward, and lots of plans to make, and —

CYNTHIA: Do I fit into those plans, Joel?

JOEL: Cynthia, be —

CYNTHIA: I want to be with you. I want to be part of those plans. Just say you want me, and I'll go to every party, club, and show. Parks and leapfrog and everything else can wait till later, but don't lead me on. At least say you need me for something.

JOEL: Of course I need you, Cynthia. I need you for a million and one things.

CYNTHIA *(very pointed):* Really? What are the million? I was hoping it would just be the one.

JOEL: Cynthia, I thought you wanted to have fun, a real vacation. I want to show you all the exciting things this town can offer. Don't you want to feel free for once in your life? Meet new people, let go, relax? Isn't that why you came here?

CYNTHIA: I came here to find out what I really wanted, Joel. Where is it?

JOEL: Cynthia, you've got to grow up. You're as bad as Alan in your way. Sure I like you, but there's so much more — we're not anyways near ready to settle down, get in that old Midwestern rut. You can't turn New York into Coldwater, Minnesota. You have to be realistic.

CYNTHIA: Yes, I do, don't I?

JOEL: We'll discuss all this later. Don't worry. You want to live it up just like I do. And we will. Just let me phone Radzie and get a few things taken care of, and tonight we'll have the greatest bang-up party you've ever seen. Singing, dancing, all that nonsense. You'll love it. *(Into phone)* Hello, Radzie? Joel. Yeah, listen, — hey what are you doin'? (CYNTHIA *has slammed down the receiver)*

CYNTHIA: Joel, I want to go away right now. And I want you to come with me. I don't care where. Not Minneapolis. Not New York. The Moon! . . . anyplace, just the two of us?

JOEL: Cynthia!

CYNTHIA: Will you come, Joel?

JOEL: To the Moon, huh?

CYNTHIA *(pleading):* Forget about this nightclub deal. Forget about Radzman, Parkay, the whole bit, and come away with me. You don't need them. You've proved to yourself you could make it. You don't need to struggle around here anymore. Let's go away, just the two of us. Please!

JOEL: You've been talking to Alan. I can see his infl —

CYNTHIA: No, Joel, I'm talking to *you.* If you love me, come away now, while we're still young enough to enjoy ourselves, still silly and dreamy enough to wipe out everything that's happened in the last five years. I want to, Joel. I want to.

JOEL *(finally):* Cynthia, I can't. I won't leave everything I've worked for to go willy-nilly in search of lost youth. I'm too old to be a child!

CYNTHIA: Not even for me?

JOEL: Not for anyone.

CYNTHIA: I'm sorry, Joel. I loved you more than anything in the world. The idea of you, anyway. But I'm going to have my fun . . . I've got to. "Childhood," as you call it, is all too grand a thing to toss out the window. I left Minneapolis to find myself, to kick up my heels and have a high old time in this world looking for what I am. I thought you were the biggest part of it, Joel. A miscalculation on my part. But with or without you, I'm gonna have my vacation. My Chopsticks Concerto, I guess.

JOEL: Cynthia . . . *(He kisses her)*

CYNTHIA: Good luck, Joel. And goodbye.

She exits through the door R.; JOEL *sits alone. He starts to pick up the phone to call Radzman, when* ALAN *enters from his room, all bags ready.*

ALAN: Where's Cynthia?

JOEL: She's gone.

ALAN: For good?

JOEL: Oh, she'll be back. Whenever there's a rainstorm and she's scared of the thunder. Whenever she starts to realize that nobody else makes mud pies and sings loony songs. Whenever she grows up enough to see that life isn't just like in the movies, she'll be back to try and mold me all over again.

ALAN: And you're letting her go, just like that?

JOEL: It was her decision, Alan. I would have liked her to stay. She made me feel good inside sometimes. But I couldn't make any of the promises that would stop her.

ALAN: Oh, Joel, Joel, look at me. Run after her. Run like crazy; she loves you, Joel, and you need her.

JOEL: Alan, you don't know anything about this. Leave me alone.

ALAN: I'm going to, Joel. I'm a new man, today, and I've got places I have to go and things I have to do there. And they're things I *want* to do. That's the big irony of it all. Thank you, Joel, for putting up with me. This summer was a difficult time. Really. But look, we've made it through, haven't we? I owe you a lot, Joel, but all I can say is thanks.

JOEL: Alan, I'm sorry about everything.

ALAN: I know. *(He kisses him lightly on the forehead. The telephone rings)*

JOEL: Oh, God. That's Radzie. I hung up on him. *(Answers it)* Hello, baby, I — Alan Reynolds? Yes, he's here. It's for you.

ALAN: Oh, God. Not John Smith. *(Takes phone)* Hello? Yes, this is . . . yes. Yes. That's great. I mean, it's wonderful, but I can't. You see, I'm leaving New York today. Yes, I was just here on a vacation, and now it's over, so . . . so I won't be able to. But thank you, anyway. What? Oh, yes, I understand. Oh, before I go . . . could I ask you just one question? Who is Gregor Pedestri? Oh, well, thank you anyway. Thank you. *(He replaces phone)*

JOEL: Mr. Smith?

ALAN: No, no the TV show. They wanted me to be a contestant. I guess I didn't know so much after all.

JOEL: And you turned them down? Alan, baby, with your brains you could have made a fortune.

ALAN: Maybe. But what would I have done with it?

JOEL: Why you could have bought — I don't know — clothes, a whole new wardrobe. You could have taken trips — a big holiday to Europe, or . . . or anything.

ALAN: I've had my holiday, Joel. I don't think I could take another one. You know what the lady said when I asked her about Gregor Pedestri? She said, "I don't know. I just work here."

He is still smiling as ELVIRA *comes in from off the fire escape.*

ELVIRA: Hey, what's going on down here this morning? Everybody jumping around, screaming, crying? *(To Joel)* Oh, congratulations. I hear you're a star.

JOEL *(with pride):* There's the contract, Elvira.

ELVIRA: All in a night's work, I guess.

JOEL *(trying to recapture the magic):* And pretty soon little children will start shouting in the streets. Hollering to beat the band.

ELVIRA: Yeah? That's nice. I heard one kid yelling this morning. A dog bit him. *(To Alan)* You're all packed, huh? Things won't be the same without you. How am I ever gonna entice all the John Smiths upstairs all by myself?

ALAN: Just let the John Smiths see the real you, Elvira, and they'll come running in droves.

ELVIRA: Yeah? Stampeding across all those hollering urchins on the sidewalk.

JOEL: Oh, I've got to call Radzie. *(The phone rings just before he picks it up)* Damn. Damn. Damn. Hello, Radzie, I — who? Oh, Tony. Tony, yes, of course I remember you. We should be gettin' together one of these days and . . . what? Well, I can't, you see. As it turns out, I'm moving myself. Yeah, in with my agent. We can work better that way, and . . . what? Elvira's number? Well, it's — wait a minute, she's right here. *(Hands her the phone)* It's for you. An admirer.

ELVIRA *(low, seductive voice):* Hello. Yes, Tony. Why, why, yes, of course. And Ingrid too? She is? She isn't! Yeah? That's nice. This afternoon, then? Oh, you naughty boy. *(For Joel's benefit)* Me to you. Bye bye.

JOEL: What the hell?

ELVIRA: That was Tony, my new roommate. We're gonna have puppies.

RADZMAN *enters in a fury.*

RADZMAN: Just what the hell is going on around here? Did you hang up on me, you ungrateful —

ALAN: Oh, God.

JOEL *(soothing):* Radzie, Radzie, I've been trying to get ahold of you, but our phone keeps ringing, and —

RADZMAN: Why did you hang up on me in the first place?

JOEL: I didn't. Cynthia threw the phone down in her temper tantrum, and I —

ELVIRA *(jumping to life):* Oh, my heavens, Cynthia. Alan, I almost forgot. She's gone.

ALAN: She's . . . already?

RADZMAN: Well, thank heavens for that.

ELVIRA: Shut up a minute, will you?

JOEL: Elvira, you can't —

ALAN *(interested):* You, too. Shut up.

ELVIRA: She came running upstairs, woke me up, and told me goodbye. Left me an address in Minneapolis to mail her stuff to, and then she just walked out. She said she was gonna see Central Park, come hell or high water.

ALAN: Joel, Joel, she's still here; you can catch her.

JOEL *(nearer Radzman):* Alan, for heaven's sake, what are you talking about?

ALAN: Joel, go after her.

JOEL: Alan, I can't.

ALAN: You mean you won't.

JOEL: All right, I won't!

RADZMAN: Well, that's more like it. Someone's talking sense, anyway.

ALAN *(the final realization):* Joel, you don't really love her at all, do you? Admit it, you're relieved that she's going away aren't you?

RADZMAN: Well?

JOEL *(no pretense):* Yes. Yes, I am, frankly. Relieved about the whole situation.

ALAN *(making up his mind):* Elvira, how long ago did she leave?

ELVIRA: Well, it couldn't have been ten minutes —

JOEL: And just where do you think you're going?

ALAN: After her.

RADZMAN: I don't understand any of this.

JOEL: And what do you hope to prove by that?

ALAN: Prove? Nothing, really. I did all the proving that was necessary last night. I'm gonna hunt her down, and . . .

JOEL *(amused, but jealous):* Yes, and what?

ALAN *(quite simply):* Tell her I love her. Tell her I need her. Because I do. And hope in time she can care enough to —

JOEL: This is almost funny. Do you think she'd have you? Want you?

ALAN: I don't know, Joel. But I can hope so. I've made an awful lot of mistakes in my time — mistakes damned hard to overlook. Especially for a woman like Cynthia.

JOEL: Woman? She's a ten-year-old child.

ALAN: No, Joel, a woman. And I'm gonna try like hell to be a man. To make her believe in me again. She said she liked me . . .

JOEL: Like she likes peppermint candy and Whittier and —

ALAN: Maybe so. But I like those things, too. And what's more, *I* believe in her. If she wants to make mud pies, I'll cook up the thickest damn mud pies you ever tasted. If she wants to play leapfrog, I'll leap . . . *we'll* leap, and never stop till we go over that metaphorical moon.

ELVIRA: Well, then, don't make speeches. Run, before it's too late.

JOEL: Dreamer.

ALAN: Elvira, about last night. Can you ever forgive me?

ELVIRA: Don't mention it, Alan. It was the nicest thing anyone's ever done to me.

ALAN: But what if you get . . .

ELVIRA: Pregnant I won't get. Maybe I can't tell when the water's boiling, but some things I can calculate. Now run.

ALAN *(kisses her):* You're wonderful. Joel, goodbye.

JOEL: Alan, you're a hopeless child.

ALAN: Maybe, but as long as I know where that yellow brick road is, on it I stay. And if it's a concerto she wants, she'll hear the loudest damned version of Chopsticks she ever imagined. *(He is off)*

RADZMAN: Quite a live wire, that boy. A real individual. Genuine, to say the least.

JOEL: I thought you hated him.

RADZMAN: I do. Because I'm intensely jealous.

JOEL: But there's the tragedy. They'll never make it. They're both senseless children trying to play make-believe. Happily ever after doesn't follow what's in his past. Someday, they'll wake up, very sad, old people and realize life isn't one long movie.

ELVIRA: Maybe so. But until that day —

JOEL: And she won't have him. Not after what —

RADZMAN: Well, let's not waste time speculating. You have some packing to do yourself.

JOEL: Yes. Yes I do.

RADZMAN: So let's see them off with a drink.

JOEL: The poor fools.

RADZMAN: To Alan and Cynthia.

ELVIRA *(beaming):* I'll drink to that. By the way, did I tell you what I dreamed last night?

THE CURTAIN FALLS.

NEITHER HERE NOR THERE

David B. Jones

FADE IN:

1. *ESTAB SHOT COLLEGE CAMPUS — DAY*

A square or open area of a college campus. In the background to the right is a union building. In front of the union building is a raised pavilion, with tables, most of which are occupied by students studying, drinking coffee, etc. In the background to the left is an auditorium. There is an open pathway to the right of the union building and pavilion. The pathway opens on the near end to the square and on its far end to the street. On the near left, between the CAMERA and the auditorium, is a SPEAKER haranguing into a microphone. On the near right a small group of DEMONSTRATORS are carrying signs proclaiming free speech, abortion, and anti-war sentiments. They are passing to and fro in front of a table stacked with pamphlets. One GIRL DEMONSTRATOR sits at the desk handing out pamphlets. Opposite the demonstrators, on the other side of the square (near the auditorium), a small group of COUNTER-DEMONSTRATORS carry signs supporting morals and the war in Vietnam. In front of the pavilion, in roughly the center of the square, is a kiosk plastered with posters of various kinds. It is a bright sunny day. Students and faculty are walking and riding bikes to and from classes.

The CAMERA moves forward into this scene focusing roughly on the kiosk, which is not necessarily distinguishable initially. The speaker's voice is loudest as the CAMERA passes him and will fade out as the CAMERA nears the kiosk.

SPEAKER *(gesticulating wildly):* . . . so the real heroes are not in Vietnam. The real heroes are *here,* in this country. They're in the South, fighting for civil rights. They're in Delano, fighting for downtrodden workers. They're on the college campuses fighting for peace, for *truth,* for *mankind!!* They're here! Right here, demonstrating, marching, protesting! They're giving speeches . . . *(embarrassed at the unavoidable but logical extension)* . . . like me . . . *(recovering himself)* that is, like *you,* out there. The heroes are the artistic socialists, the individualistic communists, the creative anarchists . . .

As the speaker fades to the left out of the moving CAMERA'S view, the CAMERA passes by the speaker's audience, all except one of whom seem to be paying little attention to the speaker but rather are enjoying the sun and relaxing on the grass. The lone ROOTER, with clenched fists and gritted teeth, resembles a boxing fan rooting for his favorite fighter. With the speaker's voice still heard, though fading, we hear the rooter mutter.

ROOTER: Attaboy . . . get'em . . . you tell'em . . .

As the CAMERA continues forward, the signs of both the demonstrators and counter-demonstrators are readable just before they fade out of view to the right and left, respectively. An AMERICAN and ORIENTAL STUDENT stop at the kiosk and read the posters, their backs to the CAMERA. The speaker's voice fades completely out of hearing as the CAMERA approaches the kiosk. The pavilion is now clearly distinguishable in the background. The Oriental says something to the American. As the American replies, the CAMERA is close enough to catch it.

AMERICAN *(matter-of-factly):* Yeah, he's an ape, with a Ph.D. *(looking at the Oriental with expression of mild surprise)* How long have you been in this country, anyway?

As they move on, a Southern student stops at the kiosk. The CAMERA moves up to read the poster. It is among many other various announcements.

The Faculty Club

presents

DR. JOSEPH YOUNG

My Former Life as an Ape

Thursday 4:00 P.M. Forum Hall

2. *KIOSK — MED. CLOSE SHOT*

The Southern student is open-mouthed and puzzled.

SOUTHERN STUDENT *(heavy accent):* Them *damn* Kennedys.

3. *PATH RIGHT OF PAVILION, MED. LONG SHOT — DAY*

A 2- or 3-year-old car is parked on the street at the end of the path. DR. JOE YOUNG, his assistant FRITZ, and the FIRST FACULTY MEMBER are on the near side of the car walking up the path toward the CAMERA.

4. *PATH TO RIGHT OF PAVILION — MED. CLOSE SHOT*

Young is an ape, conventionally dressed in a suit, shoes, etc. His face is as much like an ape's as possible while still allowing him freedom of expression. Except for his face and the palms of his hands, all visible parts of his body are covered with fur. He walks with a slight but noticeable limp. He carries a briefcase in his left hand. The first faculty member is on Young's left (CAMERA'S right). He is a thin, balding, bespectacled man in his thirties. Though dressed quite correctly, he appears a little unsure of himself. On Young's right is Fritz, a young Nordic with a slightly rebellious expression. He doesn't seem to like Young very much. He is carrying a film projector.

FIRST FACULTY MEMBER *(obsequiously to Young):* We have some minutes. Would you care for some coffee? There are some guests . . .

YOUNG *(voice like any Midwesterner):* Certainly. Fritz, go to the auditorium and set up the projector.

Fritz walks on ahead of them.

5. *REVERSE ANGLE — MED. CLOSE SHOT*

The CAMERA follows the two men as Fritz heads toward the auditorium across the square. The demonstrators and counter-demonstrators become visible in the background. Young and the faculty member are talking, though we don't hear what they are saying. The CAMERA moves forward and pans some to the right to two COEDS, who have halted their bicycles and are looking at Young, who is off-CAMERA. Their short skirts ride up their legs revealing most of their thighs as they straddle their bicycles. Although attractive, they appear aggressive.

FIRST COED *(smiling; to her friend):* Wow! I bet *he* can do it!

The CAMERA swings back to follow Young and the faculty member. Now at the end of the path, the two turn to the right and on to the square. As they turn, they pass a NEGRO and a WHITE STUDENT walking toward the

CAMERA, which pauses on the two students for a moment.

NEGRO STUDENT *(to his friend):* . . . but would you want your daughter to marry one?

6. *CAMPUS SQUARE — MED. CLOSE SHOT*

Young and the faculty member are passing along the side of the square next to the pavilion. They are heading toward the stairs leading to the pavilion. The kiosk is on their left. CAMERA behind Young. Few of the various students or other people notice him. Two SHAGGY HUMANS, otherwise quite similar to Young, pass him from the opposite direction without noticing him.

7. *PAVILION — MED. CLOSE SHOT*

Young and the faculty member mount the stairs to the pavilion as the CAMERA follows them. An entrance to the union building is directly in front of them across the pavilion. There are occupied tables to both the left and right of the open aisle. On the right, immediately alongside the aisle, are three tables, successively occupied by (1) a MAN reading a paper, (2) an OBESE REBEL, flanked by a GIRL REBEL and an ADMIRING REBEL, all wearing sunglasses, and (3) a male AFRICAN STUDENT and a WHITE GIRL. As Young and the faculty member walk toward the union door, the CAMERA pans slightly to the right and closes in on the man reading the paper. The man is facing the CAMERA and we don't necessarily see his face behind the paper. The CAMERA pauses a moment, close-up, on a large, front-page photo featuring a presidential-like person, seated and facing the CAMERA, raising his shirt with one hand, and pointing with the other to a large scar on his large, exposed belly. The CAMERA moves on, as Young and the faculty member pass the second table, and pans slightly to note the three people sitting there. The OBESE REBEL is facing the CAMERA, which moves forward, following Young's path, but still aimed to right to catch the three, none of whom notice Young. The OBESE REBEL has an air of great importance as, leaning back in his chair, his hands folded behind his head, he stares upward. He is motionless. The girl rebel is seated on the obese rebel's right. We hear the SOUND of an occasional monotone "plunk" of her guitar as she stares creatively out into space. The admiring rebel, barely within the CAMERA'S view to the right, is gazing admiringly at the obese rebel as he talks to him. He looks and sounds effeminate. He talks over the occasional "plunk."

ADMIRING REBEL: . . . need something new, you're perfectly right. This Vietnam thing's getting old, *(with affectation)* passé.

He passes out of the CAMERA'S view.

ADMIRING REBEL: Besides, it looks like America's winning.

As the CAMERA moves forward to the third table, the admiring rebel's voice fades out. The African is talking intently to the girl, who doesn't appear especially interested. As Young passes by, she notices him and, forgetting the African, gazes curiously at Young. Young and the faculty member reach the door and enter the union. Over the entrance is a banner reading, "Alumni Week."

8. *INSIDE UNION BUILDING — MED. CLOSE SHOT*

Young and the faculty member pass through a hallway open at least on one side. CAMERA follows. More tables inside the building on one side of the hallway. The SOUND of a Barry Sadler record is heard. Two CONSERVATIVE STUDENTS are at one of the tables grimly conversing. As the CAMERA passes them by, we hear one of them.

FIRST CONSERVATIVE STUDENT *(grimly and with respect):* And exactly how does the art of Ayn Rand fit in with your concept of aesthetic capitalism?

At the end of the hallway is a staircase rising from right to left as the CAMERA sees it. Below the upper part of the staircase is a bulletin board. As Young and the faculty member walk toward the stairs, the THIRD and FOURTH CONSERVATIVE STUDENTS are seen taking down a poster reading, "Support our Fighting Men in Vietnam." To the right of this poster, at the edge of the board, is a Marine Corps poster reading, "The Marine Corps Builds Men." As Young and the faculty member prepare to mount the stairs, the CAMERA focuses on the Marine Corps poster. The two conservative students, carrying their poster, turn away from the board to leave in the direction of the CAMERA. Young's legs are seen as he climbs the stairs. Fur is visible between the cuffs of his trousers and his socks.

THIRD CONSERVATIVE STUDENT *(to his companion):* It's getting tiresome. *(passing out of view to the left)* Besides our side seems to be losing.

9. *SECOND FLOOR UNION BUILDING — MED. SHOT*

From top of stairs CAMERA watches Young and the faculty member walk down a hall.

10. *INSIDE RECEPTION ROOM — MED. SHOT*

About fifteen people are walking around, chatting, waiting for Young. Coffee is being served. Among the guests are a MIDDLE-AGED LADY, an ELDERY FACULTY MEMBER, a STATE DEPARTMENT REPRESENTATIVE, a PEACE CORPS REPRESENTATIVE, a SECOND FACULTY MEMBER. The CAMERA'S point of view is from the side of the room opposite the entrance. The CAMERA focuses on the State Department representative, a short, chubby, balding, cigar-smoking man, whose voice is heard over the other chatter as he speaks to the Peace Corps representative, a tall Negro.

STATE DEPARTMENT REP *(confidentially, and like a salesman):* And so the Secretary, fearing Chinese involvement, feels we should get in there and democratize them first, the theory being that a band of hostile apes in the heart of Africa would pose a direct threat to our security . . . You know, dominoes. Well, that's my game. What's yours?

PEACE CORPS REP *(pipe in hand):* Same. Except I work for Sargent —

Before he can finish, the door across the room opens and Young is ushered in by the first faculty member. The guests turn and welcome them.

11. CAMERA behind Young, follows action. Among the five or six people around Young are the first and second faculty members, the elderly faculty member, and the middle-aged lady. The other guests are in groups of two or three, within earshot of Young's group. The SOUND of the other guests' conversation is barely heard.

MIDDLE-AGED LADY: Isn't this the first time you've spoken at our university?

YOUNG: Yes, it is, and I'm delighted at the opportunity.

MIDDLE-AGED LADY *(smiling smugly):* Well, we're certainly glad to have you.

FIRST FACULTY MEMBER: We sure are! You know, we're one of the first universities to —

ANOTHER ANGLE

SECOND FACULTY MEMBER: Say, Dr. Young, being quite interested in the derivation of names — I have, in fact, published several works on the subject, and am in the process of preparing my . . . let's see . . . nineteenth book on names — I was —

YOUNG *(innocently):* Excuse me: your name . . .?

ANOTHER ANGLE

SECOND FACULTY MEMBER: Oh, I'm sorry. *(smiling)* Dr. Richardson. T. Henry Richardson, professor of English language and literature here — though I'm not teaching this year, but —

FIRST FACULTY MEMBER *(breaking in; smiling happily):* We have graduate students for that!

SECOND FACULTY MEMBER *(irritated at the interruption):* Not teaching, but rather am on a grant — publish or perish, you know — a grant doing research on the correlation of names with — *(halts)* Well, that's neither here nor there. My question has to do with . . . *your* name, Dr. Young. Your parents, obviously, did not —

ANOTHER ANGLE

YOUNG *(unabashed):* As you may or may not know, most creatures in a zoo have names. Zookeepers, particularly, like to bestow names on . . . those with whom they work. Anyway, as I understand it, there have been several Hollywood films made about . . . apes, the most popular of which, they tell me, was one called "King Kong." Well, another ape, an old one in the cage adjoining mine, had already been given that name. My name, so I am told, was suggested by one of these films, an obscure one which one of the zookeepers had seen on television about the time of my assignment to the zoo —

FIRST FACULTY MEMBER *(breaking in):* What zoo?

ANOTHER ANGLE

YOUNG: San Diego. An obscure movie called, "Mighty Joe Young." Hence, the name, Joe Young. Not *Joseph* Young, by the way.

SECOND FACULTY MEMBER: Thank you, Dr. Young. Excellent material!

FIRST FACULTY MEMBER: Dr. Young *(nodding toward Young's legs)* as we were walking over here, I noticed you were . . . limping.

CAMERA behind Young, facing the conversants opposite him.

YOUNG: Oh, yes. The result of a, shall we say . . . wanton shot by the woman — yes, woman — who felled me in Africa. *(forced laugh)* My introduction to Western Civilization, you might say.

FIRST FACULTY MEMBER *(grimly):* Hmmm.

ELDERLY FACULTY MEMBER *(with a suggestion of senility):* Haw-Haw. You're lucky her aim wasn't a little higher. *(he chuckles)*

The middle-aged lady blushes; the first and second faculty members look toward the old man disapprovingly.

YOUNG *(seriously):* A higher shot would have killed me. Here,

As he continues, he bends over slightly, unbuckles his trousers, and drops them and his shorts. His backside and legs are completely covered with fur. The CAMERA scans reactions. Everyone is stunned. The middle-aged lady gasps but continues to look. The elderly man frowns and looks up sadly at Young. The other conversation groups drop whatever they were talking about and rush over. The young woman runs up and stands on her tiptoes to look over the shoulder of one of the faculty members. She is eager to see, but is puzzled, and, after a second or two, drops her curious but puzzled look and stares disdainfully at Young. The tall, athletic-looking faculty member, who has a very close crew cut, looks first worriedly but then relaxes.

YOUNG *(continuing; with scientific detachment):* As you can see, the bullet, a thirty-ought-six hollow point round, entered the inside upper thigh. The impact deflected its path upward and to the left. At this point, according to an ammunitions expert with whom I discussed the matter, the bullet had expanded — from the initial impact — and thus, through its velocity had been greatly reduced, the bullet was now a whirling piece of lead of irregular shape. Consequently —

FIRST FACULTY MEMBER *(a little shaken):* Excuse me, sir, but . . . it's almost four. *(looks at his watch)* Shall we head over to the auditorium?

Young looks up quickly, a little surprised. He pulls up his trousers. CAMERA moves to near the door. The first faculty member takes Young by the arm and leads him toward the door. As Young passes by the CAMERA, we hear him muttering more or less to himself.

YOUNG *(irritated and hurt):* When the truth is in question, great minds discard the niceties of refinement!

The other guests trail Young and the first faculty member out the door. They are still amazed. The State Department and Peace Corps representatives look at each other and shake their heads as if to say, "*He* won't do." The athletic faculty member, as he passes the CAMERA, looks disgustedly at the young woman.

ATHLETIC FACULTY MEMBER *(muttering):* The savage!

12. *SECOND FLOOR UNION BUILDING — MED. SHOT*

CAMERA point of view from top of stairs. The group enters the hallway and walks toward the CAMERA. The athletic faculty member and the young woman hurry past Young.

13. *INSIDE UNION BUILDING — MED. SHOT*

CAMERA point of view hallway at bottom of stairs. Young and the first faculty member descend. SOUND of Barry Sadler record is heard.

14. *PAVILION OUTSIDE — MED. LONG SHOT*

CAMERA at pavilion stairs, facing direction of union entrance. The third table is now occupied by the third and fourth conservative students. At the second table, the girl rebel still plunks at her guitar every three or four seconds and we hear its SOUND. The obese rebel is sitting exactly as before. However, the admiring rebel's chair is now unoccupied. The athletic faculty member and the young woman emerge from the building and approach the stairs and CAMERA. As they near the CAMERA, Young and the first faculty member emerge from the building. As the athletic faculty member passes the CAMERA, he speaks to the young woman.

ATHLETIC FACULTY MEMBER *(with a suggestion of relief):* It just proves his ape nature is not yet out of him.

As Young and the faculty member approach the CAMERA, a REPORTER, with camera and notebook, enters the scene from the stairs and rushes toward the union entrance, brushing Young but not noticing him. As Young and the first faculty member pass out of view, the second faculty member emerges from the building. The reporter rushes up to him. The CAMERA moves forward for a medium-close shot.

REPORTER *(eagerly; out of breath):* Mister, what's this about some guy running around here nude?

SECOND FACULTY MEMBER *(grimacing):* Well. . . .

The reporter's next five questions sound as much like commands as they do questions.

REPORTER *(automatically):* Who?

ANOTHER ANGLE

SECOND FACULTY MEMBER: Joseph — er, Joe Young. But —

The admiring rebel emerges from the door carrying two cups of coffee.

REPORTER: What?

SECOND FACULTY MEMBER *(proud of his expression):* Blatant exhibitionism! *(catches himself)* Well, not exac —

The admiring rebel, overhearing, stops and listens with interest.

REPORTER: When?

ANOTHER ANGLE

SECOND FACULTY MEMBER: Just now, but —

REPORTER: Where?

SECOND FACULTY MEMBER: Upstairs. But that's not —

REPORTER: Why?

The second faculty member, taken aback, glares disapprovingly at the reporter.

SECOND FACULTY MEMBER *(haughtily):* One doesn't ask that question at an institution of superior quality.

REPORTER *(correcting himself):* That is, how?

The second faculty member relaxes, smiles, reaches to his belt absently, unbuckles it, and starts to drop his trousers.

SECOND FACULTY MEMBER: He bent over thusly, unbuckled his trousers, dropped —

He catches himself and, embarrassed and looking at the reporter as if he were to blame, buckles his trousers. The CAMERA focuses on the admiring rebel, whose expression indicates he has just received a bright idea.

REPORTER *(may be off camera):* How utterly depraved. I wish I had a picture . . . Upstairs, you say.

The reporter is caught in the CAMERA's picture as he

rushes into the building. The CAMERA pans to the right to momentarily follow the admiring rebel as, precariously balancing the two coffee cups, he hurries excitedly to his table.

15. *PAVILION — MED. CLOSE SHOT*

CAMERA opposite obese rebel, whose position remains as before. The girl rebel still plunks at her guitar every few seconds (SOUND). The admiring rebel enters the picture and sets the coffee on the table, in front of the obese rebel, spilling some of it in his excitement. The third and fourth conservative students at the third table listen.

ADMIRING REBEL *(wanting to please):* O, Great One! Listen! Some poor guy, all he did was take down his Levis in front of some people, and they're going to put him in jail or somethin'.

The obese rebel's position and expression remain unchanged.

ADMIRING REBEL *(continuing):* Oh, who cares? The point is: Puritanism! Hypocrisy! Persecution!

The obese rebel remains impassive.

ADMIRING REBEL *(hurt by the silence):* Well?

Without altering his position, the obese rebel emits an extremely loud, Tarzan-like jungle cry. Neither the girl, the admirer, or anyone else visible in the background appears shocked or surprised by the cry. Rather, they don't seem to notice at all.

OBESE REBEL: AHWWAHOHEEEEYAW —

His cry ends abruptly with a gurgle.

16. *SKY — MED. SHOT — DAY*

CAMERA on ground, looking upward. A bird flying.

17. *PAVILION — MED. CLOSE SHOT*

CAMERA opposite obese rebel, who remains impassive and silent for a moment. Then he slowly sits up in the chair, removes his hands from the back of his head, and, grimacing just slightly, takes a sip of his coffee, washes it around in his mouth for a second, and spits it out on the ground to the side of the chair. The girl remains impassive.

18. *PAVILION — MED. CLOSE SHOT*

CAMERA point of view behind obese rebel. As the obese

rebel assumes his former position, five more rebels arrive opposite him and assume a roughly military position, in line, opposite the obese rebel. They are, from right to left (from CAMERA), SHOSTANSKISLAV, who doesn't appear Slavic; OGG, about whom nothing appears unusual except his name; MARIE LE FLEUR, a homely, sad-looking girl; OBSIDIAN, a light-skinned Negress; and HO, a tall, heavy young man with long blond hair. All wear sunglasses. As he receives his assignment, each rebel gives a salute-like nod and departs off CAMERA.

OBESE REBEL *(staring upward, not looking at the five):* Shostanskislav: signs . . . Ogg: table . . . Marie Le Fleur: handbills . . . Obsidian: marches . . . Ho: microphone . . .

CAMERA opposite obese rebel, who sits back up in his chair and reaches for his coffee.

OBESE REBEL: Artistic socialism cannot stand idly by as persecution is permitted.

He takes a sip of coffee, washes it around his mouth, and spits again to the side.

19. *PAVILION — MED. CLOSE SHOT*

CAMERA point of view back of obese rebel, looking at third table. The two conservative students are grim-faced.

THIRD CONSERVATIVE STUDENT *(grimly):* Jay! The Galtmobile! Aesthetic capitalism will not remain detached while perversion is promulgated.

20. *OUTSIDE AUDITORIUM — MED. LONG SHOT*

CAMERA pavilion stairs, looking across right side of square, toward the auditorium. Young and the first faculty member can be seen as they enter.

21. *INSIDE AUDITORIUM — MED. CLOSE SHOT*

CAMERA is offstage at left. The stage is visible at the end of a small passage. A podium is on the stage; a screen is set up behind it. A small microphone is on the podium. A visual-aid chart, on a stand, is beyond the podium. (These details about the stage are not necessarily visible at this point.) Young and the first faculty member are in front of the CAMERA, their backs to it. The first faculty member has his arm around Young as if to encourage him. He leaves Young and walks out to the podium.

STAGE — MED. SHOT

A shot of the audience. Chatter dies down.

FRONT AISLE

The first faculty member does not use the podium, but is out in front, or to the side, of it. With hands folded politely across his stomach, he bends graciously toward the audience as he speaks. The visual aid is to the left (his right), but only the empty cover page is visible.

FIRST FACULTY MEMBER: Ladies and gentlemen. The faculty club is extremely proud to present to you, Dr. *Joe* Young, an extremely fascinating a — . . . man, whose words never fail to provoke the mind to questions that may some day be answered through diligent research. *(looking to his left and extending his arm)* With no further ado, I present to you, Dr. Joseph Young.

Applause. Young walks out. CAMERA moves forward for close shot. As they shake hands, the first faculty member, still smiling, whispers to Young.

FIRST FACULTY MEMBER *(pleading):* Please, nothing graphic. Alumnae are present . . .

The first faculty member walks off stage and off-CAMERA to right. CAMERA follows Young.

YOUNG *(perfectly at ease, though a little pompous):* Honored members of this university! I am here to give you an account of my rise from ape to man. *(turns to the chart and takes up the pointer)* My progress can be divided into three stages . . .

Young lifts up the cover sheet on the visual aid. In large letters, the chart reads simply:

- OCEAN VOYAGE
- VARIETY STAGE
- EDUCATION

Young stands back and looks proudly at the visual aid as he points his pointer at "ocean voyage."

REVERSE ANGLE

Audience is straining to see the chart. Those in the back rows are standing up, squinting, etc. One man pulls out a pair of field glasses. Several people are taking notes.

YOUNG *(off camera):* First, the voyage. The first thought I ever had that I could verbalize in human terms . . .

FROM FRONT AISLE — MED. CLOSE SHOT

YOUNG *(continuing):* was a desire . . . not for what you call freedom . . . but a desire for a *way out,*

DISSOLVE TO:

22. *OCEAN — LONG SHOT — DAY*

A modern transport ship at sea.

YOUNG *(continuing; off camera):* a way out from the excruciatingly

23. *INTERIOR TRANSPORT SHIP MED. SHOT*

In the guts of the ship. Pipes, machinery, etc., abound. A sign reading Boiler Room is on a wall. The sound of engines, etc., is heard. Young, unclothed, his face completely ape-like, is cramped inside a small cage. SEAMEN walk past about their jobs.

YOUNG *(continuing; off camera):* uncomfortable cage in which I found myself.

FIRST SEAMAN *(walking by Young):* How ya doin', ape?

SECOND SEAMAN *(tossing a pebble at Young):* Hi, skipper.

CAMERA FROM YOUNG's POINT OF VIEW

A THIRD and FOURTH SEAMAN enter the boiler room, moving a little surreptitiously. The third seaman is carrying a prominently labeled bottle of whiskey. A FIFTH SEAMAN enters.

THIRD SEAMAN *(to fifth seaman):* Keep an eye out.

FOURTH SEAMAN *(excitedly):* Do you think he'll drink it?

ANOTHER ANGLE

THIRD SEAMAN: Whaddya say, ape?

FOURTH SEAMAN *(scratching):* Fleas again!

As the third seaman takes out his pipe, the fourth seaman spits at Young. Young spits back. Young wipes his face clean; the seaman does not. Saliva can be seen on the fourth seaman's cheek . . . CAMERA follows action.

ANOTHER ANGLE

The third seaman offers his pipe to Young, who takes it, raises it to his mouth, puffs at it, chokes a little, but keeps working at it for a few seconds until the third seaman takes it back. CAMERA follows action.

FOURTH SEAMAN: Not bad for an ape.

The third seaman raises the whiskey bottle.

THIRD SEAMAN *(to Young):* Watch me!

FOURTH SEAMAN: Aw, he can't underst —

THIRD SEAMAN *(still looking at Young):* Watch me!

The third seaman slowly uncorks the bottle, raises it to his lips, drinks, puts the bottle down, and rubs his belly, grinning.

THIRD SEAMAN *(extending his bottle to Young):* Here . . . No, wait. *(to the fourth seaman)* Get me an empty one.

The fifth seaman, having overheard, enters with an empty bottle. He gives it to the fourth seaman, who gives it to Young. Young looks at it curiously. The third seaman again goes through the motions; Young follows him. When the bottle is at Young's lips, he gets sick, makes a choking sound, and throws the bottle away, breaking it. Then he rubs his belly and grins.

FOURTH SEAMAN *(disgusted):* shiii . . .

THIRD SEAMAN: Give him time.

DISSOLVE TO:

24. *INTERIOR TRANSPORT SHIP — MED. SHOT*

Same setting as before. Young in cage.

SHOT FROM YOUNG's POINT OF VIEW

The third and fourth seamen lead the other seamen into the room. They seem in good mood. Most of them have bottles. The third and fourth seamen have the same brand of whiskey as before.

FOURTH SEAMAN *(skeptically to the third):* This is your last chance, Teach. They're unloading him tomorrow.

FIRST SEAMAN: You still playin' with that ape? Shiiit.

ANOTHER ANGLE

THIRD SEAMAN *(to fourth seaman):* Give him your bottle.

FOURTH SEAMAN *(protesting meekly):* But it's almost full.

The third seaman looks at him sharply. The fourth seaman reluctantly hands the bottle to Young.

FOURTH SEAMAN: Okay.

THIRD SEAMAN *(to Young):* Now: follow me.

ANOTHER ANGLE

The third seaman takes his bottle, uncorks it, and drinks. With no hesitation, Young takes his, uncorks it, raises it to his lips and drains it dry. CAMERA follows action.

FIFTH SEAMAN *(wide-eyed):* Look at that!

ANOTHER ANGLE

Cries of amazement from the group. Young casually sets the bottle down, rubs his belly, and grins. The third seaman smiles for the first time. CAMERA follows action.

YOUNG *(crudely, but distinct enough):* Shiiiit, man.

The seamen joyously cheer, jump up and down, etc. Two do a little jig. The third seaman leans back and laughs, grinning from ear to ear.

YOUNG *(narrating; off camera):* And with that short utterance I had broken into the human community. The words, "Listen, he's talking,"

DISSOLVE TO:

25. *INSIDE AUDITORIUM — MED. CLOSE SHOT*

CAMERA point of view from front aisle. Young is off the podium, wiping his forehead with handkerchief.

YOUNG *(continuing):* swept like a soft caress over my sweat-drenched body.

26. *OFF-STAGE AUDITORIUM — CLOSE SHOT*

CAMERA from Young's point of view. Off-stage, the first faculty member is paying little attention to Young. He is sitting on a chair reading a massive tome, "Data: This and That," underlining significant sentences and making notes on three-by-five cards.

YOUNG *(continuing; off camera):* They were good creatures, in spite of everything. But there was no attraction. . . .

The first faculty member yawns, stretches, gets up, and, lighting his pipe, walks down the passageway away from the stage. CAMERA follows him.

YOUNG *(continuing; off camera):* for me in imitating human beings. I had no choice. *(voice grows weaker)* It was either the cage or humanity *(voice fades out over shot 27)*

27. *END OF PASSAGEWAY — MED. CLOSE SHOT*

CAMERA at side of first faculty member, who is standing at a door or window looking out into the square. He stares outside, draws on his pipe. His mouth falls a little open; his eyes widen with curiosity.

28. *CAMPUS SQUARE — MED. LONG SHOT — DAY*

CAMERA at door or window where the faculty member is standing. Across the square, Shostanskislav, Ogg, Marie

Le Fleur, and Ho are approaching the demonstration table. All except Ho are carrying signs, which cannot be read from this distance. The demonstrators are carrying on as before with the same signs. There are still some counter-demonstrators on the near side of the square. The SOUND of the speaker's voice is heard again, though weakly. A 1966 Lincoln convertible approaches the square from the path to the right of the union and pavilion.

SPEAKER *(off camera):* . . . and in the university of the future there will *be* no grades. There will *be* no classes. There will *be* no instructors. There will *be* no texts. Ah, brothers and sisters, education will be but one big . . . long . . . happening.

29. *CAMPUS SQUARE MED. CLOSE SHOT*

CAMERA at center of square, looking toward demonstration table. The demonstrators are pacing back and forth with their signs. They look bored. Shostanskislav, Ogg, and Marie Le Fleur enter CAMERA picture from the left. We still cannot read the signs they are carrying at their sides. Ogg walks up to the demonstrator who is carrying the "Make love, Not war" sign. The demonstrator's expression indicates he is subordinate to and a little afraid of Ogg. With his back roughly to the CAMERA, Ogg raises his right hand, places it against the demonstrator's sign, and forces the sign to the ground as he speaks. As he speaks, Marie Le Fleur is seen standing at the table. With one authoritarian sweep of her hand, she knocks off the handbills and pamphlets the frightened girl was displaying, and replaces them with new ones. The speaker's voice is heard throughout.

OGG *(as he pushes down the sign):* Man, that's *Camp.*

SPEAKER *(off camera; weakly heard):* We demand: abolition of the grading system. We demand: abolition of professorial status. We demand: salary for students.

30. *CAMPUS SQUARE — MED. SHOT*

CAMERA at center of square, looking towards speaker. Ho approaches the speaker.

SPEAKER *(louder):* We demand: the right to establish curriculum. We —

The speaker stops short as he notices Ho. Ho says something to the speaker which we don't hear. Ho makes first a downward motion with his thumb and then an upward, backward motion with the thumb, indicating the speaker is to leave. The speaker walks dejectedly away.

31. *CAMPUS SQUARE — MED. SHOT*

The counter-demonstrators are carrying on as before. The Lincoln convertible enters the picture from the right. It is driven by Jay, the fourth conservative student, who is wearing a huge pair of sunglasses. The car is occupied by several other students. There is a large dollar sign on the front and another on the side of the car. Also in the car are more signs, which are not readable. CAMERA at center square. Auditorium is in the background.

32. *PASSAGEWAY (INSIDE AUD. BLDG.) MED. CLOSE SHOT*

CAMERA at door or window. The first faculty member turns and heads back to his chair off stage. CAMERA follows for a moment.

YOUNG *(off camera; weak):* It was in San Diego . . .

33. *INSIDE AUDITORIUM — MED. CLOSE SHOT*

CAMERA at front aisle. Young is holding his pointer on the second line of the visual aid.

YOUNG *(continuing):* that I saw there were two paths open to me; the zoo or the variety stage.

DISSOLVE TO:

34. *ZOO — MED. SHOT — DAY*

Young is sitting in a spacious cage, with a small rock ledge and a watering hole. A TRAINER enters the cage carrying a whip and a stool. He sets a stool down next to Young. The trainer has a small mustache. He is pompous and sedate, though a little uneasy. CAMERA follows action from front-inside cage.

YOUNG *(off camera; continuing):* Naturally, I chose the latter.

TRAINER *(stepping back from chair; speaks unnaturally):* Well, how are we today?

YOUNG *(as ape in cage):* Fine.

The trainer jerks a little, but not much, indicating this is not new to him, even if still upsetting.

TRAINER *(snapping his fingers):* Sit!

Young goes to the stool and sits down on it in a very

human-like position. Trainer is a little worried. He lays his whip down.

TRAINER: Stand!

Young stands up on the stool.

TRAINER *(worried):* Lie down!

ANOTHER ANGLE

Young obligingly gets off the stool and lies down. He does it easily and looks bored.

CAMERA OPPOSITE CAGE DOOR

The trainer is perspiring and shaking lightly. Behind him, outside the cage, a short, cigar-smoking AGENT and his young ASSISTANT arrive and, standing next to the cage door, watch through the bars.

TRAINER *(shaken):* That's enough for today.

CAMERA AT SIDE OF CAGE, INSIDE — MED. SHOT

The trainer turns to leave. Young walks over and picks up the whip. CAMERA follows action.

YOUNG: Stay!

The trainer turns around, horrified.

YOUNG *(handing the whip to him):* You forgot this.

CLOSE SHOT

The trainer's eyes suggest madness. Perspiring and shaking, he grabs the whip without saying anything and rushes toward the cage door.

35. *OUTSIDE CAGE — MED. CLOSE SHOT*

CAMERA at side of door opposite agent, outside. As the trainer exits, the agent grabs him by the arm. Trainer is startled. CAMERA follows action.

AGENT *(to the trainer):* Hello, again. Just want you to know the deal's closed. I've bought the ape. When can I have him?

TRAINER *(insanely):* Now! Take him away! He's inhuman. I mean, he *is* human! Take the ape!

The agent lets go of the trainer's arm. The trainer runs away howling.

AGENT *(to his assistant):* Have him boxed up and shipped tonight.

YOUNG *(narrating; off camera):* How I learned things! People began

DISSOLVE TO:

36. *INSIDE AUDITORIUM — MED. CLOSE SHOT*

CAMERA at front aisle.

YOUNG *(continuing):* to treat me less and less like a dumb animal and . . .

DISSOLVE TO:

37. *FARM COUNTRY — LONG SHOT — DAY*

A speeding train. Sound of whistle and engine.

YOUNG *(continuing; off camera):* more and more . . .

38. *SMALL TRAIN STATION — MED. CLOSE SHOT — DAY*

Young, now dressed rather snappily, and the agent get off the train.

YOUNG *(continuing; off camera):* like a human being.

39. *TAXI STAND — MED. CLOSE SHOT — DAY*

CAMERA to side of Young and the agent, who are waiting for a taxi. Young is behind the agent. Several groups of NEGROES are waiting, ahead of Young and the agent. A taxi pulls up, passes slowly by the Negroes, and, seeing the agent, stops. The WHITE DRIVER is looking the other way as Young enters and does not notice him.

40. *OUTSIDE HOTEL — MED. CLOSE SHOT — DAY*

The taxi pulls up abruptly to a hotel. Young and the agent exit. The agent pulls out his wallet and extends a dollar bill toward the driver. Without waiting for the dollar, or closing the door, the driver speeds his cab away. Peeling SOUND is heard. CAMERA pans to follow taxi momentarily.

ANOTHER ANGLE

The agent shrugs as he and Young turn to enter the hotel.

41. *INSIDE HOTEL LOBBY — MED. CLOSE SHOT*

CAMERA inside hotel entrance looking toward desk. A well-dressed, dignified-looking NEGRO and his FAMILY are at the desk. The CLERK, facing toward the camera, is shaking his head. As Young and the agent come on CAMERA and approach the desk, the clerk can be heard speaking. He has a strong Southern accent.

CLERK *(frowning, to the Negro):* We simply have no vacancies at this time, at this moment.

The Negro family walk dejectedly away. The clerk spies Young as he and the agent arrive at the desk.

CLERK *(brightening up):* Oh, Mr. Young, sir. We received your telegram. *(obsequiously)* You may have your *choice* of rooms.

42. *INSIDE BURLESQUE HOUSE — MED. CLOSE SHOT*

CAMERA on stage. A small dirty theatre. Except for one man, a football COACH, most of the audience are either old men or wide-eyed kids. The theatre is packed; the crowd is rowdy.

OLD MAN: Ya dumb ape!

CAMERA FROM AUDIENCE POINT OF VIEW

Young, dressed dapperly, is on stage with a scantily-clad, fading BURLESQUE QUEEN, who appears uncomfortable. Young is embracing her. Catcalls of the audience are heard as Young speaks.

YOUNG *(to queen):* Come with me to the forest. I will not take no for an answer.

FIRST VOICE *(as Young speaks):* Put it to her, ape!

SECOND VOICE: Kiss her! Kiss her! Kiss her!

43. *OFF STAGE, BURLESQUE HOUSE*

Young and the queen are off-stage, walking toward the CAMERA. Sound of applause dying down is heard. The agent is waiting for them. He looks worried.

QUEEN *(to agent):* I've had it!

YOUNG *(to agent):* Can't you get me a better writer? I feel like an idiot.

The football coach appears on CAMERA and approaches Young.

COACH *(Ozark or similar accent):* Mr. Young, my name's Buff Granger. I want to talk to you. Let me buy your supper.

Young walks off camera with the coach.

44. *INSIDE RESTAURANT — MED. CLOSE SHOT*

The coach and Young are sitting at a dining table. They have finished eating and are now talking. CANDLE-LIGHT.

CLOSE SHOT — YOUNG'S POINT OF VIEW

COACH *(the hard sell):* With an education, Joe, you can go much further in this world. Southern Nebraska will make you a scholar-athlete. *(aside, to waiter)* Boy, how 'bout some more coffee!

The waiter's black hand is visible as he refills their cups.

COACH: At Southern Nebraska, Joe, you will be treated as an equal. *(smiling candidly)* You *will* be equal . . . *(abruptly):* That is, you will have certain handicaps, at first. Special tutors, of course, will be provided.

ANOTHER ANGLE

COACH: It's a helluva opportunity, Joe, Edjacation . . . book-learnin' . . . human girls . . .

CAMERA profiles the two. The coach pulls a piece of paper and a pen from his pocket and sets them in front of Young.

COACH *(eagerly):* You just sign this letter of intent. Admission is tough, but I'll get you in.

Young signs the paper without hesitation. They rise. The coach extends his hand. They shake.

COACH: Just call me "Coach," Son.

YOUNG *(narrating; off camera):* I jumped at this chance . . .

DISSOLVE TO:

45. *INSIDE AUDITORIUM — MED. CLOSE SHOT*

Young marks the third line of the visual aid with his pointer. CAMERA at front aisle.

YOUNG *(continuing):* for an education.

46. *OFF STAGE AUDITORIUM — MED. CLOSE SHOT*

CAMERA from Young's point of view. The first faculty member gets up again from his book and walks through the passage leading to the door.

YOUNG *(continuing; off camera):* The stage had become only another kind of cage.

47. *END OF PASSAGEWAY — CLOSE SHOT*

CAMERA at door or window. The first faculty member gazes out.

48. *CAMPUS SQUARE — MED. CLOSE SHOT*

CAMERA at center of square, looking toward demonstrators. They are carrying their new signs. One reads, "Drop Trousers, Not Bombs"; another reads, "Scientific Exhibitionism, Yes; Sadistic Militarism, No"; a third reads "Privates, not Generals." The demonstrators are gazing menacingly in the direction of the counter-demonstrators. The SECOND SPEAKER's voice is heard.

SECOND SPEAKER *(off camera):* We cannot submit to the absurd insistence on clothes. We see nothing wrong with objective nudity . . .

REVERSE ANGLE

The counter-demonstrator's signs are now readable. One reads, "Clothes Make the Man — Adam Smith"; another reads, "Stripers, Not Strippers"; a third reads, "Explosions, Not Exposures." They stare menacingly in the direction of the demonstrators. The second speaker's voice is heard.

SECOND SPEAKER *(with righteous indignation; off camera):* We uphold a man's right to appear in public however he wishes. We support free display of the genital area . . .

49. *END OF PASSAGEWAY MED. CLOSE SHOT*

CAMERA at door or window. The first faculty member is watching apprehensively. After a second, he turns to walk back to his chair off-stage.

50. *INSIDE AUDITORIUM — MED. CLOSE SHOT*

CAMERA angle from front aisle.

YOUNG *(to back of room):* Fritz!

Lights go out. Flashing on the screen is a sports promotional film. As the coach narrates, we see a football player throwing passes, kicking, etc.

COACH *(narrating):* So we feel this fine boy will help us out a lot next year.

The film now cuts to shots of Young dressed casually, walking down a campus street carrying a book, then to Young in football gear, except helmet, throwing passes, kicking, etc. Though clumsy, he looks formidable.

COACH *(continuing; slightly apologetic tone):* Our next fine freshman prospect is Joey Young. This fine young . . . lad had little experience on the gridiron, but me and my fine staff feel we kin develop this fine boy into a fine ballplayer.

The film cuts to a shot of Young and several other mesomorphic players dressed in gym shorts. They are facing the camera, arm in arm, smiling.

COACH *(continuing narration):* Young Joe is happy here at ole Southern Nebraska. We treat him just like one of the family.

The film now cuts to a shot of a short, smiling, round-faced player facing the camera in a lineman's stance. His head appears to be bald on top.

COACH *(continuing narration):* Our next fine prospect is Hubert —

YOUNG: Cut!

The film clip dies off. The lights go back on.

YOUNG: Football interfered with my growing interest in books. I gave the game up, supporting myself with an occasional performance,

DISSOLVE TO:

51. *INSIDE LIBRARY — MED. SHOT*

An open library room, whose walls are lined with shelves of books. Young, carrying a large gunny sack, walks up to one shelf of books, extends his arms to either end of a long row of books, and lifts them off the shelf, the books still intact as a row.

YOUNG *(narrating; off camera):* and immersed myself in the academic life . . .

CAMERA pans with Young as, carrying the books, he takes them over to the LIBRARIAN, raises one end of the books and sets the other end on the desk, forming a vertical stack. CAMERA zooms closer. The librarian first looks at the stack in amazement and then at Young. Her face relaxes with a smile of understanding, indicating that this is s.o.p. for Young. She starts taking books off the top of the stack and stamping them, and starts a new stack of stamped books. CAMERA follows action.

52. *INSIDE LIBRARY — MED. CLOSE SHOT*

Same as before, ANOTHER ANGLE. The stack of stamped books is now the high one. As the librarian stamps the last book and stacks it, Young opens his gunny sack, sweeps the books into it, throws the sack over his shoulder, and walks away. CAMERA follows action.

53. *INSIDE SOUTHERN NEBRASKA UNION — MED. SHOT*

Young is sitting alone at a four-place table. His stack of books is on one of the chairs. He has a newspaper; he appears lonely. All the other tables are occupied. Some students are dancing to the SOUND of twist music. Young looks around, and as students pass by, he adjusts the empty chair next to him so that someone might more easily sit down. No one does. He is not snubbed; he simply has no friends. He opens his paper. CAMERA zooms forward as Young appears to be reading something with interest.

CLOSE SHOT

An advertisement for computerized dates, with a questionnaire. Young's hands are visible as he tears out the ad.

54. *SO. NEB. CAMPUS STREET — MED. SHOT — NIGHT*

CAMERA angle from street. Young is walking alone, his sack of books over one shoulder, an envelope in the other hand. As he passes a mailbox, he drops the envelope in it and walks on.

DISSOLVE TO:

55. *INSIDE YOUNG'S STUDENT APT. — MED. SHOT — DAY*

A small, booklined room. A desk, bed, and telephone. A small table under the phone. A window. An open doorway leading to a bath. CAMERA at entrance to room.

REVERSE ANGLE

Young enters his room. He is dressed differently from the last scene. He looks down as he enters, and stoops to pick up two envelopes lying on the floor. He walks over to the desk, sits down, and looks at the envelopes.

CLOSE SHOT

Young's hands are visible as he looks at the envelopes. The first is a letter from a Marine Corps recruiter; Young tosses it away without opening it. The second is from "Computerized Couples, Inc." Young opens it.

56. *INSIDE YOUNG'S APT. — MED. CLOSE SHOT*

Carrying the letter, Young walks over to the telephone, dials.

YOUNG *(into telephone):* Hello. May I speak to Marilyn. . . . *(looking quickly at the letter)* Hapsburg-Jones, please? . . . Well, would you have her call Joe Young at the men's dorm please? Thank you.

Young hangs up. Whistling a light, cheerful tune, with his back to the CAMERA, he undresses completely. The CAMERA follows the hulking, furry mass into the bathroom.

57. *INSIDE SHOWER — MED. SHOT*

CAMERA follows Young from his waist up as he showers. A bar of soap is intermittently visible in one hand as he soaps down. The first time we see the bar of soap, it is huge. Each succeeding time we see it, it is smaller, until the last time, when nothing is left but lather. Young's body is white, completely covered with soap. Young sings "There's Nothing Like a Dame" as he showers. The phone rings just as he finishes rinsing off.

58. *INSIDE YOUNG'S APT. — MED. CLOSE SHOT*

CAMERA at entrance to room. Young emerges from the bathroom with a towel wrapped around his waist. Still wet, he answers the phone.

YOUNG: Hello? Joe Young here.

VOICE *(British accent):* This is Marilyn Hapsburg-Jones — Hapsburg *dash* Jones — I had a message to call —

ANOTHER ANGLE

YOUNG *(nervously):* Yes. I received a notice from Computerized Couples —

VOICE: I know. I just got a copy today. . . . It says here that you are from Africa. . . . Are you *(forced sweetness)* . . . a Negro . . . boy?

YOUNG: Oh . . . no.

CAMERA zooms closer as Young answers. The upper half of his body is visible as he wipes himself dry with his towel.

VOICE *(relieved):* Oh, I just was curious. My cousin's family is from the colonies, too. What a coincidence!

YOUNG *(laughing):* Yes. Do they hunt?

Young finishes drying himself. He picks up a bottle of Jade East and pours some on his upper body.

VOICE: No. Tell me more about yourself . . . Are you on a scholarship?

ANOTHER ANGLE

YOUNG: Oh, no. I don't require assistance.

VOICE *(relieved):* My family's financing my tour of the states, too. I'm glad we're both from . . . good families — Not that . . . I'm a snob, but . . . you know. Well, another coincidence!

Young picks up a comb and runs it through his fur.

YOUNG: Well, I don't . . . Shall I take you for a walk tonight?

VOICE: Fine. Would eight-thirty be all right? I —

YOUNG *(gaily):* Eight-thirty is great. I have your address.

ANOTHER ANGLE

VOICE *(excitedly)*: Great! You know, the way this computer has been so right so far, I think maybe I could, as the Americans say, go *ape* over you. *(laughs)*

YOUNG: Hope so. Well, bye.

VOICE: Yes. Bye-bye.

Young hangs up.

59. *INSIDE YOUNG'S APT. — MED. CLOSE SHOT*

CAMERA by phone. Young, snappily dressed in tie, sport coat, etc., adjusts his tie as he leaves the room, whistling a happy tune. He carries a book with him.

60. *OUTSIDE GIRLS' DORM. — MED. SHOT — NIGHT*

CAMERA on loading zone. As a taxi pulls away, Young walks up to the entrance to the lobby. A GIRL and her DATE pass him from the opposite direction, toward the CAMERA. The couple smile warily at Young. As they approach the CAMERA, the girl speaks to her date.

GIRL: His name is Young, isn't it?

DATE *(frowning)*: Yeah . . . I wish his kind didn't smell so bad.

61. *INSIDE GIRLS' DORMITORY — MED. SHOT*

CAMERA opposite entrance. CAMERA is looking across a waiting room to the entrance. At the desk to the left of the door, several men are waiting for their dates. A woman DESK CLERK is assisting. One couple is leaving. The CAMERA focuses on MARILYN HAPSBURG-JONES and her ROOMMATE, who are sitting in the waiting room. The desk clerk's voice is heard through an intercom as the two girls talk.

DESK CLERK'S VOICE *(over the girls' conversation)*: Miss Louise Williams. You have a caller at the main desk. Miss Louise Williams.

ROOMMATE *(American)*: You say your date's from Africa?

HAPSBURG-JONES: Yes, but I told you, he's not a Negro, *(quickly)* though it wouldn't make any difference. I'm not like American girls, you know.

ROOMMATE: No, I meant . . . Isn't that ape-man one sees running around the library . . . named Young?

Across the room, Young enters and goes up to the desk. The girls do not see him.

HAPSBURG-JONES *(mouth falls open):* I . . . don't . . . know.

ROOMMATE *(giggling):* What would you do?

HAPSBURG-JONES *(worried):* Well, I . . . *(stiffening)* I would, of course, adhere to the principle of equality, as I always have.

DESK CLERK'S VOICE *(tremulously):* Miss Hapsburg-Jones, you have a . . . caller . . . at the main desk. Miss Hapsburg-Jones.

She rises and walks toward the desk.

CAMERA AT YOUNG'S POINT OF VIEW

She walks toward the CAMERA. As she sees Young her eyes widen, her face contorts in horror, her body shakes. Her roommate rushes over as she emits a sort of soft cry. She swoons into her roommate's arms. Young appears in CAMERA's picture as he reaches to help.

ANOTHER ANGLE

The roommate wipes Hapsburg-Jones' forehead with handkerchief. She comes to.

HAPSBURG-JONES *(delirious determination):* I . . . shall . . . continue.

CAMERA at opposite desk, near door. Hapsburg-Jones turns and looks upward at Young in horror.

HAPSBURG-JONES *(barely conquering her horror):* Good evening . . . I'm Marilyn Hapsburg-Jones. You must be . . . Joe. . . . Hi, Joe.

She recovers herself, and walks out toward the door with Young. CAMERA pans right to follow. CAMERA stops at the desk and zooms forward to the desk clerk.

DESK CLERK *(in wonderment):* Them foreign girls just don't have no sense of rectitude.

62. *CAMPUS SIDEWALK — MED. SHOT — NIGHT*

CAMERA in street. Young and his date are walking on opposite sides of a wide sidewalk. Young's date looks at him as if she were afraid he might attack her at any moment. Young is reading his book in the dim light as they walk.

63. *ANOTHER SIDEWALK — MED. CLOSE SHOT — NIGHT*

Hapsburg-Jones has moved a little closer to Young, who is still reading his book as he walks.

HAPSBURG-JONES *(politely):* Joe, what courses are you taking?

Young looks up from his book to answer.

64. *ANOTHER SIDEWALK — MED. CLOSE SHOT — NIGHT*

They are walking side by side now, though not touching. Young carries his book down at his side. CAMERA faces them, backing up ahead of their steps.

HAPSBURG-JONES *(sincerely):* You . . . are quite surprising, Joe.

YOUNG *(embarrassed):* Oh . . . what do you mean?

ANOTHER ANGLE

HAPSBURG-JONES: Well, you're a very serious student, aren't you?

YOUNG *(laughing):* Such a student of mankind the world has never seen!

They both laugh.

65. *BENCH — MED. CLOSE SHOT — NIGHT*

CAMERA faces Young and his date, who are sitting on a bench in a clearing among some trees. MOONLIGHT. She is sitting close to Young, who is at one end of the bench reading his book. She looks at him; she wants his attention.

HAPSBURG-JONES *(softly):* Joe, why don't you put your book down?

Young complies and looks at her. She puts an arm around his neck.

ANOTHER ANGLE

HAPSBURG-JONES: I think I rather like you.

MED. SHOT

She lays her other hand on his chest as she talks. She slips her fingers inside his shirt between buttons. Young remains impassive. Her desire for Young becomes almost uncontrollable. She throws both arms around him and presses her body on him. Young looks uncomfortable and reaches for his book. CAMERA follows action.

HAPSBURG-JONES: Oh, Joe, Joe. Please. I'm not afraid . . . Kiss me, Joe . . . kiss me . . .

She starts climbing all over Young. Young, quite uncomfortable, picks up his book and starts ostensibly reading.

HAPSBURG-JONES *(near-hysterical laugh):* If Mums could see me now! Oh, Joe, hold me . . . Joe . . . don't you want me?

She gets up, backs away from Young. CAMERA follows action.

HAPSBURG-JONES *(shaken):* Beast! *(angrily; backing away)* To think that I deigned to cast my pearls . . . *(starts to cry)* . . . before an *Ape!*

She runs away, broken up.

CLOSE SHOT

Young, standing, looks sadly after her, sits down, and resumes reading his book.

YOUNG *(narrating; off camera):* My one attempt at companionship having failed,

DISSOLVE TO:

66. *INSIDE AUDITORIUM — MED. CLOSE SHOT*

CAMERA in front aisle. As Young speaks, the SOUND of rioting is faintly heard from the outside.

YOUNG *(continuing):* I excluded everything from my life but scholarship . . . *(looks over to his left, where noise is coming from)* As the public began to take a real interest in my progress, as I received scholarships and grants, *(looking again to his left)*

CAMERA AT YOUNG'S POINT OF VIEW

The audience is paying little attention to Young. They are looking to their right in the direction of the SOUND. The SOUND of a police siren is heard.

YOUNG *(continuing; off camera):* I began to engage teachers for myself, establishing them in five communicating rooms, and taking lessons from all at once by leaping from one room to another . . .

67. *OFF-STAGE AUDITORIUM — MED. CLOSE SHOT*

CAMERA at Young's point of view. The first faculty member is sitting up in his chair looking back through the passageway. He is very worried. He looks at his watch. The SOUND of several sirens is now heard. The audience is getting restless and noisy.

YOUNG *(continuing; off camera):* Within a short time, I achieved the cultural level of the average American; a few months later, of the average European; and a few months more, the average Oriental.

68 *INSIDE AUDITORIUM — MED. SHOT*

As Young is winding up his speech, several members of the restless audience get up and hurry out, passing in front of the CAMERA, which is facing Young. Young's voice is barely audible over the SOUND of people getting up and leaving, and the SOUND of the riot and sirens outside.

YOUNG *(continuing):* On the whole, I have achieved what I set out to achieve: a way out. But do not tell me it was not worth it . . .

The first faculty member walks out on to the stage from the right.

YOUNG *(hurrying; trying to make himself heard):* In any case, I am not appealing for any man's verdict! I am only imparting information; I am only making a report. I —

Before Young can finish, the faculty member takes the mike and hurriedly speaks as the crowd disperses.

FIRST FACULTY MEMBER *(shaking Young's hand):* Thank you, Dr. Young, for a most stimulating . . .

They start to leave to the right.

FIRST FACULTY MEMBER *(finishing up):* address.

69 *CAMPUS SQUARE — MED. SHOT — DAY*

CAMERA on pavilion stairs. A general riot is in progress. . . . The demonstrators' table is overturned; the Lincoln convertible is upside down. Signs are flying through the air. Several police cars are parked in the square. The red lights are turning, their sirens SOUNDING. Some POLICEMEN are herding some students into a paddy wagon, but they seem to have no control over the riot, in which even some faculty are participating. Several students and faculty have been, or are being, depantsed. One policeman has lost his trousers. Trousers and skirts are flying through the air; others are trampled on the ground. The whole student body seems to be involved. A THIRD SPEAKER has taken over the mike. His pleading voice is now and then heard throughout this scene.

THIRD SPEAKER: Students . . . *Faculty!* Please . . . Alumni week . . . money . . . the future of our university . . . sabbaticals . . . grants . . . new buildings . . . please cease . . . stop this horseplay . . . please, students . . . alumni week . . .

The CAMERA focuses on the speaker in the distance, across the square. He is mobbed by several men and women, disappears, and reappears, trouserless. The CAMERA pans right to the Auditorium entrance. Young, carrying his briefcase, Fritz, carrying the projector, and the first faculty member emerge from the auditorium.

CAMERA IN AUDITORIUM

As Young, Fritz, and the first faculty member descend the stairs, the CAMERA follows behind. The first faculty member is heard speaking, more or less to himself. A student is descending the stairs within earshot.

FIRST FACULTY MEMBER: Oh dear . . . There goes my three-year, two hundred thousand dollar grant for the study of the Eskimo toenail . . . Oh dear . . . I may have to teach . . .

ANOTHER ANGLE

STUDENT *(pained):* Oh, *dear!*

At the bottom of the stairs, they stop. They shake hands. The first faculty member looks worriedly out toward the rioters.

FIRST FACULTY MEMBER *(hurriedly):* Dr. Young, I'm sorry, I'd *like* to escort you to your car, but there is a meeting . . . Your fee will be mailed . . .

Young silently nods, and he and Fritz start to cross the square toward the path to the right of the pavilion. As Young and Fritz begin to penetrate the rioters, an opening opens magically before them and closes behind them. CAMERA pans and follows their progress from stationary position. None of the rioters notice Young. After they have gone about half-way across the square, the reporter, with his camera, weaves his way through from the opposite direction. He brushes Young, but doesn't see him. After the reporter brushes Young, the CAMERA pans back, following the reporter.

CAMERA BEHIND REPORTER — MED. CLOSE SHOT

The reporter rushes up to the first faculty member, who has started to leave in the other direction.

REPORTER *(yelling; nearly out of breath):* Hey!

The first faculty member turns around.

REPORTER: Where's that ape?

The first faculty member frowns disapprovingly at the word, "ape," but nods in the direction Young left.

FIRST FACULTY MEMBER: Over there.

CAMERA AT KIOSK — MED. SHOT

From top of kiosk, CAMERA spots Young and Fritz emerging unscathed from the rioting onto the path to the right of the union.

REVERSE ANGLE

The reporter is rushing toward the CAMERA, trying to

catch Young. The reporter gets knocked down by one of the rioters, gets up, and weaves through the rioters, getting knocked about some more.

70. *PATH TO RIGHT OF UNION — MED. SHOT*

CAMERA about a third of the way down the path. Fritz and Young approach the car parked at the end of the path. Fritz opens the door for Young and goes around to the driver's seat side. As he enters, and starts up the car, the reporter comes into view from behind the CAMERA. Now pantless, he runs down to the end of the pathway, waving wildly and still carrying his camera. By the time he reaches the road, the car is quite far, though still visible. The reporter lifts his camera and takes a picture, then relaxes.

71. *RESIDENTIAL AREA — MED. SHOT — DAY*

Young's car is moving from right to left down a street lined with middle-class homes. CAMERA moving with Young's car, to the left and a little behind the car. Each house the car passes has a "For Sale" sign on the front lawn. At least one Negro family and at least one white family are outside on their respective lawns packing furniture and other belongings. Young's car stops at the first house without a "For Sale" sign. The next houses beyond Young's also have "For Sale" signs. Young, with briefcase, and Fritz, with his projector, get out of the car.

CAMERA AT CAR — MED. SHOT

Young and Fritz near the door.

72. *INSIDE YOUNG'S HOUSE — MED. CLOSE SHOT*

Young's living room. CAMERA inside door at door's right. CAMERA starts with right side of room, panning right to left. In the far right corner of the room is a television set. A chair is placed in front of the set, facing it. An open doorway is on the far wall leading to the rest of the house. A book-and-liquor cabinet is in the far left corner. Along the left wall, near the cabinet, a chimpanzee is sitting on a chair, chained to one of its legs. The chimp is dressed in a jumper. Next to the middle wall is a table. As the CAMERA pans further left, to the door, it moves out to along right wall. Young and Fritz enter and walk toward the table. CAMERA pans with them.

ANOTHER ANGLE

Fritz lays the projector on the table. Young lays his briefcase on the table and pats the chimp casually on the head. She is very excited now. As Young walks over to the television set to turn it on, Fritz teases the chimp, who slaps him.

ANOTHER ANGLE

FRITZ *(complaining to Young):* Com'on, tell me about that so-called *(sarcastically)* "frightened, insane look of the half-broken animal" she's supposed to have . . . Jesus.

Young is back at the cabinet. As Fritz speaks, he takes a bottle of whiskey down from the cabinet. It is the same brand that was on the ship. He pours some in a glass and walks back over to the chair in front of the television as he answers Fritz.

YOUNG *(low):* Only I can see it.

CAMERA FROM BEHIND TV

Young sits down in the chair, facing the CAMERA.

YOUNG: Fritz, that will be all for today. Goodnight.

FRITZ *(leaving):* Goodnight.

Young sits impassively, takes a sip at his drink, as the Voices of the ANNOUNCER and then the SONGSTRESS are heard from the television set.

ANNOUNCER: The noted educator concluded his testimony by emphasizing the importance of underdeveloped nations modeling their educational systems after ours. Stay tuned for the weather.

SONGSTRESS: Oh, there's something about . . . an aqua-velvet maaaaaaaan . . .

FADE OUT

FOUR: AUTOBIOGRAPHERS, ESSAYISTS, JOURNALISTS

FIRST COMBAT

Charles Coe

The United States has the nuclear weaponry to destroy most of the world. Our scientists send rockets to the moon and the planets. Our doctors stop the human heart, repair it, and start it again. Our children grow taller and stronger with each generation. We live in a highly refined age, an age pointing to the future and calling proudly for all to follow. But with all our technical achievements, with all our social flexibility, with all our smug Twentieth Century sophistication, there are a few things we cannot change. And we are engaging in one of those things today in a place called Vietnam.

If you haven't slogged through the waist-deep mud of a coastal rice paddy, if you haven't looked for an enemy who only identifies himself by shooting at you, if you haven't torn your feet bloody clambering up a mountain a thousand meters high (that didn't show on the maps), if you haven't felt the noonday sun at 125 degrees and gladly drunk green paddy water to keep from going mad, if you haven't done these things, then you will never understand what it was really like. You just weren't there. You are an outsider. You can't know the strange pride that those who were there—who are there—share. It isn't talked about much. It doesn't have to be. If you were there, you know.

There are many ways of being initiated. You may be on patrol and have your daydream about that cold beer shattered by the first terrible crack of an incoming round. You may be talking to a Don or a Bill or a Sarge when a mortar shell explodes—and he doesn't answer any more. You may not know for a long time. You may never know. But for most people initiation comes on the first combat operation.

After it's over you know you'll never be the same. You feel older—much older. Things that were boyishly important scant hours before no longer matter. It's like the first Christmas you knew there was no Santa Claus. Or when you had your first woman. Or when your mother died. You want to cry, but you know you can't. You're different. The world is different. Or maybe you're both different. And you know that for the rest of your life it can never be like it was.

You don't know yet whether what has happened is good or bad, but you know it has happened. . . .

The first combat for the 2nd Battalion of the 1st Marines came at a place called Vung Mu. It was hardly more than a porkchop of sand and scrub brush sticking out from the coast a few miles south of Qui Nhon. Vung Mu doesn't roll off the tongue quite the way that Valley Forge does. Or Shiloh. Or Verdun. Or Iwo Jima. But for the 2nd Battalion it was every bit as significant. For those who died there it was more so.

The time before an amphibious combat assault is a peculiar mixture of exhilaration and solitude. The officers and staff bustle to and from briefings. Maps are issued and probable enemy fortified positions are marked. Operations orders are reviewed for the thousandth time. Everyone has an extra letter to write. Everyone has a special good luck piece to tuck away in his pack or on his dog-tag chain. Clerks scurry about the company areas making sure everyone has his Geneva Conventions card—just in case. You want to talk and joke with your friends. You need them and there are many things you want to say. But talk doesn't seem to come now.

There are questions to ask yourself. Will I do all right? Will I panic and run? What is it like to get shot? Can I really kill a man? I wonder who'll get it? You can't answer them yourself. But they will be answered.

I don't suppose anyone sleeps much before his first combat. Later on you sleep during it and are thankful for those precious moments of rest. But this is before combat. You are still a virgin. You still have ideals. You're dry and you're safe and your belly is full. You have a lot to be thankful for. And you'll tell yourself that many times in the next few days. You wish you'd joined the Navy. You wish you could see your girl—just for five minutes. You wish you could sleep. But someone you ate supper with is not going to come back. And you wonder.

For the first time in your service career no one has to wake you. People start getting up hours before they have to. You take extra care shaving and dressing. It helps, but not much.

By now most of the troops have developed a certain bravado. They have come to terms with their fear and are practicing Shakespeare's advice about brave men dying but once. Most of them have never read *Julius Caesar,* but that doesn't matter. They are the stuff Shakespeare wrote about.

Steak and eggs is the traditional Marine breakfast before a landing. No one feels much like eating now. Your mouth is dry and the food tastes like cotton. Lack of sleep and emotional tension are taking their toll. You'll regret not eating in a few hours. But right now that might as well be in the next century.

You can hear the helicopters warming up on the flight deck.

The carrier trembles slightly as she swings into the wind. The bo'sun's mate snarls into the ship's intercom: "Set condition one alpha." You know you'll soon be ashore.

By this time everything works automatically. Training has taken over. You go through the prescribed routines you have performed dozens of times. By the numbers. It is just as well. Your mind boggles at what is happening.

In the helicopter you keep thinking what it would be like to get shot. You have never seen Vietnam before and you wonder if it is really like all those briefings you got back in the States and on Okinawa. You remember the officers and men who briefed you on their experiences in combat. They seem strange, distant. You wonder if you'll become like them.

Suddenly the helicopter is on the ground and you are out of the hatch and running. Your helmet keeps slipping down the side of your head. You're very conscious of the packstraps cutting into your shoulders. The ground feels strange after so long at sea. Your legs are heavy and you can't move like you want to. It's like the childhood nightmare of having to run in slow motion while the neighborhood monster sprints after you at full speed.

Everyone is shouting and pointing and the sand is soft and you can't get a good foothold. You fall down and curse because you are embarrassed. But no one hears. There are strange faces everywhere and you feel lost because they are all doing something. Or seem to be.

Your company is setting up a perimeter defense and you begin to recognize faces and forms. For the first time you realize your fear doesn't own you any more. The familiar faces, the officers looking at their maps, the sergeants yelling, the muffled gunfire in the distance—you are a part of it. You are suddenly very aware that you have a job to do. And that job is the most important thing in the world at the moment. You know you are being depended upon to get it done. And you know you will. You still haven't answered a lot of these questions, but they are beginning to answer themselves. Answers you can live with.

By noon you are a veteran. You haven't been shot at yet, but you know you'll react all right when it comes. And somehow that is more important than being shot at.

No one in your company has been hit yet. That will come later. You have seen a few bodies wrapped in ponchos being carried back to the CP for evacuation. That is different. You didn't know them. But you will.

The company is moving again. Orders have come down to replace Foxtrot Company on a ridgeline for the night. You move into their defensive positions and joke with them about how soft they are—going back to the CP just when things are beginning to get tough.

You check your foxhole to make sure you have a grenade sump

and that there's room to get all the way down. Someone comes by and talks about clearing fields of fire. You chop some more brush away from your position.

You realize how very tired you are. And hungry. Steak and eggs is just a dream now, and so is that soft rack back on the ship. The water in your canteen tastes of chlorine and metal, but it's still good.

You begin to relax a little. Somebody throws you a C-ration. Ham and limas again, but it doesn't matter. They all taste the same at this point.

It will be dark soon and the man you're sharing the foxhole with—your runner—offers you a cigarette. Your mouth is dry, but you smoke it anyway. You check your magazines to see they are all loaded and handy. One of the battalion staff comes by checking positions. He says to get some sleep now because they never attack until after midnight. You ask about casualties, but no one seems to know. You lean back against the parapet and close your eyes.

You open them a month later and find that a couple of hours have gone by and that it is dark now and very cold. The artillery is firing "H & I" every fifteen minutes or so and the muffled explosions sound miles away. Every now and then one of the destroyers cuts loose with a salvo at an enemy position. Nothing makes quite the same sound as naval gunfire and you jump in spite of yourself.

A machine gun opens up somewhere off to the right and the night is alive with tracers stitching in all directions. You want to fire, but you can't see anything to shoot at. Your runner is crouching down deep in the foxhole. You realize he is more afraid than you. You feel superior. And you feel responsible for him. You reach out and touch his shoulder and squeeze. You wink at him in the dark. He can't see it, but he knows and feels better.

It's quiet again. It must have been a false alarm.

You hear a sentry's challenge in the distance and rifle fire seconds later. For the first time in your life you hear the sharp flat crack of incoming enemy fire. You instinctively duck into the hole and when you look up flares are going off. Everything flickers in a nightmare-green glow.

It takes a few moments for your eyes to adjust. You can make out forms in front of your foxhole. You can't tell where the men leave off and the shadows begin. But you're very aware that they are both coming to you.

You punch the safety off and point your rifle at the shadows. They are about a hundred meters away. You fire three or four rounds and look to see if you have hit anything. But you don't have time to look. The shadows are closer and you can see muzzle flashes and tracers cutting the night. A shadow is throwing a grenade at a foxhole on your left. You point your rifle and empty the magazine. There is a roar as the explosive goes off. The shadow has vanished.

Your own artillery begins a prepared barrage. The shells are landing less than a quarter of a mile away. The ground shakes as they go off and you are vaguely conscious that your ears hurt. You are yelling something at your buddy, but he is too busy firing to pay any attention.

Your hand stings. You burned it by holding the barrel of the rifle while you fired it. But that doesn't matter now. You won. They tried to take your ground, and you beat them off. Your hand begins to swell and pain throbs through it. It is your badge of honor. You accept the discomfort because it reminds you that you won.

Exhilaration is a sometime thing. As the pain in your hand increases you begin to think about whether any of your buddies got it. Your CO comes by checking on casualties and you want to mention your hand. You wonder if you will get a Purple Heart. You think about the stories they will write in the hometown papers. But the CO tells you the third platoon position was overrun and you don't feel much like a Purple Heart any more.

It's a long night. The longest you have ever spent. Nothing more happens. You hear a lot of strange sounds. Once you think you see some more shadows moving toward you, but it's nothing.

Dawn brings more than a new day. It brings a new way of life. As the sun comes up the shadows of the night before become crumpled and twisted caricatures of men sprawled around your area. They look like boys—a lot younger than you are. And the flies come. And the stench. They tried to take your ground. And you won.

You have to bury them. First they are searched, and then a bulldozer scoops a shallow trench and you help to throw them into it.

Your CO sees your swollen hand and sends you back to the battalion aid station for treatment. You see some of your friends who have been wounded. And you see the bodies wrapped in ponchos waiting for helicopters to take them away. The enemy dead don't look so young any more. They just look like enemy dead. And they can't hurt you now. They can't hurt anyone.

You get a tetanus shot and some salve for your hand. You go back to your position as soon as you're released. You are embarrassed by your hand now that you have seen some of the wounded. And you feel sick to your stomach when you look at the bodies—your bodies—neat in their rows.

You survive the rest of the operation. It's all the same. The fear will always be the same—and the frustration—and the anger—and the sorrow. But you are different. You think about that in the helicopter on the way back to the ship. You don't really think about it, you just have an awareness. You can't put the feeling into words. It's like so much about the war—all tied up in personal sensations. You can't explain them. You don't want to. Those who were there will know. And somehow that is all that matters.

LSD ON THE CAMPUS

David L. Bieber

Excerpts from a Series in the Daily Kent Stater

I

They're frocked in pea coats and posh coats, flaring bells and Burgundy jumpers, v-necks and dirty necks, ties and t-shirts.

They're found at the Hub, the Rat, the Frat, the dorm, the superfluously plush new apartments and roach-infested rooms.

They're from New York City, Cleveland, Chicago, Los Angeles via Akron, Boston and obscure areas in between.

They're flipped on LSD, marijuana, dexamil, dexadrine, benzedrine, lighter fluid, catnip, ether, cough syrup, amphetamines, morning glory seeds and hashish. They attain various mental heights.

The common linkage is that all the "theys" are students at Kent State University.

Every student who admitted being "on the take" had stories, drawn both from personal experience and hearsay, of drugs at Kent State.

Paranoia engulfed many. The popular concensus is, as one student said, "The others probably disapprove right now of my even talking to you."

"The others" is a vague term, but suffice it to say that the category is not necessarily limited to the people who supposedly "look the part."

The drug world at Kent State is populated by students of numerous departments, and the popular concept that "it's the artist and actor element," as voiced by one student, is a vague and erroneous generality.

"My roommate's in poly sci and I'm a chemistry major. We know people in art, theatre and philosophy. We either smoke pot (marijuana) or take acid (LSD). Attendance at a pot party has no scholastic prerequisite," a local fraternity man noted.

Within the realm of the major drug in-group on campus, there is, in essence, much interrelation of people of various backgrounds.

To a degree, people meet each other because they look the same, in an arty way. One person may walk up to a total stranger and simply say, "You look like I should know you," and a relationship is generally established. Furthermore, unless a student "pot smoker" or "acid head" is totally self-reliant in obtaining and taking psychedelics, eventually most users on campus get together.

However, even when "copping" from fellow students, there is a unifying bond which eliminates the fear of exposure by "lip-wagging loose talkers."

"The whole scene is much more subtle here than the things one hears and reads about the West Coast," an art major from Cleveland noted.

Other students referred to many campuses far more abandoned in drug indulgence than Kent State.

"I've been to Ohio State and Penn State for week-ends," one coed said, "and it's like open season for heads."

True heads are the most frequent drug users. They report that other universities, especially those in larger cities, are havens for getting what they want without too much difficulty.

The true heads constitute the elite of drug users. For creative, psychological, experimental, or a variety of reasons, they walk the campus almost continually "up." They're usually at an introspective level of drug development, smoking pot or dropping acid privately or among a few mentally compatible friends.

Often, the heads can supply the campus, mainly because they're into the hallucinogens so often themselves.

"I guess I followed the usual pattern for total involvement in the drug scene," one well-known campus head said.

"I first started using pills (dexedrine and benzedrine) nearly two years ago to relieve certain anxieties. When the physiological effects became too great, I passed out of that stage and onto grass (marijuana). I stayed on grass for about a year before moving up to acid," he continued.

"Last winter, when I couldn't find acid around here, I took off for California. Initially, I had mingled thoughts of kicks and fear as I ventured from grass to acid. The kicks aspect has since diminished, and I now look at acid as a form of intellectual expansion."

He said that acid is probably the "hardest yoga of all," because its powers of consciousness expansion are lost when the trip ends. To maintain and further the mental development he has been building, this student takes LSD three or four times a month, and sporadically smokes marijuana.

Another psychedelic regular deals in both marijuana and LSD.

He claims that drugs are difficult to obtain in Kent, but he still manages to obtain for himself and a select group on campus. "I'm not in this for profit, but I'll do a friend a favor," he admitted.

He has been using drugs for several years ("before it became a 'cool' thing to do") and he termed himself a "devoted head."

"I don't want to stop because there's so much to gain," is the recurring theme of the true head.

"I'm at the point where there's no raving, no freaking out and no spouting off about unfamiliar subjects," an introspective acid head explained.

His "highs" on LSD lead him into a world where "things are done in an unforced manner."

He says that latent creative talents such as expressive art work have risen to the surface since his indulgence began. According to him, he also has become aware of and developed deep appreciation for the arts in general, especially music.

The biggest threats to his personal mind expansion are laws which forbid possession and use of various psychedelics. He says, "I may have to move to another society because it's horrible to live here in a constant state of paranoia."

The "new heads" at Kent, who generally fall into the 18-to-22-age category, usually have migrated here for scholastic and psychedelic pursuit from the East, notably New York and Pennsylvania.

Rather than dedicate their lives to drugs like the true heads, the new heads see "turning on" as comparable to going downtown on Friday for an evening of drinking. Their appearance runs the range of Shetland-domed males in suede, leather or army cast-off to ear-exposed fraternity men in blandly traditional attire.

Their female counterparts can be pants-suited and Sassooned, or nondescript and sorority-smiling. The total population of new heads varied with each succeeding interviewee. The student concensus is that 200 new heads on campus is not an unreasonable estimate.

Within their realm is a rapidly expanding cult of "acid heads" or students granting themselves a psychedelic degree and graduating from marijuana to LSD. Most of the new heads are pot probers and have a multitude of reasons for participating in the campus drug subculture.

"I've smoked pot for about a year and look at it as part of growing up in a different sort of way," said a political science major.

"Under favorable conditions, I can isolate and therefore heighten my senses. Pot can be really nice, because I get a chance to groove on my own particular interest in an intensified manner," he explained.

A 22-year-old Clevelander revealed that when she smokes, "I can dig poetry reading or the cracks in the walls, and feel equally refreshed. If I feel like intently listening to music, I can close everything but my ears."

One of the new heads has recently been dabbling in the acid area.

"I've only taken two trips and had both good and bad experiences. The first time, I was in Boston. One of the better revelations was viewing the Charles River at night and watching the skyline lights streak across the sky.

"I could groove on patterns, shadows, lights and sounds much more than I had experienced with pot," he said. "It was like I could see inwardly and view beautiful mosaic patterns of my eyes and all they were witnessing."

One student has become so enthralled with marijuana that he wants to "share it" with all his friends. "I sometimes get a Messiah complex and want to tell the world about the fantastic effects while taking pot."

Other hippies, within the periphery of the artistic in-crowd of Kent, put down the actions and behavior of certain student members of their own subculture.

"Too many of the people taking marijuana around here are clowns," said a disgusted 20-year-old coed from New York.

She claimed that "most people on campus take their grass or acid alone or in the company of friends on week-ends. Others can smoke during the school day, but don't freak out along the way. They can go to class and maintain themselves.

"But there are kids who jump around the Hub like rabbits and make no attempt to conceal the fact that they're flying. I've seen people sitting on the grass in front of the Hub smoking pot like it had been declared legal the day before. I mean, anyone with senses can visualize the scene and smell the smoke," she noted, perturbed.

II

Accessibility to drugs is at a peak when parties take place. The social gatherings of campus drug users may be either planned or spontaneous. Prodigal pot parties are infrequent, and the proverbial "Chinese opium den" type of function is rare.

A Kent pot party is generally attended by no more than four to eight persons. The purpose of the get-together is usually to get high in an unobtrusive manner and then move on to a larger congregation of friends and heads.

"Some parties may be as large as 5 to 20," one student claimed.

The evening usually begins at a downtown bar. Everyone knows each other, and alcohol is not the motivating pleasure.

Therefore, the suggestion is made to make it to someone's place;

it could be a $135-a-month apartment or a $12-a-week slum-potential dwelling.

In any case, it's well removed from the prying pressures of campus officials and Kent cops. The freedom to do whatever comes to mind is the important feature.

If the party is small, the joint is freely passed among the smokers. Should the affair become larger, however, several students will periodically leave for another room, to turn on in private.

One girl, an education major from New York, explained her involvement in several parties.

"The guy I'm dating is a big smoker, and it gets to the point where you keep going to these little parties, and you can't resist smoking. My first experiences weren't too great, mainly because I was frightened to death, fought the stuff, and as a result, had only a slight high.

"I've since been able to cope with pot, and the parties are no longer no-reaction sessions for me," she said.

Some gatherings are for pure fantasy-invoking, mind-wandering experimentation, while others avoid the "kicks" route. If the host is especially paranoiac, pockets and purses are checked to assure nothing dangerous or incriminating is being brought in.

One group of between 50 to 70 students and 10 to 15 professors frequently congregates, but these sessions do not necessarily include pot or acid.

"The profs are very open-minded on a variety of subjects and will freely discuss drugs, if not actually take them," a 21-year-old art major from Cleveland disclosed.

However, a sophomore English major observes, "Some of these parties are like low-budget liquor parties; you bring your own."

An art major who does smoke pot at the larger parties has seen "several profs smoking" and knows of "three who are specifically on acid." She said that "these profs are fairly young and are quite close to the students on a mental and personal level."

Several fraternities in Kent have known pot smokers or acid heads as members. This revelation has come to the attention of independent users on campus because of the frat man's need to cop from the new heads.

Except for a scattered few fraternity men who indulge on a consistent basis, the majority of Greeks partaking can be placed in the classification of "collegiate heads."

"They're goofy people who want to try something once and talk about their big experiences for years. They probably don't even attain a decent high, and nobody, not even the Feds, takes them seriously because they're really nothings," an attractive Kent coed said.

A psychology major also downgraded this type of pseudo-hippie, stating, "They're stupid. So many naive people think all they need to blow up to the sky is a pinch or two puffs. It simply can't happen, and they're only deceiving themselves and being fools in this self-deceptive process.

"However, I would estimate there are just as many straight people (those with the clean-cut collegiate look) on the stuff as arty-appearing heads on this campus. The frat men just don't play up the appearance aspect, and therefore, are overlooked," he said.

III

To some students, drug usage is not a perpetual and pleasurable romp in the poppy fields. And there are psychedelic participants on the Kent campus who have failed to attain a meaningful existence with their drugs.

One student has witnessed one of her closest girl friends plunge into the category of a "crystal head," or persistent user of stimulant pills.

"She has averaged three dexadrine pills daily for the past several months, and can't get up in the morning without at least one," she noted.

Her further commentary included "the pills are as necessary to her as breathing," "she's hooked or she'd stop," and "without a pill at the proper time, she becomes extremely depressed."

While few KSU students are deeply involved in pill participation, pill poppers of various degrees comprise the greatest percentage of users of contraband drugs.

A coed who has smoked marijuana "at least a dozen times this quarter alone" said that one of her friends "sporadically goes up and down" on pills, using various stimulant and depressant pills throughout a 16-hour period.

"Some of the people I know are no better than jokers. They take pills simply to test themselves. They want to experiment and see how many they can take, yet still retain the ability to act straight and maintain themselves," an English major from Cleveland added.

The prolific use of pills during midterm and final exam weeks is often justified by students trying to cope with lengthy book sessions.

"I took dexamil as a freshman and sophomore mainly because of my confused approach to studying," a senior in journalism asserted. "I needed to stay awake and had no other recourse."

Pills are taken mainly for their stimulating powers, which last from 6 to 12 hours. However, as a junior in art warned, "Students taking pills during exams must be wary of coming down during a test.

"I was on pills most of finals week last quarter," she said, "mainly out of necessity to study. Unfortunately too many people, especially freshmen, seem to have the impression that taking pills is a prerequisite for being considered a daring college student. In the back of their minds they seem to be thinking, 'Boy, if my mother ever saw me now!' " she said critically.

Pill popping takes on its most detrimental aspects when the capsules are no longer used intermittently for studying purposes. Indiscriminate use of pills may lead to a persistent reliance on the stimulants and result in a user's using pills as a crutch. Loss of mental and physiological stability is often the price paid for pill dependence.

KSU students often impose self-limiting barriers for a number of reasons. The two most usual restrictions are their inability to cope with certain drugs and/or fear of mental or legal repercussions.

A local acid head denies the existence of hard stuff on campus, pointing to the inability to obtain it in a town as small as Kent.

"Things like heroin require a daily contact and a small fortune to supply and support the habit. Unless a wealthy student is bringing to campus month-long supplies, I'd have to conclude that it simply does not exist here," he declared.

However, the widespread movement toward greater participation in stronger psychedelics is growing. Kent students have been relatively undisturbed in the past year as far as interference from law and scholastic officials is concerned. However, while there have been no recent major arrests, there are indications that the coy cat (police) and mouse (student drug users) game is still operating, but at a low level of intensity.

"Many of the deep-rooted, notorious heads left for the West Coast fall quarter or at the end of last summer. Several of my friends were questioned by the police, who made them nervous enough to leave rather rapidly," one student revealed.

Another local head said that "last year's winter bust by the Feds brought everything to the surface. Now we (student drug users) always see straight-looking strangers who obviously don't belong in our bars and meeting places."

Rumors of Federal attention directed toward heads on campus reached a peak during fall quarter finals week.

"The word was out last December. I remember one night in a downtown bar when everyone became extremely paranoiac, left en masse and stashed all incriminating drugs. But nothing happened because the Feds don't want to come when they're expected," a junior art major revealed.

A female student recalled attending a movie downtown during finals week with a friend who is an instructor. While they sat awaiting the start of the film, they were approached by a man neither had ever seen before.

"I can still remember his exact words: 'I'm giving you and your friends a warning. You'd better be careful about what you do.' He then left abruptly, and believe me, from then on, we've been cautious," she stated.

Local police officials concede that drugs are present on the Kent State campus, but as Roy D. Thompson, Kent chief of police, views the situation, "Activity is slow right now."

"We expect greater frequency of use during spring quarter," he noted. "We're always aware of such campus activities, but our prime interest is the supplier of drugs."

Donald Schwartzmiller, KSU's chief security officer, equated the drug scene to that of unlawful gambling.

"We're continually investigating complaints and rumors about drugs both on and off the campus. However, people who want to do something illegal find ways to get around the law," he said. "We can't totally eliminate drug use on the campus," he concluded, "but we are interested in not allowing it to get out of hand."

PILGRIMAGE TO MECCA

Barbara Jean Savery

An essay on the socio-psychological relationships between the Black Muslim movement and the current crisis in Negro identity.

A Stanford University student was recently advised to take "Negro lessons" by a member of the undergraduate counseling service. Disturbed by her lack of social life and convinced that it was due to her racial status, the student had hoped for some psychological "propping up" from the counselor. Instead, to her surprise, she was told that her lack of social life was due to her failure to parade her Negroness, to act, dress, think, talk like a Negro. The counselor warned her that she was missing out on dates with Negro students because they felt she was trying to be white, suspected that she was "stuck up," that she was not proud of her race, and that further, she was missing out on dates with white students because, by minimizing her Negroness, she was failing to attract those white students—the curiosity seekers—who occasionally "take a Negro to lunch," as they half-humorously style it. "Kink your hair, rub on a little Man Tan, and thicken your accent," advised the counselor.

The information was ill-advised and ill-taken. The student, who happens to be a close friend of the author, was neither willing nor able to take "Negro lessons." She had already finished the course, and her problem—the problem of identity, in both an individual and a racial sense—is a problem shared by almost all of America's 18 million Negroes. James Baldwin called it "facelessness," and once remarked bitterly, "Nobody knows my name." The Negro Stanford student merely complained, "I'm not trying to hide the fact that I'm a Negro, but I'm not going to parade around looking like I'm fresh out of the jungle to prove it either."

The American Negro is seated squarely on the horns of a dilemma of identity. He is both American and Negro and neither one. "American citizenship" implies, almost simultaneously, "whiteness"; it is inseparably associated with white European morals, attitudes, culture, dress, social and religious patterns. The Negro is not white, and hard conks and repeated skin bleachings cannot change the fact that he is black, and that because he is black, he cannot be, will not be allowed to be anything but a second-class American. Neither, however, can he be a Negro. Deprived of his Africanness, of his own black culture, morals, speech, and religion through slavery, the Negro was literally forced to accept the white European culture into which he suddenly found himself injected; he became, culturally, a European. In the larger sense, however, he became a mongrel—a creature in which two diametrically opposed identities were haphazardly wedded. Physically, he remained Negro; culturally, he had become European and, because European culture despised him, he began to despise himself, to hate his Negroness.

Jean Piaget conducted a study of young school children as part of the research for a book entitled *A Child's Conception of the World.* In simple experiments designed to test childhood prejudice, Piaget asked the children to state their preferences in situations in which black and white were alternative choices. Repeatedly, the Negro youngsters chose white. Asked why she chose white, one Negro child answered, "Because white is better." Convinced by a culture that is not their own that they are inferior, most Negroes at least subconsciously reject themselves, reject their Negroness, and seek, almost pathetically, to Europeanize or Americanize themselves—they conk their hair, bleach their skin, invest in the symbols of middle-class white American success and, almost invariably, the results are only a tragic loss of identity because white America does not want them and because, in spite of the Cadillacs, they remain Negro. Thus, the Negro, unable to reconcile the warring African and European elements in his personality, unable to become All-American because society will not allow him to, and unable to become 100 percent Negro because he neither can nor wants to, becomes a No one, a Nobody going Nowhere in a subculture that robs the lives of its members of all meaningfulness.

Historical explanations for the problem of Negro identity are not, of course, lacking. Four hundred years ago, slavery was introduced into the New World and the peculiar American twist given the institution—the "goods and chattels" innovation—greatly facilitated the de-Africanization of those brought to the New World as slaves. Because they were considered property, Negroes were denied much of the consideration accorded more "human" beings, and the division of families and larger tribal groups, forced cohabitation, less than humane physical treatment, and the total physical and psychological subordination of the Negro population to the white "Massahs" became common.

The results were profound and, as we are realizing only today, 400 years later, tragic. Demasculinization of the Negro male, the emergence of a matriarchial sub-culture, and the associated instability of the Negro family structure were results, as was the equally important loss of racial and cultural identity. The products of chattel slavery are readily recognizable in 1967 in the absence of stability and unity in the Negro family and community, in the lack of racial pride, in the sense of rootlessness, and, most importantly, in the lack of identity, in the sense of "namelessness" that pervades Negro society.

The history of the Negro since the promulgation of the Emancipation Proclamation has provided few, if any, solutions for the problems raised under slavery. White prejudices, fostered by the dogmatic assurances of Negro inferiority issued by the slave masters, have been consistently confirmed by the Negro's inability to progress economically or socially, and the Negro's inability to progress has been, of course, functionally related to white prejudice. This impotency, while reinforcing white prejudices, wreaks its worst havoc on the Negro and embroils him in a vicious circle of self-hatred. By failing to make economic progress, the Negro is only proving to himself that all the things the white man is saying about him are true, and so, besides despising himself because he is black, he begins to hate himself for those things that his Negroness implies in white society: stupidity, laziness, irresponsibility, immorality, inability to get and hold a job. The result is apathy. Writes Charles Silberman, "Precisely because they have been acculturated into middle-class values, their inability to climb out of the lower-class slum persuades them that the cards are stacked against them, or reinforces their sense of worthlessness. In either case, the evidence of their lives suggests that there is no use in trying."[1]

The history of the Negro in America since Lincoln has been a disheartening one. North and South, he has been relegated to the back of the line, the back of the bus, given second-class schools, housing, public facilities, and citizenship. Lacking vocational skills when he emerged from slavery, he has been consistently denied the chance to get them by a society that enlisted him to do the necessary jobs that no one else wanted to do: street-sweeping, shoe-shining and, today, if he's lucky, car-washing. The Negro has always been American society's "boy"—stupid, somewhat irresponsible, incapable of holding a steady job, but good enough to do the dirty work.

Good enough for the dirty work, but because he was immoral and dirty and diseased and black, not good enough to live next door, and so the "boy" was segregated from the company of his "betters." The impact of the prolonged segregation forced upon the Negro cannot be over-emphasized. To accept segregation was to accept the thesis of undesirability on which it rested, to concede the assumption of inferiority which accompanies its practice,[2] and the Negro had no alternative other than the acceptance of segregation because there was

1. *Crisis in Black and White,* p. 47.
2. *The Negro Personality,* p. 153.

no possibility for him to protest it; all the conventional social and political avenues of protest were closed to him, if not openly, then indirectly. In the South, he was denied the right to vote; in the North, he was bought by political machines. In the South, he found himself unable to vote; in the North, his vote was manipulated. He was never allowed the realization that his vote was potentially influential, that, voting as a community, he was potentially powerful. The result, again, was apathy, this time of a political nature, and ignorance of identity, this time in a political sense.

The American Negro lives today in a ghetto, separated from the mainstream of American life through his relegation to tenements and shanties, by his relegation to menial work, through his segregation from political activity, and by the consistent denial of his humanity on the part of the non-black population, a denial whose justification he repeatedly confirms to himself. The American Negro is a nobody going nowhere living in a society which hates him and which has made him hate himself. Like Old Man River, he's "tired of livin' " and "skeered of dyin'." Pathetically, all he has found to do is to "jest keep rollin' along."

To ignore the existence of Negro self-help organizations would be, however, a serious oversight. The fact that they have existed at all is an indication that the Negro is not satisfied with merely "rollin' along," and that, given greater opportunities and different circumstances, he would be only too willing and able to change the social and political patterns of Black American society. That the Negro organizations have until so recently failed to play decisive roles in civil rights, failed to create solidarity within the Negro community, and failed to effectively tackle the problem of Negro "facelessness" is, of course, as much an indictment of the Negro community as it is of the white, but it is only too obvious that the failure of the majority of Negro organizations is due to the apathy of the Negro community, and that the apathy is induced almost exclusively by the political and social barriers erected by the white community.

The Negro Church has enjoyed perhaps the longest and most complete support from the colored community. Founded in 1786, the independent Negro Church has, however, played a regrettably passive role in Negro affairs. It has attempted to reconcile the Negro to his status rather than militating for reforms. . . . The intensity of suffering in this life is directly proportional to the intensity of bliss in the next, and the Negro will be walking on clouds "in dem golden slippers," the Church assures, while the white man roasts in hell. This religious Uncle Tomism is not only regrettable, but harmful, and provides a religious sanction for Negro apathy.

Admittedly, there have been more activist Negro groups. Noble Drew Ali, who founded the Moorish-American Science temple in 1913, and attempted to sell an Ethiopian inheritance to the American Negro, made perhaps the first real assault on the Negro identity problem and was an important forerunner of the more militant Black Muslim group. Marcus Garvey, a contemporary of Drew Ali's, formed the Universal Negro Improvement Association and African Communities League on August 1, 1914. Often characterized as a "Back to Africanist," Garvey did not actually advocate a wholesale displacement of American Negroes to Africa, but preached, instead, a philosophy of racial purity and the restoration of colonial Africa as a homeland for Africans at home and abroad. He was convinced that "the Negroes of the world, united together by a consciousness of race and nationality, could become a great and powerful people."[3]

Neither Drew Ali nor Garvey, however, although they enjoyed fleeting periods of real power and commanded, momentarily, the allegiance of fairly large segments of the Negro community, were able to hold the attention of that community for long. The white population was able to successfully ignore both of the self-appointed nationalist leaders, and the lack of response from the white community soon convinced the Negroes of the ghetto that neither of these men would be able to effect radical changes in black status.

Since the 1930's however, several important developments in world and national affairs have precipitated significant changes in Negro attitudes and expectations.

World Wars I and II resulted in the wholesale migration of Negroes from the South to the North where the more casual segregation and more relaxed racial attitudes initiated important changes in the Negro's aspirations and outlook. Allowed to ride in the front of the bus, he decided he didn't want to ride in the back at all. The front seats were more comfortable. Tentatively, he even began dreaming of riding in the driver's seat. "Discontent by itself," Eric Hoffer has written, "does not invariably create a desire for change. Other factors have to be present before discontent turns into dissatisfaction. One of these is a sense of power."[4] The Southern emigrant to the North was tasting power for the first time. He was allowed to vote, to walk into a restaurant and order—and be served, to send his children to school with white youngsters. His appetite was whetted; agitation began to build for the extension of Negro rights. Life in the North showed the Negro what he didn't have, gave him a taste for what seemed just out of reach, made him audacious enough—still dizzy and glorying in his first taste of power—to demand he be given the rights and opportunities he was being denied.

When the white man, surprised and somewhat intimidated by these first displays of Negro belligerence, began granting limited rights

3. *Black Nationalism,* p. 50.
4. *The True Believer,* p. 17.

to the Negro community, and even offering lip service to the "atrocities foisted on the poor American Negro," Negro discontent swelled to a roar. Improved conditions enlarged Negro discontent, precipitated an increase in Negro demands because the Negro began to realize what he didn't have; he began to understand what he was entitled to, began to sense how close he was from having what, by virtue of his American citizenship, was his, and he began to believe that the white community might eventually be forced to give it to him. "Discontent," remarks Hoffer, "is likely to be highest when misery is bearable, when conditions have so improved that an ideal state seems almost within reach."[5] More succinctly, "Our frustration is greater when we have much and want more than when we have nothing and want some."[6] The Negro had some and he began to want more.

The emergence of the African nations after centuries of colonial control was a factor of explosive importance in the development of racial pride and a sense of racial identity in the American Negro. To deny its importance is to deny the obvious. The American Negro community takes tremendous pride in the resurrection of an Africa whose now antedated image as a jungle land of idiot cannibals is being replaced by that of a land of sovereign black nations rapidly forcing the white man out and proving to the world that black men can rule as effectively as white.

The Negro is experiencing a tremendous resurgent pride in his African origin, and simultaneously—and somewhat ominously for the white community—an irrepressible desire to liberate himself as his black brothers in Africa have done. Africa is returning racial identity to the American Negro because Africa is proving that the Negro can be proud of it.

The speed with which the Negro community has sought to identify itself with Africa, and the extremes to which some Negroes go to display their sense of identification are impressive and, occasionally pathetic. A certain Mrs. S., who works in the Stanford Social Research Department, delights in loud African prints, totem earrings, ethnic sandals. She wears her hair "natural." She claims she is proud of being Negro, proud of her African heritage. Negro students who work with her on interview projects in East Palo Alto find her extreme, are embarassed by her attempts to "make like an African." In the search for identity, she has failed to reconcile her Negroness with the fact of her American citizenship; she has gone overboard, she has lost her balance. She has not really found a solution.

More popular with Negro students is Mrs. B. "Me?" she asks, "I'm just a plain old Nigger." She laughs hard, but not too hard. She's active in civil rights, is concerned about Negro apathy. Disgusted with one apathetic slum family she had just interviewed, she once remarked,

5. *The True Believer,* pp. 33, 34.

6. *The Black Muslims in America,* p. 3.

"That's the kind of colored people I've been trying to get away from all my life." Mrs. B. is an "American Negro" trying to shorten her title to "American, period." The emergence of Africa, the sudden boost to sagging Negro self-respect, the appearance of a solution to the confusion of Negro racial and cultural identity have inevitably resulted in some imbalances, in the Africanization of a large number of Negroes. Hopefully, however, the new racial pride and the growing sense of racial and cultural identity will provide the Negro community with a foundation for assuming a more confident American citizenship because the Negro will never achieve a resolution of the identity crisis until he realizes that he is American as well as black and begins to fulfill himself as an American.

The development of a black bourgeoise middle class has exerted a somewhat detrimental counter-influence to that exerted by the liberation of Africa. The most notable result of its development has been the propagation of class consciousness within the Negro community. The Negro community has long been characterized by a homogeneity that existed in none of the other racial or ethnic sub-cultures in the United States. Slightly increased educational and economic opportunities have, however, allowed a small number of able Negroes to advance to white middle-class economic status. These privileged few, rather than retaining their ties with the old primarily lower-class Negro community, have almost consistently sought the society of the white citizenry. The reasons are, of course, clear: they are still trying to be white, and the minute they are economically and socially secure enough to sever their ties with the Negro community—the symbol of their own blackness—they do so.

The psychological effect on the Negro ghetto has been explosive: not only is the white community rejecting them, so too are members of their own racial group. The result is an increased lack of willingness to let those "integrated" Negroes represent their problems and needs to the white man. Lower-class Negroes neither respect nor identify with the "boot-lickers," the sycophants who plead for gradualism and restraint in civil rights, and assure the white man that Negroes are grateful that he is finally condescending to indulge them in a few of the privileges that were their birthright.

Lower-class Negroes either totally ignore or are violently opposed to moderate organizations like the NAACP, feeling that they are selling them out. Often, after sporadic support of such organizations, they leave them totally disillusioned, repulsed by the image of Martin Luther King prostituting his dignity and theirs for the sake of a minor reform that the white man finally tosses them like scraps from a dirty plate. CORE, SNCC, NAACP: the majority of Negroes have no use for them. They are run by a black bourgeoisie that uses them to conceal Negro discontent from the white man and so to preserve its own precarious middle-class status.

Fearing that knowledge of Negro dissatisfaction will turn the white man against them, members of the Negro upper crust deliberately sell their own community out. In so doing, they destroy the claim of Negro moderates to leadership of the black community, and accelerate the ascension of black nationalist groups such as Elijah Muhammed's Black Muslims.

"I charge the white man with being the greatest liar on earth! I charge the white man with being the greatest drunkard on earth. I charge the white man with being the greatest gambler on earth. I charge the white man with being the greatest peace-breaker on earth. I charge the white man with being the greatest robber on earth. I charge the white man with being the greatest deceiver on earth. I charge the white man with being the greatest trouble-maker on earth. . . ." In a play entitled *The Trial,* by Minister Louis X of Boston, the Negro nation fires a volley of charges at the American white man and proceeds to find him guilty on all counts. "Ladies and gentlemen of the jury," roars a Negro attorney, "I ask you to return a verdict of guilty." Returns the jury, "Guilty as charged."

The Muslim Nation has tried, convicted, and hanged the white man. Once styled "the hate that hate produced,"[7] the Black Muslims, under the leadership of the Honorable Elijah Muhammed, have managed to build a nation of 100,000 militantly nationalist Negroes who, united by a common hatred of white America and a professed rejection of white society, are attempting to solve the problems of Negro identity and racial pride under the banner of a somewhat adulterated Muslim. Explains one member of the movement, "All my life I was in darkness, I knew something was lost. . . . I wanted the customs of my people whether they are good, bad, or indifferent. I wanted something to represent what I was. . . . When I first heard the Minister of Muslim declare, 'You are God's chosen people,' it was not new to me. . . . When I got here, I found myself, I found my people."[8]

Author of the movement was a light-skinned self-proclaimed holy man from Mecca who was variously called W. D. Fard, Walli Farrad, Farrad Mohammed, F. Mohammed Ali, or more simply, Professor Fard, and who announced that he had come to save his "Uncle" living in the wilderness of North America. He suddenly appeared in Detroit in 1930, peddling raincoats and silks, and within four years had supposedly recruited 8,000 Negro followers. He soon enlarged the movement to include Chicago, the city which now, dominated by the massive Temple of Muslim #2, serves as the unofficial capital of the black nation.

The initial success of the Muslims was extensive, but it was not

7. Mike Wallace on WNTA-TV Broadcast, New York, July 10. 1959.

8. *Black Nationalism,* p. 110.

unusual. Garvey, Drew Ali, and the Back-to-Abyssinians all drew strong if ephemeral support from the Negro community. Their failure to become more than transitory expressions of Negro discontent was and unfortunately remains characteristic of virtually all Negro organizations that do not receive white support. The Black Muslims, who have continued to enlarge their membership, are an important exception, and to understand them is to gain important insights into the rapidly changing attitudes and social pattern of the American Negro.

Initially, several distinctive features distinguished the Muslims from the more typical Negro organizations, and particularly favorable social and political circumstances assured them a more than usually sympathetic reception in the black community. Fard appeared during the Great Depression, a period which hit the Negro much harder than the white. More importantly, perhaps, he made his initial appeal to a community of Northern Negroes—the most frustrated segment of the American Negro population. Irked by their inability to get more than a taste of the economic and social rights once completely denied them in the South, the Northern Negroes were totally frustrated when the Depression destroyed the minimal progress they had been able to make.

Eric Hoffer has noted that, "The milieu most favorable for the rise and propagation of mass movements is one in which a once compact corporate structure is, for one reason or another, in a state of disintegration."[9] Not only was the black community collapsing, so was the white as well, and for the Negro who had always regarded the white man as somehow impervious, who still endowed him with all the infallibility of the "Massah," the psychological blow was tremendous. The result was panic, and despair born of the evidence that even the white man was failing; if the white man was impotent, how much more impotent was he. The Negro was trapped.

Fard provided a violent panacea. Placing full blame for Negro impotence on the white community of "blue-eyed devils," he made a series of brazen denunciations of the white man. Negroes were admiring, attentive, amazed. Hatred, which often springs more from self-contempt than from a sense of legitimate grievance,[10] was directed at the white man who began to serve as a convenient scapegoat for all Negro woes. The long years of wallowing in the nausea of self-contempt, of segregation, of rights denied, or ego-destroying sycophancy, and the new frustration, the new anger aroused by the small taste of civil rights and economic opportunity he had been given by sob sister liberals in the North began to fulfill themselves in the Negro's readiness to listen to Fard, to concede that the white man was the devil, to hate the white man with a terrifyingly intense passion. Hatred

9. *The True Believer,* p. 45.
10. *The True Believer,* p. 69.

requires an object, a devil; Muslim inherited a ready-made one; the strength of a movement is almost directly proportional to the tangibility of the devil;[11] the white man was nothing if not tangible.

As long as Muslim engendered enough hatred, it was assured of success; a mass movement is most successful when it deliberately fosters and aggravates the frustrations and hatreds of its adherents:[12] by fanning violent emotions, a mass movement assures that its members will not come to terms with themselves,[13] will not be able to resolve their conflicts, will not achieve an equilibrium which would possibly make them psychologically secure enough to leave the movement. The members of the Black Muslim movement do not find themselves able to achieve psychological security outside the movement. Neither, for that matter, do the non-members.

In *Black Nationalism,* Essien Udom describes three basic types of Muslim converts. The first type joins because he wants "to lead a better life"; the second type because he is dissatisfied with the status of "blackness" in America and disgusted with the Negro middle-class exclusiveness and leadership; the third as a reaction to his own emptiness, his own lack of identity, and as part of his conscious search for a political-religious outlet. "They are not," Udom stresses, "fanatics. The choice of the Muslim movement springs from the historical and psychological roots of the Negro's situation and predicament in America."[14]

The typical Muslim convert is a young man from the lower class who has had minimal education and is a first generation Northerner; he is a Negro who feels most acutely the frustrations that being Negro entails in the United States. His masculinity is outraged by a matriarchial family structure and his inability to play the conventional bread-winner role. His membership in the lower class assures that he feels the prejudice of both the white community and the black bourgeoisie most acutely, and so becomes one of the more frustrated members of the Negro ghetto, most plagued by the lack of even an identity to cling to. His recent immigration to the North assures that his frustration is most intense, his awareness of the rights and opportunities which he lacks most acute, having been so recently whetted by his first taste of them in the North. He is the outcast, the misfit, rejected by both white and black societies. He is the man who becomes a Muslim.

One of the more explosive aspects of Muslim is its avowed white hatred and its total rejection of white society. Advocating the complete segregation of the white and Negro races, the Muslims refuse to vote,

11. *The True Believer,* p. 85.
12. *The True Believer,* p. 80.
13. *The True Believer,* p. 80.
14. *Black Nationalism,* p. 96.

conduct as little social and commercial intercourse with the white community as possible, and viciously denounce the Christian religion as a tool of the white power structure used to keep the Negro "down and out." "White Man's Heaven is Black Man's Hell" is the title of a song by Minister Louis X, and Muslims are taught to despise what Muhammed characterized as an Uncle Tom religion that distracts Negro attention and energy from this world to a fairytale Christian heaven that, according to Muslim doctrine, doesn't even exist.

The psychological effect of this brazen rejection of white culture, and condemnation of the white man is to imbue the Negro with a tremendous sense of power and a resurgent confidence in himself; in doing something he has always wanted to do but never before dared, in telling the white man that he hates him, the Negro is daring, for the first time, to be himself. The change in roles from that of a "boot-licking Nigger" to that of an "Asiatic Moslem" who dares tell the white man that he is a "bastard" makes the Negro feel tremendously powerful; he is suddenly the equal of, if not better than, the white man, and the fact that he succeeds in scaring the white community rather than eliciting the usual disinterest or annoyance is a tremendous boost to his ego. He begins to be less afraid, he begins to respect himself.

Although the rejection of white American society may be justifiably characterized as merely the manifestation of withdrawal by a group of psychotically insecure individuals rejected by that society, the Muslim withdrawal provides several important psychological benefits to its members. Withdrawal initially implies that the Muslims no longer consider white standards and expectations applicable to them. This immediately frees them from the censure of white society, and the burden of failure, as measured in the white world, is lifted. More importantly, withdrawal provides Muslims with an opportunity to create their own society, a society in which each member is able to play an active role, to perform some useful function, and in which, among the select company of equals, he can achieve respectable status—an accomplishment which would be prohibited him in the larger white society in which he has repected membership.

Significantly, Muslim status symbols are often identical with those of American society in general. Negroes have so thoroughly internalized American middle-class attitudes that they are unable to apply any other system of success evaluation to themselves. Psychologically, however, as more Muslims become economically buoyant, the fact that they are succeeding even on a white level will provide a boost to the Negro ego; knowing that he is playing by the white man's rules and beating the white man at his own game will tremendously strengthen the pride the Negro takes in himself and force him to positively re-evaluate his own abilities. Similarly, the ability of Muslims to fulfill the white Christian code of morality, the fact that they can compete at a moral level with the white man and even, occasionally, prove to be his moral superior, provides a sense of power and an important increase in self-esteem to Negroes taunted with charges of immorality for hundreds of years.

The primary explanation for the enduring appeal of the Black Muslims lies, however, in the doctrine of Black Supremacy. Breeding half-truths from African history to a rabid racism, the Muslims assure followers that black was the original race, and that the white man is only a black mutation to whom Allah gave control for 6,000 years until the black race should reassert itself.

In a fantastic tale of creation, the Muslims allege that Yakub, a scientist in the old black nation, once discovered that, through mutation, black people could be given brown, red, and yellow complexions. Knowing this, he eventually created the white man, a task which took him over 600 years. Since his intent in creating the white man had been "to make a devil," he and his kind were cast out of Paradise (Asia).[15] According to the Muslim eschatology, "The white is inferior physically and mentally. He is also weak because he was grafted from the black. He is the real 'colored' man, i.e., the deviant from the black color norm. His brain capacity is smaller than that of the black man. The original man is handsomer and his women more beautiful. Black people brought civilization to mankind before the Caucasian race was created. When the black man was at the height of his civilization, white people were living in the caves of Europe after they had been thrown out of Asia."[16]

Although the adroit manipulation of the word "colored" is too obviously name-calling, the implications of the creation story and the dogmatic Black Supremacy of the Muslims are extremely important. The subtle re-orientation of the American Negro to an Africa whose present significance lends credibility to Muslim claims of its glorious past provides a satisfying solution to the problem of lacking cultural and racial identity, and complements the Negro's current inclination to identify with Africa. Too, it reinforces, and, more importantly, justifies, Muslim rejection of white society, and eliminates the lingering temptation to compete consciously in white society on white terms with the inevitable results of frustration and self-contempt. Told that he is better than the white man, the Negro finds it increasingly easy to divorce himself from white society, the greatest source of his frustration; he no longer needs to be ashamed of being black, instead, he is taught, he can be proud, thankful that he is not white.

More important, however, than the solution to the problem of cultural and racial identity is that to the important problem of

15. *Black Nationalism,* p. 150.
16. *Black Nationalism,* p. 151.

individual identity. Acceptance into the Muslim movement is characterized by a "re-birth phenomenon" unique to the movement. The Negro applying is requested to copy a letter stating his readiness to return to his own, and is then granted his "real name" by Elijah Muhammed, the supreme leader, himself. The "slave name" is discarded, the member adopts the Muslim "X" and becomes a member of the world-wide community of Muslims. This internationalism is critical in instilling the new member with a heightened awareness of his own new status and importance. He becomes part of a world-wide confraternity, of a nation bigger and more important, so he's told, than the United States; he has all of Africa and Asia behind him. Psychologically, this facilitates his rejection of white America because he is supposedly becoming part of something far superior. More importantly, however, it provides him with a secure ethnic identity reinforced by Muslim dress, dietetic, and social restrictions.

Entrance into the Muslim Nation is equivalent to total personal renewal. The convert receives a new name, a new racial identity—he is, he is told, Asiatic, not Negro—a new way of life that includes significant changes in the people he associates with, his moral and ethical practices, his dress and diet. Characteristically Negro patterns of dress, morality, eating, and drinking are eliminated by being forbidden; the Negro is divorced from the things that characterized Negroness, from the habits associated with his old life, with an identity connoting inferiority. He becomes, and this is not to be taken lightly, a new man. Perhaps more accurately, he becomes a man for the first time because he begins to know, for the first time in his life, who he is.

Black Muslim builds ego. By demanding rigid observance of moral and ethical standards often ludicrously similar to those of the white middle class, Muslim proves to its members that they can be moral. By strictly encouraging its members to work hard, and by demanding economic self-sufficiency, the Muslims teach members that they can be responsible workers, that they can achieve economic security on their own, that they can be productive members of a society. By reversing the characteristic maternalism of the Negro family, the movement has restored a sense of importance to the Negro male and precipitated the development of a more stable family structure in which the ego demands of all members are more satisfactorily answered.

The secrecy and exclusiveness of the movement—the "dress down" of everyone entering a temple, the fact that no white men are allowed into the movement or into a temple—a heady exercise in discriminating against the white man, and the conviction that he is, often for the first time in his life, superior to someone, to the "blue-eyed devil," provide sources of pride to the Negro. "I don't hate the white man anymore," remarked one Muslim, "I just feel sorry for him."

Support for the slumping black ego is also provided by the close communal solidarity fostered in the Muslim movement. The history of the Negro community has been one of consistent disunity and, often, violent internal dissent. The history of this incompatibility extends to the original slavery situation in which the black men imported from Africa were haphazardly torn from different tribes and thrown together in a strange land under a system that forced them to live together and, eventually, to cling together in misery. However, the fact that the Negro's own community offered then, and continues to offer today, few economic or social rewards, forced the Negro to depend on the white man and white society for whatever recognition he was able to obtain. The result was that the Negro was directed away from rather than into his own society, and that he was competing against members of his own group for crumbs from a white devil against whom all should have united.

The Black Muslim movement promotes Negro solidarity by preaching a doctrine of total social and political separation from the white community, by encouraging Negro economic independence through its "Buy Black" programs, by endowing adherents with membership in a religious community that is all black and international, and by consistently exhorting members to be loyal to one another.

Great emphasis is placed on a Muslim's obligations to his Sisters and Brothers, on his obligations to the Negro community, to the salvation of his ignorant fellow black men. The emphasis on solidarity is an important aspect in the reclamation of Muslim Negroes as individuals, and as a community. Because he is no longer concerned only about himself, but about other Negroes as well, a Negro finds it more important that he succeed, that he become somebody, that he be respectable. No longer does his success or failure affect him alone. The sense of responsibility to save and assist others in the struggle against the white man forces the Muslim to work hard, to remain moral. Simultaneously, however, the knowledge that he is a member of a community that accepts and needs him, that he is a part of a thing larger than himself which is working in his interest gives the Muslim a sense of well-being and confidence.

The sense of self-esteem many Negroes gain through Muslim is partially responsible for the fact that they are better friends. The increased sense of personal worth results in the greater assurance that they have something to offer another person and that he is not interested in them merely because he is "out to get something" from him. The suspicion so often latent in many Negro friendships, the sense of competition to be "most white" are absent in Muslim relationships. The pride in Negroness brings them together where shame in it once forced them to avoid one another, and the heightened sense of identity and self-esteem has released them from the crippling conviction that other members of their race see them merely as stones to step on, as tools to use in a mad race to prove to the white man that they're as good, as white as he is, and that they have no use for "Niggers" either.

Muslim offers the prospect of a better world now. Unlike any previous or present Negro or white civil rights or reform organization, Muslims want changes, reforms, improvements right now. Totally rejecting Christianity and its promise of rewards on the far away Day of Judgment, rejecting the promises of white moderates that gradualism will earn them the improvements they demand, the Muslims preach a fiery doctrine of reform while the living can benefit. "The grave," they warn, "settles it all. It is justice we want."[17]

Explained Minister Lucius X in Chicago, "Heaven is a condition. That condition the white man now has. The Bible teaches that rich people will not go to heaven, yet .the white man continues to amass wealth, but the Negro is to be patient and wait for a reward in heaven. If reward of hell is for the rich, and heaven for the poor, as the Bible says, who is catching hell here and now? It is the Negro. If heaven and hell are conditions, then it follows that Negroes have their hell right here in the United States. The so-called Negroes must get out of this hell now."[18] The demand for immediate changes in Negro conditions attracts Negroes who have spent most or all of their lives enduring indignities because the white community and the black bourgeoisie told them to be patient. The Muslims encourage impatience, which serves as an important source of steam-letting, a safety valve that heightens the self-esteem of the Negro because he feels he is finally powerful enough to get away with saying things he has wanted to say for a long time.

Awkwardly coupled with its emphasis on immediacy of reform is the millenialism of the Muslim movement, but the two in no way contradict one another. The Muslim eschatology teaches that the white man was given a chance to rule for 6,000 years so that the Black Nation would learn to appreciate justice during that time. At the end of that 6,000 years, however, supposedly in 1970, power will be restored to the Black Nation. Thus, Muslims predict the coming of a Golden Age. Muslims do not want to reconcile Negroes to the present, they want to disaffect them from it. Thus, the millenialism complements the demands for immediate reforms because it assures the Negro that he is superior, and encourages him to participate in the building of the Black Nation through Islam.

Black Muslim has elicited violent reactions from all sides of the American community. C. Eric Lincoln accuses them of siding with the disease against the cure,[19] and white moderates have labeled them "Black Nazis." The black bourgeoisie, composed of men like Martin Luther King, has charged the Muslims with seriously threatening the civil rights progress more moderate groups have been able to achieve. The Muslims themselves do not claim to be revolutionaries, as every-

17. *Black Nationalism,* p. 154.
18. *Black Nationalism,* p. 154.
19. *The Black Muslims in America,* p. 253.

thing is under the control of Allah and they are merely participants in a plan he has already laid out. The sanest approach seems to be that by E. U. Essien Udom who explains, "The nation of Islam is important not because it tells whites how bitterly Negroes feel about their present conditions, but for showing the Negro masses 'why' they feel the way they do, 'how' they may get out of their degradation and 'how' they may become self-respecting citizens."[20] The Muslim Nation has proved to the Negro community that Negroes can be moral, economically successful, socially respectable, that, acting in concert, pulling together rather than apart, they can provide one another important support and effect important changes in their conditions themselves. Moreover, as the Muslims become increasingly successful in imparting self-esteem and self-respect to their membership, as individual Muslims become increasingly successful commercially, and as members become more confident, more satisfied with themselves, the movement will inevitably become more conservative.

"The value of a mass movement," writes Eric Hoffer, "lies in the awakening and renovation of stagnant societies."[21] Muslim, in spite of its disturbingly outspoken racism, has and is performing an important role in the liberation of the American Negro and in the restoration of his personal identity and dignity. In making the pilgrimage to Mecca, 100,000 American Negroes have also begun the final pilgrimage from the back of the bus.

BIBLIOGRAPHY

1. *The Negro Personality* by Bertram P. Karon. Springer Publishing Co., New York, 1958.

2. *What the Negro Thinks* by Robert Russa Moton. Doubleday, Doran and Co., New York, 1929.

3. *Crisis in Black and White* by Charles E. Silberman. Vintage Books, New York, 1946.

4. *The Autobiography of Malcolm X* by Malcolm X. Grove Press, New York, 1964.

5. *The True Believer* by Eric Hoffer. Harper and Row, New York, 1951.

6. *Black Nationalism* by E. U. Essien-Udom.

7. *The Black Muslims in America* by C. Eric Lincoln. Beacon Press, Boston, 1961.

8. "The Social Power of the Negro" by James P. Comer. *Scientific American,* April, 1967.

20. *Black Nationalism,* p. 363.
21. *The True Believer,* p. 149.

A ONE-TIME TRIP

Barry Herem

Midnight: I have just swallowed a small white capsule containing approximately 200 micrograms of the drug LSD. A friend of mine from the University of California at Berkeley is with me. He purchased the pill in Berkeley for $6, and is himself a veteran of two "trips." I have set out typewriter and paper to record as much of what happens as possible.

In spite of long preparations, much reading and interviewing, and in spite of my earnest preparations, I now know that I had no idea what was about to take place. I did not—and could not—know that I had dropped a penny in a one-armed bandit that would soon spill overflowing heaps into the lap of my consciousness. But I did know that I was gambling.

As it turned out, I did not produce very much more than a page of type between first swallowing the pill and sleep 22½ hours later. What I wrote during those hours is indented here while the rest is an effort, but only an effort, to explain what I believe happened.

Before taking the pill, I was naturally apprehensive about the possibility of a "bad trip" for I knew that deep-seated horrors sometimes afflict people under the drug's influence. Not only had I read a great deal about LSD, but I had gathered considerable firsthand information from several LSD users. I was aware, therefore, that chances of a highly upsetting experience are diminished when the drug is taken in comfortable and familiar surroundings with at least one trusted friend nearby.

In my case, Ron, an old school friend, acted as my guide. I had just returned from a six-week trip to California and, though I had obtained the pill in Berkeley four weeks before, I wanted to be home in Seattle, Washington, when I took it. Even so, I probably would not have dared to do so if I had not also obtained a powerful sleeping pill from a psychiatrist friend of Ron's. This, I felt, might at least limit the length of a "bad trip," and so I was willing to take the chance.

I never doubted that at least some chance was involved. In strictly realistic terms, I wasn't certain that, if needed, the sleeping pill would work, let alone that the trip would be good, or that the LSD capsule contained a carefully-measured amount of the drug—not certain, that is, in the sense that none of us is ever really sure of anything. But I was convinced that under the circumstances I had taken maximum care. Even so, I barely looked at the pill. I knew myself too well. I swallowed it instantly.

> *2 a.m.: Just found LSD capsule sticking to the collar of my shirt where it was accidentally coughed up just after having taken it two hours ago. We have been waiting in perplexed anticipation for two hours wondering why it hasn't begun to take effect. I have swallowed the pill again now and expect some action soon. God!*

This was hardly funny at the time. For two hours I had fought off sleep interpreting every infinitesimal sting, itch, taste, scent and sound as the beginning of "the experience." Since Ron's trips had taken only 45 minutes to an hour to begin, we agreed that something had gone wrong.

After a thorough search of pants cuffs, pockets and floor, we found the pill stuck to my collar. Now I really had doubts. Was that an omen? Should I go ahead? After all, it was 2 a.m., and the trip was almost guaranteed to last at least 12 hours. That meant the whole day.

At this point I was inclined to give up, but my now-or-never philosophy got the upper hand, and I swallowed my doubts—and the pill—for a second time. Quickly.

> *5:45 a.m.: We got tired of waiting and went to bed at 4:00 a.m. when at 5:30 I was aware that something was happening. Everything is in jags, like peaks—my fingers, these keys and everything about me appears in some way to be associated with mountain vertigo and hiking. I feel at a great distance, looking down on my hands as a part of a mountain range, and this white paper seems like snow, with the type blurring into crevasse lines. I am unable to express it in any other way than to say that everything is "hiking."*

It had started. After three and a half hours it had awakened me and begun. The relationship of everything to mountains and hiking was, on reflection, quite understandable. The day before, Ron and I had just returned from a three-day hike in the North Cascades of northern Washington state. We had camped above a mountain pass and hiked up onto the snowfields of a nearby mountain. The many crevasses we encountered were the first I had ever seen and I found them terrifying.

At the time I took the pill I was living in the peak of a three-story house with sloping walls, and the LSD changed my room into a mountain cabin, and all of the hiking gear (sleeping bags, backpacks, boots, ropes and mess kits) lying around the bedroom loomed nauseatingly larger than life. I walked dizzily down a hall that was a dark crevasse, then into my sloping, somehow mountain-oriented living room. The corners of my desk and bookcase became cliff edges, and the ocher walls changed into the subtle autumn colors of the Alpine slopes of the mountains.

I couldn't get away from that damn mountain and all the hiking. I returned to the bedroom, but couldn't stand the sight of the equipment there and turned the lights out. Ron, who was up now, greatly enjoyed my fixation on hiking. I clearly remember telling him: "I'm so *sick* of hiking. Everything is hiking." He said I had invented a new adjective—and we laughed.

This opening phase couldn't have lasted more than 45 minutes, from 5:30 a.m. to perhaps 6:15. What followed was so unearthly engrossing that it took me at least an hour to focus the energy needed to write the two simple sentences which follow.

> *7:20 a.m.: Everything is beautiful. All the hiking is over.*

I am all but a teetotaler, and with the exception of LSD, I have never had any experience with hallucinations from either drink or drugs. Because I have excellent vision, I was astonished to see the walls begin to change color. The change was not drastic as, say, from red to blue; rather, circles and chips of pastel pinks, blues, greens and yellows emerged from the walls, iridescent and yet harmonious with the wall color.

Soon my attention shifted from the walls to the ceiling. Wrinkles in the white plasterboard began to fuse and change and swell and retract in skeletal formations, as though I could see three-dimensionally into the inmost structure of the ceiling. Noticing every mark and distortion, I thought the ceiling incredibly ugly and wanted to turn away, but, like fire, it fascinated me. When I did manage to turn away and stand up, I found the entire room had changed into a luminously beautiful place. It must have been at this time that I typed, "Everything is beautiful."

I have never read or written a more pregnant sentence. The room had become resplendent. I was relieved by its new beauty, as the "hiking" phase had left me tired and displeased with the room. Now, however, all of the natural reds, yellows and browns of my clothes, the furniture and the walls had blended into a pulsating russet warmth. Everything seemed large and cozy, and I felt especially at home with the blurry, soft reds.

I was coherent and active at this time, though frustrated by how fascinating everything had become and how little time I felt I had to enjoy it all. Small, close-up things did not interest me, only large areas and spaces of room color. I walked around the room many times, turning, looking, turning, lying down on the floor to observe the changing ceiling, getting up again and down again, touching the walls and turning, always smiling, and delighted with the whole effect. At some time during this phase I got hungry and ate a banana and, though it had the usual taste, no banana ever looked better.

Up to now the experience had been entirely visual, and had it ended there I would have been left more than sufficiently awed. But it was far from concluded; in fact, the real esthetic crescendo had only just begun. It began with a chair; a chair I had used during many nights of study and writing, a chair I had picked out of the garage as just a nice, comfortable chair. I clearly remember that it was while lying on my back on the floor that I noticed the chair and picked it up. I turned it upside down and crawled under it.

I found it necessary to entwine myself under, around and in that chair, and as the drug reached its peak, I became physically engrossed in the curving shape of its legs and back. From a very high plane of visual acuteness, I had now moved into an even higher realm of tactile awareness.

At this point in my memory I lose the sequence of events which followed. I was unanchored, drifting in the most intense pleasure of my life. My hands felt puffed and thick with sensitivity. It is strange to write—and will be even stranger to read—but my hands not only felt, they *saw*. Eyes shut, I followed them over the curves of the chair and was enthralled. Whatever they touched drew gorgeous images of multihued circles, gyrating spirals and arabesques, all sequin-bright in torrid blues, reds, and purples. Still the primary pleasure was not in what I envisioned but in a concentrated experience with form, with shape, roundness and curve. My concentration was so intense that for a short time I had the transcendent sensation of *becoming* that chair.

Then, for the first time, I understood the naturalness of sweeping, curving, round proportions in painting, sculpture and architecture. Asian art struck me as particularly natural. In a phantasmagoria of abstract and human shapes, I saw the pattern-on-pattern designs of Persian rugs and saw space filled with round-rumped Indian gods and goddesses, arms and legs flowing with that anatomical Asian grace so admired but little understood by Westerners.

All curving and circular symmetry in art made sense as it never had. I envisioned and reappreciated the roundness of figures by Rubens, Renoir and Michelangelo and some of Saarinen's and Wright's buildings. To say that this preoccupation with art, form and curve was sensual would be to understate it. The room and these hundreds of sensations fell down around me with a voluptuousness that was all but sexual. Images and colors careened warmly through my mind, and my physical reactions were like those of a slow-motion somnambulist.

At some time the chair lost importance, and I stretched out on the floor. I involuntarily threw my hands out to the sides where one of them touched Ron's knee. I was immediately fascinated by the curving kneecap and bones beneath the skin.

I rubbed and plied the knee, allowing it to evoke swirls of sharp color and highly stylized mathematical curves. The knee became many things, all interfused and dissociated: a lump of sun-warmed loam, a ball of clay, a smooth, brown sponge. I moved my hand, first pressing and rubbing it along the floor and then touched his face (he was very patient). His brow became a curving mountain range and my hand a giant thing, drooped over and sweeping along the curve. The eye sockets were immense circular blue pools separated by a mountain ridge, which was his nose.

I slowly drew my left forefinger and thumb to the top of the ridge, and as I did so, it became a slope up to one of the peaks of my psychedelic fantasies. To my touch it was not a nose but a powerfully evocative shape, and when I reached the tip, I slowly, gently and slightly twisted it.

The effect was fabulous. It was as though an enormous battery of stadium lights had been switched on, illuminating the moist floor of a rain forest. In that super-light the shape of the nose appeared as a low forest hump mantled with an exquisite, dewy, jewel-green moss. It was a simple image, yet intensely vivid in its greenness, as if the color had been boiled, steeped and ladled thickly and sparkling onto the forest floor. It was a kaleidoscope green, something from the Land of Oz.

By now it was daylight on a cloudy morning, and I went back into the bedroom to look out at my view of nearby mountains and Seattle's Elliott Bay. The new view was very pleasing. The gray clouds were puffed with swelling shades of lavender, the streets glowed a darker purple and, nearby, an aura of magenta pulsed from the dark leaves of a large maple tree. All of the movement, the swelling and retracting color, happened so swiftly that it tended to keep me off balance. My head wobbled and swung in arcs, and I half-fell, half-dived onto the bed, caressing my soft, green bedspread. It felt and looked like mint-colored fur, as though it had been dusted with powdered opals.

When I returned to the living room, Ron was playing Mozart's Violin Concerto No. 5 in A major (I learned later), and I began swaying to it, turning, eyes closed, smiling, limply moving, seeing colors, colors, colors, crisp in curving shapes that wound and swiveled across my mind. I was in this euphoria when I went to the couch, stretched out on my back and became fascinated with my own legs.

My legs are sound and healthy and they get me where I want to go—but now they were hypnotic pieces of living, flexing anatomy, and I watched them with the kind of awe a young surgeon might feel at his first sight of a human heart uncovered and beating.

They were wonderful legs, symmetrical, flowing with rhythm, and I soon had them moving, pedaling in the air to the sounds of Mozart. Next I brought my arms up, watching them with the legs, like seaweed in a moving sea, swaying to the sound. I had produced my own Fantasia and was beginning to hypnotize and lose myself in that combination of music and motion.

For a few instants I floated, free of the couch, free of the room, and drifting, suspended purely in music and form. As in everything else, the sensation was warm, comfortable and profoundly physical. Music was still playing, as it was most of the time, and though I enjoyed the sound as always, its value became as much visual as auditory. I clearly *saw* the music. It came in undulating curves of color, matching, complementing and interfusing with the tone. I reacted to the music not only visually but also physically, swaying and moving to the waves of sound and color. Everything possessed rhythm.

At all times my reaction to the LSD was athletic; at least I found it impossible to sit still. I kept moving, turning, pushing, pulling, plying, twisting, stretching, swinging my arms, walking about, even writhing on the floor. In fact, I spent so much time rubbing my head on the carpet and the upholstered furniture that a raw spot developed on my chin.

During all this peak time I had been unable to write a word—unable to do anything but enjoy myself. Even so, I thought of writing and even tried a couple of times, but found myself unable to rivet my attention on any goal long enough to achieve it. Carrying out anything planned or contrived was futile. All resolves melted before the enjoyment of the immediate.

Finally, as time passed, I began to move down far enough from the peak of the experience to feel that the power of the drug was centered at the back of my head, just above the neck. The intense, deliberate throbbing was very much like a headache, but a headache of pleasure. In throbs the color gushed and spun through my mind. Although I sensed nothing specifically adverse, I was, for the first time, unnerved by the power I could now feel. It was as though two grappling hooks had caught me beneath the back of my skull and were dragging me through a fun-house of pinwheel colors.

I was the captive of color-hemorrhaging hallucinations. It was beautiful but frighteningly uncontrollable. I realized then, as I do now, that had the drug turned sour, I could have suffered something hideous.

> *12:30 p.m.: The fantastic sensual, tactile, visual beauty is gone now and things have taken their regular shape and form but I am much more pensive . . . still not entirely responsible . . . a bit numb at the back of the head.*

By 11 a.m. the peak of the LSD experience was over. It had lasted for five and a half hours. I had come out of it swiftly and steadily. I felt comfortable, but was nonplussed at having to return from such heights to a state of reality which showed my rooms a mess of misplaced furniture, scattered papers—and the walls only covered with water-base paint after all. I thought the experience was over now, and sat on the floor, smiling reflectively, looking at the cover of a magazine. My mind was drifting, deeply but not sleepily, when I realized with a start that the face on the cover of the magazine was changing shape.

It was a photographed statue of a Roman citizen. While I watched, the man grew older, younger, fat, slender, high and low cheek-boned, heavy-browed, narrow-faced, bearded and clean-shaven. He became a multitude of Romans, a whole forum full. Then I went into the bathroom and looked in the mirror.

A similar thing happened. I became many men, constantly changing, aging, fattening, growing taller, shorter, younger, and on and on. It was entertaining but ultimately took more concentration than I was able to muster. I had no mental discipline. I was in a semi-somnolent stupor, as though I had just awakened from a heavy sleep. The back of my head was no longer the center of pulsing pleasure but of pulsing numbness.

> *3:15 p.m.: Left and back of head and body still numb, but recovering. A lingering interest in shapes, forms, curves, etc. The experience has been overwhelmingly form-centered, with a tremendous preoccupation for all curves, arabesques and natural flow lines, either in the body or in wood. I have spent the entire afternoon so far touching, rubbing, handling and entwining myself around a piece of driftwood. I am hoping that my interest in it will last. My own anatomy (legs, biceps, neck and shoulders and torso) and the natural swirls of the driftwood fascinate me.*

The cloudy morning had turned into a sunny afternoon—perfect for coming home from a trip. The return was comfortable, with a few surprises of its own. As the LSD wore away, I took to an old piece of driftwood which had been lying on the porch for several months. Suddenly, it seemed overwhelmingly sensuous, curvacious, pleasurable. I felt healthy and very warm, quite enraptured with the day, the sun and the driftwood.

I became intensely interested in the driftwood, nuzzling it, leaning on it, constantly lifting, shifting and turning it and arranging myself against it. I traced its cracks and curves with my fingers and pressed it against the back of my head to relieve the numbness there. Periodically the numbness shifted from left to right and back again, taking over whole sides of my body at a time. It was not at all painful, or even intense, just there.

> *7:30 p.m.: We have just returned from a two-hour walk. I can still feel the numbness at the back of my head—the drug's waning effect. I have taken the driftwood everywhere. It is a great solace—reassuring, necessary and wonderfully interesting.*

I slept with the driftwood that night, and slept well. I had spent two hours walking around with it slung across my shoulders, both arms and hands resting on its extending ends. It was dearly essential, like Linus' blanket. I understood it, appreciated it, empathized with it. It was meaningful, pleasure-giving, almost with a warmth of its own. After months of lying on my back porch, it had taken on beauty, and my response to it was not only esthetic but emotional as well. I *liked* it.

By 10:30 that night I was ready for bed. Although I had scarcely slept in 38 hours, I was not sleepy, just tired of being up. After 16 hours the effect of the LSD—the persistent numbness—was keeping me more or less alert. Finally I took a sleeping pill and dozed off and didn't dream. The last vestige of the drug clunked to the floor in the middle of the night when I kicked the driftwood out of bed.

Several months have now passed since that night and yet, today, the experience is still so vivid that I think it can safely be called indelible.

As far as I can tell, LSD did not drive me over any psychological brink, nor has it made me necessarily unhappy with reality. On the whole, I don't seem to have suffered any of the possible bad effects of the drug. Still, I am not interested in taking it again.

I quickly came to that conclusion and have stuck by it. Even a good force, if it is enormous, is frightening. LSD is a colossus. For me it was good, powerfully beautiful and profoundly affirmative—but that doesn't necessarily guarantee the same for a second trip.

It has become almost a matter of common knowledge that LSD never produces the same effects twice, and now, with a knowledge of its power, I am not willing to take another chance. I shudder at the thought of what might have happened if it had been as hideous as it was beautiful—if it had been a nightmare instead of a dream. For all of its superb potentiality, the stubborn fact remains that LSD *has* ruined *some* peoples' lives. For myself, in short, the chance of another meaningful experience is not worth the possibility of a mutilating one.

However, there can be no doubt that LSD has illuminated my life. It has broadened and heightened—"expanded"—if you will—my perceptions. To put it simply, I see more beauty and sense more harmony.

By "beauty" I mean that all of my natural senses have been sharpened—sight, hearing, taste, touch and so on. By "harmony" I mean something which is much more inscrutable, though no less actual, for, beyond my sharpened physical awareness, I have now sensed a kind of relationship between even animate and inanimate things.

I have begun to understand that, in a large sense, the sounds of a Vivaldi concerto are like, or in some way complement, the shape of leaves and the contours of a sea- or landscape. I newly recognize a certain indefinable, rhythmic similarity between the grain in wood and the pores in one's own skin, between the smell of morning and the scent of good food, between the texture of wool and the touch of bark—between, perhaps, even life and death.

I don't expect to very fully define the affirmative contribution that LSD has made to my view of life. Nevertheless I recoil from a second experience and, because of the risks, I refrain from recommending a first one to anyone else.

I gambled and won—but no one knows what might happen to you.

VISION THROUGH A VEIL

Theresa Stephens

The Deputy Directress of Education, wrapped in a white silk sari, was leaning forward on the crescent-curved green couch looking through some papers on her lap. Apa Besarupa and Apa Besakta sat on either side of her.

I glanced around the office crowded with the forty-three women teachers of Sust Raftar Girls School. I imagined that I must have been the only one who did not look bored but then I was still new, I reminded myself. Or—and the thought troubled me—could I interpret the patient, emotionless faces as veiling disinterested minds?

Begum Khudaa, in spite of her awkward massiveness, placed the papers daintily on the coffee table beside the teapot. She looked up and resumed speaking, crackling the words in her throat like sand blowing on tin.

"We must improve our school if we want to progress," she said and looked at me. I agreed with her but I wondered if she agreed with herself. Two weeks were too short a time to make a judgment. I knew that. Still I judged. "And you see here our friend, our Peace Corps Volunteer from America who has left her mother and her father to come and help us improve our school," she said and sealed my tomb with a smile. I had learned already what a terrible thing I had done by leaving my parents. A woman does that only when she marries.

Then she surprised me by asking for my suggestions on "how to improve the school." No, this is not the way, I thought, but I knew that I must say something and this would also give me a chance to find out about the typewriters. They were here; the donators had informed me before I came that they were here. No one in the school seemed to know anything about them, or even care about them. What will be the reaction if I bring it up now I wondered. I decided to dare the risk, though what risk I would be daring I had no idea.

"Ladies," I began and choked back a sour taste in my mouth, "I have been here in Sust Raftar Girls School for two weeks and I am pleased with the enthusiasm of the English teachers with whom I am working. In fact, each teacher here seems to be enthusiastic about her own subject. And so I'm very proud to be part of your school." I paused to appreciate the difference in the shy smiles of the teachers and the cautious smiles of the three leaders on the couch. Or was it the other way around? I looked again, newly bewildered, and concluded that all the smiles were alike, calm, patient, serene and bored.

"Of course I did not come only to teach, I came to learn." My eyes rested on Apa Besakta, the only relief in this still-life painting which I, like an Alice, had walked into. The assistant head mistress was sitting with one foot propped on her other knee, draping her bright yellow and green sari over her plump body like a sheet thrown over a shapeless piece of furniture, and she was chewing something. I fancied I caught amusement in her mischievous eyes, but it was vague and quickly gone, like a mirage behind a breeze-blown veil.

"And because I want to learn, I am asking your advice," I continued in spite of the discouraging thought that perhaps no one was listening. "It is about my role as a business teacher. I understand that my job is to help set up business classes . . ."

"And how are you coming along?" Begum Khudaa asked and startled me.

"I am having trouble recruiting students. We should be getting ten typewriters—new ones—from the Ford Foundation but something has delayed the machines. I think the typewriter will attract students but in the meantime, please advise me on how to handle this situation."

"Let me think on it and we will talk about it later," she said to me and I sat down, clearly dismissed.

For a week I waited and still nothing happened except that I was becoming more and more aware of an almost complete lack of interest in the school on the part of the teachers and administrators. But there *was* an interest and what it was specifically I was yet to determine. I was yet to determine and discover many things; this I sensed, perhaps out of hope of understanding this strange new old world instead of constantly peering at it as through a dark glass or a heavy veil. It was mysterious and very real at the same time, and the reality of ten missing typewriters was a very real mystery at least to me and I was beginning to suspect that it was a mystery only to me. As seemed everything else.

One day I decided that instead of going to the teachers' lounge at the recess break for conversation and tea, I would walk around. Besakta saw me go up the stairs and called to me.

"Where are you going? Come, we are taking tea!"

"I want to see the view from the upstairs veranda," I said.

"Oh yes. Then I will go with you. Have you seen the art room? There are some new displays."

"No, is it open during the break?"

"I have a key," she said and took my hand. I never ceased being embarrassed by this although it was perfectly correct for women to hold hands and men to hold hands though not with each other.

From the second story, we could gaze over the short wall of the veranda and across the whitewashed city.

"It's beautiful from up here, Apa," I said and she stopped chewing her betel nut to grin at me. Or was it an affectionate smile? It was difficult for me to interpret expressions because they all seemed to have a common thread, like multicolored beads on a single strand.

"Come, I will show you the art room," she said and took my hand again.

"What is this room?" I asked, pausing before a closed door.

"The sewing room. But it is not in use. We have a new home economics building now, you know."

"May I see it? Or do you have a key for this room?"

"Oh yes. This key fits all locks," she said and unlocked the door. She pushed it open and I stared at the typewriters.

"Here are the typemachines," she said and entered.

"Yes . . . yes. I see. When did they arrive?"

"Last month," she replied and adjusted the shoulder drape of her sari.

"Last month? Then you knew they were here. But why didn't you tell me?"

"You did not ask me," she declared and examined the one machine that was not in a box. I stared at her and then laughed.

"You are happy?" she asked.

"Oh yes, I can't tell you how happy, but do you know something? There are only six machines. I wonder where the other four are?"

She merely grunted in agreement. There was no doubt about it, there were only six typewriters in this room.

"Do you know where the other four are?" I rephrased my question.

"I don't know," she said, emphasizing the don't. "You will teach me the typemachine?"

"What? Oh yes, of course. Look, these machines in the boxes are only partly assembled. Who put that one together?"

"I don't know," she said again, chewing slowly and now watching me with great interest. Perhaps she was wondering if my temper was as short as my hair and dress.

"Well, there must be an instruction book." I pulled open the drawer in each tiny desk. "Here it is." A small pamphlet lay under some crumpled typing paper. I examined the paper. Someone had typed 'I humbly beg to state' several times but that was all. The book itself was printed in German. "Great," I said. "And all I know is *macht nichts* and *auf wiedersehen*. I'll have to use this typewriter as a model."

Besakta stood and watched me until a student came and asked her to see the headmistress in her office. She left and the girl stayed. My next period was free so I became engrossed in assembling the other typewriters. When I had completed one and sighed with satisfaction, I looked up and saw ten or twelve girls standing shyly by the door watching me. They all wore baggy white trousers, white dresses and red sweaters. White scarves draped over their bosoms and shoulders and some let their long black braids hang over their shoulders in front of them. When I noticed them, they put their scarves over their mouths and giggled. But their shyness abruptly disappeared.

"May we come in, Miss?"

"Yes, come in," I said and smiled. I caught myself wondering what kind of smile I was smiling and immediately censured myself for thinking such ridiculousness. Hadn't these girls just displayed a typically teenage reaction, giggling and acting silly.

"What are you doing, Miss?"

I explained.

"You teach us tip, tip, tip, haa, Miss?"

"Yes, would you like to be in my class?" They assured me they did, and I was happy to get volunteers. Volunteers seem to try harder somehow. Or perhaps they are more trying, they are so full of devoted interest and inexhaustible vigor. I took their names. I wanted to ask them how much of the present school year was remaining—the students were the only ones I hadn't asked—but I did not.

"Do you have a free hour?" I asked, assuming they did if they were here rather than sitting in a classroom.

"Now is our free hour."

"Good. But I can take only six of you until I get more typewriters." I circled the first six names and put brackets around the next four. "Be here tomorrow, okay?"

"We be here tomorrow okay," they said and left chattering.

When school was out for the day, I made my way to the headmistress' office to try and clear up the ridiculous matter of the typewriters.

"Okay, Miss," called a voice from a black-cloaked figure.

"Who are you?" I called back. The figure approached.

"I am Noorjehan."

"Well, lift your veil so I can see you." She did so and I saw that she was one of the girls who had signed the roll for my new typing class.

"No, you're not a 'typical' teenager."

"What, Miss?"

"I'll see you in class tomorrow, Noorjehan."

"Yes, tomorrow," she said and covered her face.

Besarupa's office was open but she was gone. Well, tomorrow, I thought.

The next morning after the national anthem and prayer, I followed Besarupa into her office and told her about the typewriters. "I found six of them," I said.

"Oh, very good," she said and sat down behind her big desk.

"They were in the sewing room, the old one. Will that be my classroom?"

She pulled the drape of her sari from off her head and smiled at me. "Yes. Is it suitable to you?"

"Yes, it is, but I'm worried about four missing typewriters. Should I write to the Ford Foundation office and ask if they are coming?"

She had been shuffling the papers on her desk and now she looked up at me. "No, I don't think that is necessary. They must be here someplace." Her phone rang so I left the office feeling puzzled. What did she mean by that?

Not one of the six girls showed up for the typing class. I had brought paper and a keyboard chart I had spent hours preparing—but no students. Some new girls wandered in and asked to join the class.

"Come back Monday," I told them, not as inspired at their interest as I was with the first group. "If my other students don't come, then I'll write your names in their places."

The morrow came but the girls still did not. I sat alone in the classroom for half the period and then dejectedly walked out to the veranda. It was Friday, the Muslim Sabbath, and school would close at noon. It was now eleven o'clock. I leaned on the wall and looked down at the garden. The circular fountain sprayed beads of water into the shimmering pool, and as I gazed through the vaporous veil in that bewilderingly beautiful moment, I felt even myself momentarily transformed like a bead of water flung through the air and finally falling back into the comfortable water.

The lawn wore tinges of winter yellow but that was the only sign of the season. Bright peach, pink and red roses blushed shyly under the bold gaze of the aggressive desert sun, and lining the high wall of the secluded school compound were mango trees and broad-leaved banana plants and *raat-ki-raanii* vines. *Raat-ki-raanii,* queen of night—those sweet-scented white blossoms that the students who roomed in the hostel would pick in the evenings and bring to me in small bouquets. There are enough pleasant things in life, I sighed to myself, and turned around startled to find myself looking into a classroom. Some of the girls nearest the wide door had been watching me.

One girl I recognized as one of the six. . . . But she had told me this was her free period. I looked closer and recognized another girl. The teacher was sitting on a chair on a platform and reading from a thick paperback book. I realized then that I was causing a distraction as all the girls who could see me were now staring and smiling. I walked back to my classroom and picked up the textbook and visual aids for my next class and on my way down the stairs I thought about what had just happened. Would I ever reach the stage when things would begin making sense to me?

My next class was entirely absent, and I finally accepted the fact that I would have no students during that period either. Wearily, I made my way around the lawn to the headmistress' office only to find that she was not there. Her car was still parked by the gate but I did not look for her because through the open door behind her desk looking out into the playground, I discovered my English students playing volleyball across a drooping net. There was no organization to their game, I observed sadly, and there was no physical education teacher about to instruct them. I decided to go out to them but I had to use another door as steps had never been built from this one.

"Come, Miss, teach us to play!" one of the girls called when she saw me.

"Is this your physical training period?" I asked as they surrounded me like curious and loving but larger Lilliputians.

"Yes, Miss, p.t." replied another girl.

"Then where is your teacher?"

"We don't know, Miss. Please you be our teacher."

"Well, I am your teacher and this is our English period, isn't it?"

"No, Miss, on Friday we have p.t."

"But you didn't have p.t. last Friday."

They looked at each other as if as equally puzzled as I was. A lovely almond-eyed girl then replied, "Apa was sick last Friday."

"Oh. Then perhaps she is sick today," I pursued.

"No, Miss, she is here."

"I give up," I muttered and stared over their heads at the high wall enclosing all of us.

"What, Miss?"

"Nothing. Give me the ball." It needed air badly and I decided to take care of that after school as well as attend to some other matters.

When the bell clanged loudly dismissing school, I hurried back to Besarupa's office hoping I would catch her before she left. She had just covered her head with her sari when I entered the door.

"Apa Besarupa, may I speak with you?"

"Yes, of course," she said and smiled vaguely.

"Well I have four questions and I'll try to ask them quickly as I see you're getting ready to go."

"There is no hurry. Time is no matter," she replied, though it was apparent to me that her philosophy had been somewhat corrupted by Western influence. I wanted to sit but she did not suggest it and I proceeded to speak under the pressure of not wanting to be heard.

"Some students signed a roll for my fourth period typing class saying that was their free period but—"

"No students have free periods. They have eight periods and eight subjects."

That was the most logical thing she had ever said to me. I felt I was getting somewhere. "Then how could they come to me Wednesday and tell me their fourth period was free?"

"Perhaps their teacher was absent," she said and smiled patiently. The thought struck me that patience was, must be, the thread, the single strand and the beads were merely sub-categories of patience. And what was the classification of her patient smile. Boredom? Was she patiently putting up with an uninteresting situation. . . . I had to admit that I still did not understand for I was trying to calculate and judge on the basis of my own understanding which, I concluded, must be inadequate.

"I see. Then there is no use in trying to start my typing classes until the next school year begins?"

"You may teach to those students with free periods."

"But . . ." I caught myself; there was a semantic problem here. "Do you mean that when teachers are absent, their students may come to me for typing lessons?"

"Yes. Is that suitable to you?"

I looked at her and wondered if she was just making up words. Surely she didn't believe that she had just given me sound advice. "No, Apa. How can I teach effectively," I reasoned, "if I can't depend on regular students?" I was losing patience and the small remaining amount of respect I had had for Besarupa. Then she spoke and what she said humbled me.

"Don't worry. You must now allow many students to come to you so you may develop their interest and then select those who do best and show the most interest.

"You mustn't forget that this is a new subject for our girls, and, yes, even undesirable from our point of view. Many parents will object, for only men work in offices, you know. But there are higher authorities who insist that we introduce the subject, so do what you can with it."

Do what you can . . . how sad and lovely . . . and lonely. I looked anew at this woman whose very modesty of dress and speech and graciousness hung on in spite of a changing world and in the contrast was made more beautiful, like an old and precious locket lying on the smooth shiny surface of a modern dresser. And to her, I was an agent of the change. I had come in the sweep of a cold West wind to huff and puff and blow down everything old and to whip and swirl and efficiently build up everything new. She did not accept it nor did she reject it. She did a much rarer thing: she simply acknowledged it.

"There are some other matters?" she asked.

"Yes," I said, still pondering this new thought. "But may I speak to you about them tomorrow?"

"Yes, if you wish."

"Thank you," I said and walked slowly to the green-curtained door leading to the garden. I stood there thinking and watching the old gardener in his worn coat and ragged, red turban meander through the flowers. He looked up and saw me and grinned shyly like a little boy. Then he took something from his coat pocket and expertly snipped a rose from its stem. I watched him limp slowly toward me, tenderly holding up the flower.

"Shukriiaa," I said taking the delicate rose from his gnarled fingers. *"Bahot shukriiaa."*

So here was something else new. Something more delicate and beautiful than the flower itself. A new smile. A new intent. He turned without saying a word and resumed meandering in his garden.

I glanced at the small building at the end of the garden, the clerk's office. Then I remembered the typewriters and it suddenly came to me that I had missed something and as I hurried toward the building, I felt foolish that it hadn't occurred to me before.

"Hello, may I come in?" I asked as I waited before the mat hanging in the doorway. A voice replied and I pushed the curtain and entered.

A man of about thirty with a high forehead and a strong jaw sat behind a desk cluttered with folders, papers, carbons, pencils, pens, ink, a stapler, some stamps and one of the missing typewriters. He stared at me and his face was without expression, like a bronze statue that had been placed there centuries ago and would remain for centuries more. Then suddenly the statue pushed back his chair and stood up.

"Yes, come in, come in!"

"Thank you. I thought you might be able to help me . . ."

"Please sit down," he said pointing to a large wicker chair. The room was so small that there really was not space for the awkward armchair. Unpolished wood cabinets with glass doors stood against the wall behind him and ancient tattered booklets were stuffed into them from the floor to the ceiling. A light bulb hung from a cord in the ceiling giving off a dim, inadequate glow.

"Do you find life comfortable in Takliif?" he asked.

I looked directly at him. He was smiling. Patiently, cautiously. "Yes, I find life quite comfortable. And very interesting," I added. I then proceeded to explain the reason for my visit. He listened. When he replied, it was without hesitation and without guilt.

"As you can see, we are using one of the typemachines. Yes, I assembled the one machine you found and please excuse me for not assembling the others for I have been very busy; this is the end of the school year and there is much to do. Our old typemachine is broken and it is necessary for us to use this one."

"You have an assistant?"

"Yes, he has gone to the mosque."

So that was why Besarupa had been in such a hurry to leave. She said her prayers at this time.

"Have you sent your typewriter to be repaired?" I asked.

"No, it is back here on the floor. I will call a repairman."

Will call. That meant he probably hadn't intended to at all and this annoyed me. "And the other three machines?"

At this he hesitated and I knew before he answered. "Two are with Begum Khudaa, Deputy Directress of Education, and one is with the Inspectress of Girls Schools." He stressed their titles, I noticed.

"But why?"

"They have need of them," he said simply.

"But I must have them for my students. There are many girls who want to join the typing class."

"Six typemachines are enough, I think."

"You have no right to assume that!"

"Madam, I have every right. What you have come here to do is perhaps very admirable in your country but here it is not good."

"Do you think I will corrupt the girls or are you afraid they will take away your job?" I asked, trying in vain to remain calm.

"I know what has happened in your country. Men and women work in the same confined areas . . ."

"Oh! You've been seeing too much of Hollywood's version. What is Begum Khudaa's office number?" I asked before the argument went any further. He told me, and I dialed the number but she was not in her office.

"Do you know her home phone number?" I asked and before he could answer, I renewed the argument. "What about Begum Khudaa? She is a woman who works in an office!"

"Begum Khudaa is a very big personality and highly respected."

"Oh, but she's suspect. Working with men in the same confined area! God help her. What is her number?"

Her husband answered and said she was at the Girls College but would be home in an hour. I should come to the house, he said.

Later, on the way over, as I passed through herds of water buffalo, naked children, cyclists and noisy vendors, I began to feel uneasy. I had just drowned my anger in three cups of tea before leaving the gate of the school, then feeling calm with the conviction that I was doing something that had to be done. Now I was wondering why it had to be done at all, why I had to ask the boss of my boss to return property of the school.

Then I saw the house. Several children were playing on the doorstep and I assumed they belonged to the servants but when they saw me and scurried to their unattended carts of fruit, I realized they were vendors. The house, a tall, one-story, yellow-red brick structure with a flat roof, stood directly on the street corner. The barred windows were closed from within by small wooden shutters.

I knocked and an old woman let me in and asked me to sit in the small waiting room. I seated myself on the comfortable divan opposite a large desk on which sat another of the missing typewriters.

"Hello!"

"Hello, Begum Khudaa," I said remembering to stand. She was not wearing a sari but a dress and trouser combination. "I hope I'm not disturbing you."

"How could you disturb me when I've asked you so many times to come and this is but your first visit. Will you take tea?"

"Oh no, thank you. I just had tea before I came." Somehow I felt that we were playing a game and that I was already the loser. She no doubt knew why I had come yet she had seen no reason to dispose of the typewriter.

"Then something cold. The walk must have made you thirsty. Or did you come by rickshaw?"

"I walked.'

"I thought so. I hear reports that you enjoy walking here and there." She called the old woman who had answered the door and spoke to her. I was thinking about what she had just said, 'walking here and there' . . . another indecent thing for a woman to do unless she was with a group of women. And I did it. I wanted to explain that I couldn't help being curious about this city that was to be my home for nearly two years.

"Begum Khudaa, I came to ask you about some typewriters you borrowed . . ." She continued to smile in a very calm and unperturbed way. I continued my speech. "Only six of the ten machines are in my classroom. One is in the clerk's office and I understand that you and the Inspectress of Girls Schools have the other three. Now that I've begun a typing class, all of the machines are needed in the classroom."

"Yes, as you see I have one here. The second one is in my office where there is also a great need for it." She handed me a glass of rose water "sherbat" which the servant had just brought in and I took a small drink.

I was beginning to understand something new. I thought she had done something wrong, she felt she had done nothing wrong. Her reasoning became clear. The typewriters had been given to the school; therefore, they belong to the school. She was Deputy Directress of Education; therefore, the school belonged to her. And therefore, the typewriters belonged to her.

"I think it was useless for me to come to Takliif," I finally said.

"No. You had to come. And now that you are here, you must understand your limitations."

"What do you mean?"

"I mean your position in relation to everyone else here, to your subordinates, your peers and your superiors."

"And our relationship in particular?"

"That is one."

"The most important one?" I pursued.

"If you expect cooperation." Her face was a mask of stone, impenetrable and immovable, set.

"I respect your ideals."

"Don't speak to me of ideals! Are you an ambassador for a nation of high morals?"

"Begum Khudaa," I said standing up, "I don't want your 'cooperation' under these terms. But I do want the typewriters and if I don't get them in one week, the Ford Foundation will know about it!"

She glared at me and I knew that she was weighing the consequences. This sudden knowledge that I had penetrated the mind of the unmoved mover momentarily shocked me.

"You are a very bold young woman," she said finally. "You can afford to be, as an unpaid foreigner. Financially you have nothing to lose by your insolence. You can't even lose your job. Otherwise, little ambassador, you have just lost everything." With that, she stood up and left the room.

I let myself out of the house and walked slowly along the street, feeling empty and bewildered. Oh, I had failed so beautifully. Surely no one could fail better than I had just failed.

"Selaam aaleekum, Miss, kaesee hal hae?"

"I don't understand," I said confronted by a host of black ghosts. If they wanted to talk they could do me the courtesy of showing their faces.

"Ah, but you do understand. And don't you know who I am?"

"How can I when you're so well hidden?"

"My *burka!*" she laughed. "I have never considered it to be a strange garment though it must be to you."

"I'm getting used to it. Now who are you, for heaven's sake?"

"Your mood is off! I am sorry. Look, I am removing two veils from my face but no more for there are men nearby. Now who am I?"

I squinted my eyes and examined the vague outline behind the gray shadow. "Rashida! Why are you playing games with me?" I demanded half amused but still half annoyed.

"I feel bad that you didn't recognize my voice. Every day we teach together and—"

"Almost every day," I corrected. "Some days you drink tea in the lounge."

"That is my bad habit," she apologized. "And you do not like my *burka?*"

"No, not yet."

"I like your answer! But someday, you know, we will be like you."

"That may be sad," I said.

"Yes, because by then you'll be somebody else."

I stared oddly at her as she replaced the two veils and said goodby.

"Yes," I said. "I'll see you tomorrow."

SAN FRANCISCO: SUNDIAL BY THE SEA

Chris Dickon

The Pacific Ocean comes in from the misted west, beyond the breakers, beyond the beach. To the east of the beach is a desolate penny arcade which stretches for blocks along the ocean, and farther east are the flatlands of the city. On a quiet, late afternoon, the beach is nearly deserted and those few of its visitors are fully clothed: dresses and hats. A few hold their shoes in their hands.

Behind the penny arcade and next to a motionless carousel sits the Geary Avenue bus at the end of its line. The bus moves slowly through this city of hills and mist, this romantic city of the American West. The streets of low, stucco houses become boring to its passengers. The bus swelters in an awkward October heat. The bus is noisy. It moves in its own gritty atmosphere. Turning a corner, it blows a shrill staccato horn to clear the way. It seems to stop at every other street, to make no progress on its journey east. Its passengers fall asleep. . . .

It is the fashion these days to speak of San Francisco as the new American city, the New York of the West. The idea is a good attempt, but it fails. Perspectives of San Francisco do not come together. Whereas in the middle of Manhattan Island there is Central Park, there seems to be a gaping hole in the middle of San Francisco; a dull gray zone of something not there, perhaps simply an absence of urban *élan,* but probably something more. The Geary Avenue bus goes from a motionless carousel on the Pacific all the way down the peninsula to the East Bay bus terminal; but completed, the trip leaves one with a sense that it has not been completed, that some corner has not been turned, or that some part of the natural succession of things has not been seen.

At the East Bay terminal, which seems to be the end of the line for all manner of bus and trolley, the people conclude their day and go away. Perhaps in the same direction from which others have come, perhaps to Oakland or Berkeley. And so the sun begins to set in the West, but the sunlight casts a disturbing color on the city. It is yellow, but an old yellow like the yellow which makes the pages of an old book brittle, or the skin of a very old man deathly. The city becomes old. The trolley cars protest their age against the otherwise quiet hum of dusk. The long avenues do not seem to fade away in perspective so much as to crumble away in the distance or to disappear under a strange illusion of desolation as if the children had grown up and gone away and left the elderly to contemplate their uselessness. The sun sets as if on the end of an age.

It strikes one that all the pictures one can remember seeing of this city have looked old, anachronistic. One wonders what truth the pictures hold. It is a mystery. The sun has set the same light on New York, but never, it seems, so morbidly. The streets of New York have been empty, lonely perhaps, but not so desolate. And whereas the airs above most of our cities are heavy with the haze of waste and dirt, the dusk of San Francisco holds something different. It brings down upon the structures of the city something worse—something unknown. Perspective of the city, once a tool of observation, seems able to turn on its beholder, to become a personal threat. There begin the makings of an existential dilemma, a threat to being; some ineffable thing not present, a premature death. There is a deception in the air, a Wildean fiction of a thing which has escaped its truth and left it locked in the attic with the artifacts of its youth. It is an enigma, not exactly bothersome; one is used to the small enigmas presented in his environment, but it is a mystery, nonetheless. The dusk hangs just above the flatlands of the city and the hills rise just above the dusk. A cable car breaks the surface.

From a hotel window atop Nob Hill one looks across the city. The building tops form a stairway down one hill and up another. The bridges are strung across the bay to a land which seems far away. Men walk about, their bodies bent forward to the hill, backward to its quick descent. Seen from above, the dusk consumes the air, and the city, viewed from the distance of height, becomes miniaturized, its features ill-defined in the haze.

Another window atop the hill. One sees only across the street, a tree which does not grow down a hill and a roof which does not decline away beneath. From this window the land levels into a plain. One sees no sky beneath him. A bird takes flight from a windowsill to a roof ledge, not wanting to stay too long in the air, as if its wings were weighted with the dusk. Movement slows. Dusk in this city brings no urgency to move; and from the window on the plain can be seen the suspension of time, a still reflection of the sun in a window across the street.

The view is elegant. The San Francisco of the hills is for those who live in elegance. The hotel is plush, its carpeting deep, its walls dark wood and velvet. Upon the wall is a portrait, artist and subject not known. Time has made it a mystery. Its brush strokes catch the study of the eyes on their way from window to window, and so, too, does one study the city which in its miniaturization, its suspension of moment, seems able to be held precisely between thumb and forefinger and examined with one eye closed. The sense of power is implicit. It is the power to observe, but withdraw, to judge, but not to descend upon the judged. The city is life's microcosm. To have it empowered would imply an independence, a certain mastery of life. It would be a life much like that of the bird whose stand upon the roof ledge suggests an immense freedom from the gravity of the earth, from the slow self movement of human life. But, too, it is the nature of the bird's freedom that the beauty of the hills is nonexistent, that the land cannot level into separate plains. The bird's freedom has only one dimension. Its life, save for the perhaps appealing reliance on instinct and whimsy, is a life of ignorance. The bird suggests that the San Francisco of the hills is a temporary notion, at best some sort of paradox.

The cable car rides the hill free-wheeling, passengers hung out from its sides at arm's length. Crowded as it is, it promotes a pleasant sense of community among men which spreads from its wooden benches within to all the hangers on without. The car thunders down a narrow street and turns a corner barely listing. In its center stands the driver, pulling at levers and squeezing on clamps in a half resistance to gravity. Crowds thicken in the streets as the car descends. The night is warm; electric rainbows light the sidewalks. One looks back up the hill at whose intersections along the way other hills begin. The car trundles down through Union Square, through the narrowing end of Van Ness and comes to a stop, its pine board brakes puffing an acrid smoke into the air. At Market Street the community disperses and another takes its place to walk the small car around on its turntable so that it may proceed up the same immense and distant hill.

One is faced with the length and width of Market Street, and it is perhaps an impression of sheer size which suggests desolation. It is not really a large street, but it seems that way; a long way to walk, a street to take when there seems no place else to go.

The life of the city when, in the dark, the hills and bridges, the bays and fogs cannot be seen, is a life of lights and sounds which somehow do not seem to converge, but to remain the strict province of their points of origin. What there is of life becomes secular, self-preoccupied. The stranger on Market Street passes through light and dark, sound and silence. The street is fairly deserted save for a bum here and there, or a group of sailors wandering aimlessly in search of something the nature of which they do not seem to know. A street car passes by slowly, in the middle of the street, its innards lit dimly, sparks clicking from its trolley.

The loneliness which, in the modern American folklore, is the province of the city, fills in the void. Market Street is like the 42nd Street madness of New York, but quietly so. It is well spaced, rather than compressed between two New York avenues; it stretches for blocks and gives no hint of its end. The major difference between the two is that 42nd Street seems fairly to explode its life from the food stands and movie houses whereas Market Street, in its dark and quiet, holds all within the doors of the building fronts which line its way. It is as if the street were a hallway between two vast penny arcades, as if, perhaps, a dim hallway in a suspiciously lifeless hotel. The rooms inside the doors are quiet except for one's own, which hums with an ascetic silence. The modern American folklore is true.

Market Street, like 42nd Street, is an avenue of movie theatres, open stands, and book stores. ("Book Store" as used here means a store which sells books and magazines concerned with sex.) One enters a store and finds one wall covered with pictures of women with their legs spread apart, another with pictures of men. The eyes are caught off guard and look from wall to wall. So, too, are the back rooms of Market Street hot dog stands, filled with movie machines which show much the same thing. The subway entrances around Times Square also have such machines, but the films are humorously innocuous. Such areas of some American cities have something of the flavor of a fabled Mexican border town. The fabled border town, however, seems to be just that; a fable and little more.

Whereas 42nd Street is garish and demonstrative, Market Street is secretive, deceptive. Forty-second Street elicits in the participating observer a defense against the dramatized aberrations of the mind which are perhaps universal, but uncontrolled by only a few. Market Street, in its nearly disingenuous aura, elicits no such defense. And whereas the loneliness of 42nd Street is of the familiar "lost in the crowd" type, the loneliness of San Francisco is one of complete separation, like the lights and sounds which do not converge. It would seem that the latter would be the more devastating of the two, but in fact it is not. It is a static loneliness, irrelevant to its beholder's sense of the impetus of time. It is without romance and, as such, not believable; more annoying than it is oppressive.

Given aspects of the city begin to take on mixed realities. If the spirit of Market Street is unconvincing, if the hills are of uncertain dimension, and if the sunlight does not seem to follow the time of day, it is doubtless that one could go on forever in his search for structural weaknesses. There is, though, a danger in excess and the danger that the traveler, moving through the city in his stream of consciousness, may abstract the city into an exclusively personal notion, draw it up from its land and imagine instead the land of hills and quiet plains which it once was, but long ago. There are many who in their ideals and idyllic dreams would like to start again. Our cities, though, are very real things; their troubles cannot be pretended away; they cannot be done over. Our cities are in crisis and their inhabitants are the agents of that crisis. It is said that the troubles of the cities have nothing to do with the cities themselves, rather that they are the product of man's response to the environment inherited, and the environment in constant change.

That there is a romance to the city, as there most certainly is to San Francisco, is perhaps indicative of man's propensity for abstraction, for bringing into personal endearment the good and the bad: for adapting. It seems to be, and perhaps must necessarily be, the only effective way of abiding life. But, too, and perhaps just as necessarily so, man has a propensity for fantasy of which abstract visions are a fundamental part. The danger is, of course, that fantasy can be deceptive. It can, in its subtle way, vitiate the necessary integrity with which one must sense his way through life.

San Francisco is called a sophisticated city, but sophistication is itself a paradox. It implies an insightful knowledge, but, too, it implies a lack of genuineness, naturalness: disillusion. It is sheer contradiction to the sense of integrity. On which side of the paradox does the city lie? Is the city lost from genuineness, submerged in the specious airs which are tools of the sophist's art? Does man in his adaptation to the city create this sophistication, and in so doing does he not perhaps lose sight of the certain realities of the self, nature, and time? To become disillusioned can be to become deceived.

In North Beach, the hill of estranged bohemia, the beat are rarely seen, as if hiding from the strange afternoon sun. At night the "topless" bars at once attract with neon, confound with tightly shut doors. The girls are injecting silicone into their breasts these days. On Broadway one sees a beat whom he has seen before in New York's Greenwich Village. In New York he seemed vital, indeed spiritual. In San Francisco he walks down a hill absently biting at his nails, seeming to hesitate with every few steps, though for no visible reason. His estrangement does not seem to be willful. There is a book store in North Beach which for once feels natural, valuable. The feeling is heartily welcomed. Here, too, the walls hold photographs of naked women, but the pictures are this time sensual, artful, as if taken in love. One remembers, though, that it is this book store, not the one on Market Street, which the sophisticated society has tried to despiritualize with its wayward law.

Retreat? If the city cannot be fought by a return to the pastoral, it can be fought as it is often fought, but as it should not be fought, by withdrawal into the self: separation. This is what the sociologists see as becoming vertical upon the horizontal plain of man. It is individualization and it, too, is a paradox. The more individual a man becomes, the more he must become dependent on other men. Specialization of one inherent resource can exclude the ability of the self to provide other resources. Autonomy is only desirable until it becomes alienation, and it is in alienation that man must come to rely on some unique element of the self, and sometimes to do so to the point of exaggeration. It is this, perhaps, which produces the 42nd Street freaks, and this, perhaps, which produces the contrasts of the city, the vertical upon the horizontal.

There is a very old bus, so old as to seem lonely in its survival from a generation long since dead—a small bus whose sole adventure in life is the challenge of Telegraph Hill. It ambles around a small path of streets at the foot of the hill as if to contemplate its task. It wheezes and stutters. The hill ascends viciously, crookedly through a growth of wispish apartment buildings which cling to it as if it were their only claim to life. The top of Telegraph Hill is small. There seems barely enough room for the bus to turn around. It is dark and quiet. Voices of the few people around do not take easily to the air. And so one stands at a railing and looks across the city as it lies down the side of Telegraph Hill and up the sides of other hills. From the top of the hill one is faced with other hills, the bays and fogs behind him. Lit as they are against the night, the hills across the way seem distant, a view of another place. They are like downtown Manhattan seen from the ferry as it approaches from the bays and fogs of the east. They would be exactly alike, were it not that while the ferry moves, Telegraph Hill does not. The old bus sits idling at the top of the hill, waiting for the cautious trip down. . . .

It has been said by some character in fact or fiction that when you get to the ocean there is no place left to go. The ocean comes toward you as you stand on a beach, but seems never to go away from you. The ocean is a mystic. The tide is constraining, keeps you running back and forth. There is no escape. You may run across a continent; you may spend a lifetime running, but in the end you will find another ocean, another tide. This, perhaps, is at least one thing that makes San Francisco the mystery that it is. San Francisco is the end of the line for a country which has always moved west. The Geary Avenue bus is the end of the line. There is no place to go but north or south along the beach. To the north there is a foggy cliff; what lies to the south is obscure. To the west is the Pacific and to the east a penny arcade, and behind that a nation.

California is the fastest growing state in the nation. It is the last word on the nation. In Los Angeles the air is oppressive, the cityscape incongruous. In San Francisco the bridges are strung from the mainland like the hands of a misshapen clock. In San Francisco the suicide rate is high. Life seems to float indecisively in the fog like figures in a sad Chagallian sky. That the sun sets awkwardly on the day is perhaps a sign that man's time can lose track of nature; indeed that man can lose track of himself.

Like the Wildean fiction, he can ignore the demands of time and assume the alternative superficiality. But time, like the compulsive movement between oceans, is a natural quality of life without which the man, the nation, or the city cannot live. In San Francisco it seems that time has gone somehow awry, but not without notice. Time, like the sun, is ubiquitous. It is metronomic in its demand to be observed. It is insistent no matter whether that insistence be in the form of an October sunset or waves upon the beach. Time is the structure for the pulse of man's anxiety, and man's anxiety is perhaps the impetus of his life. Anxiety, too, can go awry, and it, too, not without notice. It can become devastation; the road to that devastation marked with skeletal way stations, defenses, like old barns along the highway. And the highway seems to move more quickly into our cities with each passing season. Life becomes unreal. The city, becoming in the image of man, becomes unreal. The city is a creation of anxiety and at one and the same time it is a defense against that anxiety. "Come look at my hills, my bays and fogs," cries San Francisco from the shore of the sea. And from the mainland of the nation the hills are seen rising through the fog. Indeed, they seem to be afloat on the fog, to be themselves some heavenly city that might travel away above the Pacific so that there will be someplace left to go. But they are not afloat. There is no place left to go.

APPENDIX

The Authors and Their Comments

THE STORY TELLERS

Brannon, Michael: *CHASTAIN ON THE X-AXIS.* Born in Montgomery, Alabama, March 11, 1942. At present in London on a Fulbright-Hays Grant for graduate study at the London School of Economics and Political Science for 1967–68. He graduated with honors May, 1967, at the University of Alabama with a political science major. He is a member of Phi Beta Kappa. He served in the U. S. Navy, 1961–65, with assignments in San Diego, Philippine Islands, Formosa, Japan, Hong Kong and Australia. Undecided between teaching and government administration as a career.

Brawley, Ernest: *THE CHICKEN.* Born in small town in the San Joaquin Delta region of Central California, Ernest Brawley is a graduate of San Francisco State College. He has traveled extensively and held numerous jobs. He has hitch-hiked to Argentina on Highway 99, worked his way to Europe, and hitched his way across the Middle East, India and South East Asia; worked his way to Japan and has spent some time in Russia and in Spain. He has been doing graduate work in English with William Wiegand, a one-time STORY prize winner. He has worked as a railway switchman and truck driver in the United States, a reporter and translator in Buenos Aires, a bartender in Spain, an English teacher in France and Japan, a hop-picker in Kent and a dishwasher in Notting Hill Gate, London.

Harris, Derek: *A TIME FOR REASON.* Entered by a student at San Diego State College, San Diego, Calif. Mr. Harris has lived in South Africa where his father is a geologist. He was traveling at press time and further biographical details were unavailable.

Hathaway, John F.: *BARREL.* Was born July 15, 1947, in the seaside resort town of Coronado, California. Since 1965 has been attending San Diego State College where he is majoring in the study of broadcasting with a view to a career in educational television.

Logan, Louis D.: *THE BILL COLLECTOR.* 2d Prize in the short story. Born in Wink, Texas, and resident since in Wyoming, Washington and California. Mr. Logan has a BA degree in English from San Francisco State College and is married and has two children. He is employed at present on an offshore oil drilling rig near Santa Barbara, California. In 1966 he won a Wallace Stegner Creative Writing Fellowship to Stanford University for a year with an unpublished novel, which also won the Joseph Henry Jackson Award of California. He wrote "The Bill Collector" while at Stanford.

Schupan, Charlotte: *THE SLAP.* "For the last four years I have been taking as many reading and writing courses as I could at Western Michigan University. I am working toward a degree," Charlotte Schupan writes. On vital statistics she adds: "Born in January, 1927, ouch! Raised in Kalamazoo, married at 19 and have four children, eldest in M.S.U., youngest beginning the fourth grade."

Thelwell, Michael: *THE ORGANIZER.* First Prize in the short story. Born in 1938 in the West Indian island of Jamaica, Thelwell came to the United States in 1959. He has studied at Howard University in Washington, D. C., and is now in the creative writing program at the University of Massachusetts. His first published story was "Direct Action," which won an honorable mention in the STORY college short story contest in 1962–63 and was published in *Prize College Stories,* Random House. The story was also included in the Langston Hughes anthology of *Best Negro Short Stories* published this year by Little Brown & Co., Boston. While he was at Howard two other Thelwell stories, "Community of Victims" and "Nor All Thy Piety," won Honorable Mention citations in STORY College Contests, "Community of Victims" appearing in the STORY annual *The Stone Soldier,* published by Fleet in 1934. Thelwell has been active in the civil rights movement, working on the staff of the Student Non-violent Coordinating Committee and the Mississippi Freedom Democratic Party. He is working on a novel set in the rural South.

Walker (Méndez), Charlotte: *MONSERRATE.* "The past year," she writes, "I have been a graduate student in the English Department at Syracuse University where a creative writing fellowship enabled me to return to school after my recent divorce and a number of years away from formal study. With the help of an NDEA fellowship, I will spend the next few years working toward a Ph.D. in literature. As an undergraduate at San Diego State College I majored in psychology and later did a year of graduate work in social welfare. I have three children, David, Rebecca and Rachel. I have cared about writing since childhood and have published a few poems. 'Monserrate' grew out of an episode from a novel I am working on." Mrs. Méndez lives in Syracuse and her story was certified by George P. Elliott, the author, who teaches at the University.

Walton, David: *MADELAINE.* " 'Madelaine' " the author writes, "was written in March, 1967, with The Supremes playing in the background, then revised in April at Howard's Bar in Bowling Green, Ohio. It was my fifth story. I had written a little in school in Pennsylvania, and in the evening, after summer work in a steel mill. Since entering Fred Eckman's writers' workshop in Bowling Green I have been writing steadily. 'A Human Contact' is to appear in the October *Rogue,* 'Joshua Calchus' in the September *Appalachian Review* (Second Prize winner) and 'The Final Phone Call' in the *North American Review.*"

THE POETS

Abitua, Angel: *THIS OLD MAN.* Born in Texas, 1945. Junior in Pan American College, Edinburgh, Texas, studying government and journalism; planning transfer to University of Texas, in Spring, 1968. Was a contest winner, Second Prize, in the 1965 Senior Scholastic Magazine Award for a formal essay, and First Prize in the 1965 August Life Line Essay Contest sponsored by H. L. Hunt of Dallas, Texas. He writes that his ambition in life is "to be the best I can, despite 'things'... What makes a piece of writing good, I think, is that it has never been said before. As I get older I keep being surprised by the many things in life that go unsaid, undone, buried by neglect, ignorance or by human nature itself."

Allegro, Margery: *A TIME FOR MOVING.* The only child of an army family, Miss Allegro was born April 17, 1945, in Havre de Grace, Maryland. She spent her childhood in places as far apart as Tokyo and Mt. Holly, New Jersey. She graduated in June from the College of Notre Dame of Maryland in Baltimore where she had first started "her serious work in poetry" under Sister Maura, S.S.N.D. "A poem must sing," she writes, "and it must be as complete as a resolved musical composition. This must be why I so often choose the musical image and why many of my poems are circular." She plans to teach freshman English at Prince George's Community College and do part-time graduate work at Georgetown University.

Brody, Marsha: *IN A SUMMER ROOM.* Miss Brody's poetry came from Louisiana State University, Baton Rouge. Her home is in New Orleans.

Burke, Karen: *FUGUE: TO J. S. BACH; REQUIEM.* A senior English major at Skidmore, Miss Burke spends much of her free time arranging music and acting as assistant leader for Skidmore's informal singing group. The Sonneteers. Her interest in poetry was intensified as a member of a poetry workshop conducted by Laurence Josephs at Skidmore. Several of her poems have been published in the Skidmore newspaper, in *Folio,* the literary magazine, and in the *National Anthology of College Poetry.*

Confalone, Marianne: *LE CADEAU.* Born in New York in 1946, grew up in Long Island and attended St. Joseph's Academy in Brentwood. After completing three years in Notre Dame College in Baltimore, where she majored in English, she is now a student at Hofstra University, Long Island. She plans to teach English on the secondary level. "Notre Dame's proficient and highly dedicated English Department provided me with the best possible atmosphere to use and develop," she writes. "Due to Sister Maura's influence as a teacher, I would one day like to teach a creative writing course of my own. Thus far poetry has been the strongest force in my life: it has synthesized all facets of it and enabled me to interpret all experiences personally while recording them. I feel I have been greatly influenced by two outstanding contemporaries, Robert Creeley and Leonard Cohen."

Fellowes, Peter: *TO JIM . . . DEAD IN VIETNAM.* Peter Fellowes was born in Washington, D. C., in 1944, graduated from Colgate University with a B.A. in 1966 and from Johns Hopkins University with an M.A. in 1967. While at Hopkins he studied under the poet Elliott Coleman. He is studying for another M.A. in English at the University of Virginia and in 1968 is to be an instructor of English at Mary Washington College.

Henderson, Cynthia: *IF; THERE WAS SOMETHING.* A student at Marygrove College, Detroit, Mich. Biographical data unavailable at the time of going to press.

Herem, Barry G.: *WHALES; AT TWELVE; GATHER ME.* 1st Prize in Poetry shared with Eleanor Wait, and 2d Prize for Journalism with "A One-time Trip". Mr. Herem entered his material as a student at the University of Washington, Seattle. He has been traveling in England and biographical data was unattainable at press time.

Hewitt, Geof: *LETTER TO HIS WIFE.* Geof Hewitt was born in 1943 and raised in Montclair, New Jersey. He studied at Cornell University where he worked under Baxter Hathaway, David Ray, and others and holds a masters degree from Elliott Coleman's writing seminars at Johns Hopkins. His poetry has been accepted by *Epoch, Choice, New: American and Canadian Poets,* and *Poetry Northwest.* He is the founder of the Kumquat Press which he operates during vacations publishing little-known poets. At Cornell he edited the *Trojan Horse* and was an assistant editor of *Epoch.* He wants to teach writing at the college level.

Hogue, Olivia: *POEM FOR CHINA.* "I was born in Dallas, Texas, in 1945 of absolutely splendid, sufficiently weird, parents and was immediately deported to Tulsa, Oklahoma, where I have lived all my life attending either the Tulsa public schools where my mother taught art and the University of Tulsa where my father taught art. I have intended at various times myself, to teach art," she writes, "or to be an actress, a medical illustrator or a potter."

Kistler, Lawrence: *SCOUTING PARTY.* Mr. Kistler, a student of Boston College, comes from Allentown, Pa.

McGinnis, D. W.: *AFTER THE DEATH OF MY GRANDUNCLE JOSEPH PATSEY.* The grandson of a Clallan Indian, Mr. McGinnis was born in Seattle February 13, 1938. His early childhood was spent on the Olympic Peninsula with his maternal grandfather's family. The grandfather was a man of the forest who he says, "taught me the way to look at life, through nature. And the Indian tales he told by the sea are valuable memories today." McGinnis has served four years in the Navy, two years of which were spent in and around Japan. In 1960 he returned to Seattle to attend the University of Washington. His first influences were painters of the Impressionist and Post-Impressionist periods, and he found the "visual reflection rewarding." He has been published in the *Alaska Review,* the *University of Portland Review* and elsewhere and won a first prize in poetry at the Pacific Northwest Writers Conference in 1966.

Mathews, Richard: *CEDAR KEY.* Although this author's submission came from him as a student at the University of Florida, Richard Mathews is now attending the University of Virginia as an honorary Woodrow Wilson fellow to work toward his Ph.D. in English literature. He is a graduate of the University of Florida, where he edited the *Florida Quarterly,* a new literary review, and his work has appeared there, in *Trace, The Christian Science Monitor* and *Lyric.* Last year he received first place award in the *Lyric's* College Poetry Contest and honorable mention in the Kansas City poetry competition. "I look upon writing," he says, "as a kind of learning process in which I share with the reader a new discovery about some small part of the world. . . . I plan a career in college teaching."

Pendleton, Marion: *BALLAD OF A TRIANGLE.* A student at Muskegon County Community College in the advanced writing course of Mrs. Edward Kyvig, Mrs. Pendleton is a member of the Poetry Society of Michigan and has been published in its quarterly, *Peninsula Poets.* She has also been published in *Award Winning Poems* 1964, Rochester, New York, and elsewhere. She was born in New York State and graduated from the Union-Endicott High School and the New York State College for Teachers at Albany. She is married to an electrical engineer.

Rickabaugh, Rene: *THE COOKING TIPS OF JULIA CHILD; SOMEWHERE UNDER AN UNKNOWN LENGTH OF LOVE.* Born in Eugene, Oregon, August 7, 1947, Rene has been living in Portland for the last 13 years. "Disenchanted with academic study at Reed College, I transferred to the Museum of Art School (where I also teach children's art classes). The transfer was made to concentrate on subjects of interest to me. Poetry is one. Poetry is a necessary record of things I wish to remember (there are so many I don't want to forget any) and it is also a reflection of my concern with the visual world. In this respect I hope always to remain young and impressionable." He was a Scholastics Writing Awards winner when in high school.

Schneidhorst, Patricia (Mrs.): *POEM TO e.e.; LOVE IN THE WESTERN WORLD, LESSON 12; and TUESDAY.* "I was raised on a farm near Wooster, Ohio," she writes, "attended Ohio State University and in June, 1967, received a B.A. in English and Drama from Ohio Northern University. I am grateful for my schooling chiefly because I was so bored with most of my classes that I was reduced to writing poetry in them to save my sanity. I began writing poetry when I was six years old, but my only formal study of poetry was Dr. James Fullington's inspiring course at OSU. I write short stories and have experimented with playwriting. I am now studying acting at the American Conservatory Theatre in San Francisco and plan to continue in the theatre performing, directing or teaching. Nothing definite: I make life's plans in pencil. My home is in Lima, Ohio, with my veterinarian husband and our three children."

Schwartz, Hillel: *WHITTLING; THE FRENCH DOORS.* A junior at Brandeis University majoring in history, Hillel Schwartz plays tennis, makes collages and does a little choreography for modern dance performances and "in general, amateurishly, I explore things I don't know very much about." He has studied with Ruth Stone, Yves Bonnefoy and Howard Nemerov. He was a Scholastic Writing Award winner in high school.

Slowik, Mary: *HAWKWEED AND ASTER.* A senior English major at Marygrove College, Detroit, Miss Slowik hopes to continue on in a humanities program in graduate school, finding the correlation of the arts, particularly music and literature, very absorbing. She hopes to continue her study of history, "reserving a spot for some professional piano or choral work in my future too." Her family, in earlier years, participated in the Trapp Family Music Camp sing-weeks in Vermont and last summer Miss Slowik sang under Robert Shaw at the Meadow Brook School of Music, Oakland University in Rochester,

Michigan. "At home," she writes, "our days are well filled with orchard and organic gardening, evenings with reading, singing, piano and recorder playing. In this environment I have enjoyed close ties with nature and the outdoors, which inspires most of my poetry."

Sopp, Beverly: *THE GIANT YEARS.* A senior English concentrator at the College of Notre Dame of Maryland, she won a tuition scholarship last summer to the Georgetown Writers Conference. Her writings have appeared in high school and college publications and she has been editor of Notre Dame's newspaper *Columns*.

Wait, Eleanor: *ELLIE: AN INVENTORY OF BEING; PLAYGROUND.* "Honesty has always been my main index of values, and it is what I look for in both literature and life," writes Miss Wait. "When I was in high school I was the editor of a controversial school newspaper which although it came close to being banned by the Board of Education and incited an onslaught of poison pen letters, won the Scholastic Press Association of New Jersey Award that year for being the best high school newspaper in New Jersey. In my spare time I collect presidential memorabilia and have some campaign materials dating back to John Adams. For the past six summers I have worked at the Booth Bay Playhouse, a summer theatre in Maine, and was a drama major in college. I will graduate in January from Chatham College. Emily Dickinson has been my favorite poet for ten years but recently I have become enamored of T. S. Eliot, Walt Whitman, Henry Adams and William Saroyan, which one presiding at the moment depending on my mood."

Wayman, Thomas: *PREGNANT STREET; CAPES OF HORN.* Born in 1945 on the banks of the Ottawa River in a small pulp-mill town halfway between Montreal and Ottawa, Tom Wayman spent his first formative years on the north coast of British Columbia. He attended the University of British Columbia, and is now in the writing center of the University of California, Irvine. "In my writing I try to work with themes, concepts, drawn from my generation's popular music—the major force I see uniting this Can-American continent. I am by trade a journalist."

THE PLAYWRIGHTS

Felton, Keith Spencer: *THE LAST LOST WEEKEND OF MISSIONARY PEALE.* Born in San Francisco, May, 1942. His family early moved to Tennessee, then Oklahoma, finally settling in Los Angeles. He graduated from University High School in Los Angeles in 1960, and received his B.A. degree from Grinnell College in Iowa in 1964. His M.A. in Fine Arts (playwriting) came from the University of California at Los Angeles in 1967. He began writing plays at Grinnell, where he studied directing under Ned Donahoe and directed his first play, "Daniel Prince," in 1964, which was chosen as the National Collegiate Players production. His short play "Overture to a Curtain Call" was produced at U.C.L.A. in 1965, and between 1964 and 1967, he writes. "I was afforded staged readings of eight full-length plays . . . In 1967 I wrote the two plays entered in the STORY College Creative Awards Contest, 'The Blue-Tail Fly' in which a power-mad professor commits murder to gain a position he believes has been wrongly given to another; and a one-character play, 'The Last Lost Weekend of Missionary Peale,' a darkly comic solo saga of a former African missionary who agonizingly weighs the values between an exciting but questionable past and the mundane but positive preaching of his present life . . . In 1966 I returned to writing short stories and poetry (two forms which I had let lie for several years) and I have completed the first draft of a novel. In 1965–66 I received the Music Corporation of America Fellowship in Creative Writing, placed in the San Joaquin Delta College Playwriting Contests in 1966 and 1967 and was a finalist in the Samuel Goldwyn Creative Writing contests in each of the three years from 1965 to 1967." The outside support to permit his devoting time to writing, he adds, has varied "from being a Research Assistant in Mercurial Explorations to working as a chef, and from being a technical translator to selling clothes."

Gardner, Gary: *JUST LIKE IN THE MOVIES.* Was born March 24, 1944, in Danville, Illinois, and attributes the genesis of his fascination with show business to the fact that at the age of four he fell in love with a photo of Lana Turner in a magazine and vowed to marry her when he grew up. "Graduated in June, 1966," he writes, "from the University of Illinois where I majored in speech education and carried spears in numerous campus productions, as well as authoring three one-act plays, two local TV shows, and three musical reviews. (Actually this whole writing thing was a revolt against Shakespeare . . . he talked so funny—all those 'thees' and 'thous'; I swear the man was a Quaker.)" He continued his education at the University of California at Los Angeles where he is now working for a MFA degree in playwriting under Robert E. Lee and George Savage. His first three-act comedy "Just Like in the Movies" was produced at U.C.L.A. in May, 1967, and its popularity has kept the author at his typewriter ever since. His immediate plans include the book and lyrics for a musical with John Rubinstein, U.C.L.A. classmate and son of the pianist Artur Rubinstein, and the completion of his graduate study in June, 1967. He hopes in the future to teach creative writing, write plays about his two favorite historical characters, Aaron Burr and the "Bird Woman," Sakajewea, and grow fat on cheeseburgers and chocolate malts. Still single at 23, Gardner claims he's "still saving himself for Lana."

A SCREEN WRITER

Jones, David B.: *NEITHER HERE NOR THERE.* Born in New Orleans, Louisiana, and raised in Leavenworth, Kansas, which he considers his home town. Received his bachelor of arts degree from the University of Kansas, served three years in the U. S. Marine Corps, and is currently working for a masters degree in broadcasting and film at Stanford University. The motion picture script grew out of a classroom exercise at Stanford. "I think," he writes, "that much of Kafka's work is highly adaptable to film. He writes almost as coolly as a camera shoots. His style, which is often confused with his content, is an objective, self-effacing style, matter-of-factly describing a very personal and in some ways very strange world. The script fails, I think, in that it fails to provide adequate camera directions to translate Kafka's style to the screen, that it emphasizes the satirical elements of Kafka's story at the expense of other, more important elements, and that it tends to be bitter, which Kafka never is."

AUTOBIOGRAPHERS, ESSAYISTS, JOURNALISTS

Bieber, David L.: *LSD ON THE CAMPUS,* excerpts from a series in the *Kent Daily Stater.* A senior at Kent State University, Kent, Ohio, bachelor of science degree in journalism-public relations in December, 1967. Member of Sigma Delta Chi, professional journalistic society and Epsilon Nu Gamma, English honorary. Received an Alcoa Foundation scholarship in May, 1967. Has written for *Billboard Magazine, Cleveland Press, Mount Vernon News* and served as publicity director for the Kent State University School of Music, and worked the summer of 1967 in the community relations department of Cooper-Bessemer Co., Mt. Vernon, Ohio, writing for the *CB Manifold,* employe publication. "The series of articles on drug usage at Kent State University was written following nearly a month of extensive interviews," he writes. "Realizing that national periodicals had dealt with the psychedelic scene on a general, surface basis, I attempted to localize the subject. The articles are not meant to depict a proportionate representation of Kent State University students, nor to glamorize the use of depressants, stimulants or psychedelic variants; rather, the intent is to explain and present a situation as it exists on a local level. Due to the controversial and legal aspects of the articles, complete anonymity was granted the students interviewed. Additionally, each participating student was permitted to read the articles before submission to the newspaper, to delete any material of a self-incriminating nature. However, all were satisfied, and no deletions were made."

Coe, Charles: *FIRST COMBAT*. "My interest in writing began early," writes the author. "While still in grade school in Hartford, Connecticut, I won a state-wide essay contest, my school receiving a television set and I received a bicycle. (I always thought the prizes should have been reversed.) At the Loomis School I edited the literary magazine and won several gold keys in high school writing competitions sponsored by the Hartford *Courant*. One story went on to win a first prize in the short story division of the national competition sponsored by Scholastic Magazines and the Schaeffer Pen Co. In my final year at preparatory school a story I wrote was included in an anthology published by Henry Holt & Co., 'New Trails.' At Brown University, I earned varsity letters in football and wrestling and made the Dean's list but felt that student literary efforts at Brown were too much directed at shocking the reader and I stayed away from student publications. I joined the Marine Corps, obtained a commission, and spent two of my three years on active duty in various parts of Asia. In December, 1965, I was twice wounded in Vietnam and was evacuated to Japan for hospitalization. While recovering I received word that a story I had written earlier had been accepted by Merrill Books for publication in a series called Ideas in Literature. My concern with the poor quality of writing and reporting coming out of Vietnam led me to the University of California journalism program at Los Angeles, where I am now seeking my master's degree. At U.C.L.A. I was the editor of the departmental magazine, *The California Sun*. I received the *Wall Street Journal* Student Achievement Award. I also won a foreign internship sponsored by the Foreign Press Awards, and am spending four months this fall in Europe to study American newsgathering techniques abroad. My experiences in the Marine Corps sparked a real interest in things Asian and I hope to study the interaction of Asia and America at the East-West Center in Honolulu after my return from Europe. I find it very cathartic to relive my experiences by writing about them . . . The mass media treating Vietnam seem to be interested in grand strategies and philosophical trivia. I am interested in people and If I couldn't write about people I wouldn't have much to say."

Dickon, Chris: *SAN FRANCISCO: SUNDIAL BY THE SEA*. He writes: "I live on a hill above the University Circle area of Cleveland and I go down the hill each day to the University and most Saturday nights I go down the hill to hear the Cleveland Orchestra, for music is one of the few real pleasures of my life. Sometimes I go down the hill to the airport to take a plane to New York. I must visit the place as if I depended on it for my breath. I will be returning there sometime soon to live. The city I live in now is very sick as are most of our cities these days. And the people who create the sickness are to be wondered over. I am fascinated with critics and I am fascinated with the things that people do to assuage themselves. I am fascinated with the notion of freedom, with the analysis and breaking down of the psychic and environmental prisons men have built for themselves as if they could build barriers against the unknown reaches of the mind and the world. I believe that we are now searching for a better freedom and that the search is born of deep necessity. The present day reliance on drugs is a bad beginning of that search, but a beginning nonetheless. I hope, someday, to be a more responsible participant of the search. And of all my fascinations the largest is with myself—which is as it should be. The mind that writes must be an enigma. It must love itself enough to challenge the puzzle without fear." Chris Dickon was a Scholastic Writing Awards winner when in high school.

Herem, Barry: *A ONE-TIME TRIP*. See biography under Poets.

Stephens (Rashid), Mrs. Theresa: *VISION THROUGH A VEIL*. Born August 18, 1940 in West Virginia, the author is a senior at the University of Arizona in Tucson. Her entry in biography was written about one of her experiences as a Peace Corps Volunteer in 1964–65 in Pakistan. While in Pakistan she wrote a number of poems and a play. She is married.

The STORY College Creative Award Winners of 1967-1968

	SHORT FICTION
$500 1st Prize	Michael Thelwell: The Organizer. University of Massachusetts. Certified by Andrew Fetler, Assistant Professor of English.
$300 2d Prize	Louis Logan: The Bill Collector. Stanford University. Certified by R. Scowcroft, Assistant Professor of English.
$150 3rd Prize	Charlotte Walker (Méndez): Monserrate and But God Will Not Forgive You. Syracuse University. Certified by George P. Elliott, Department of English.
	POETRY
$150 1st Prize and $100 2d Prize shared	Barry Herem: At Twelve; Whales; Gather Me. University of Washington. Certified by L. G. S. Willis, Faculty Advisor.
	Eleanor Wait: Playground; Ellie: An Inventory of Being. Chatham College, Pittsburgh. Certified by Phyllis Ferguson, Chairman, Department of English.
$50 3d Prize	Karen Burke: Fugue: To J. S. Bach; Requiem. Skidmore College. Certified by Laurence Josephs, Assistant Professor of English.
	DRAMA
$500 1st Prize shared	Keith Spencer Felton: The Last Lost Weekend of Missionary Peale; The Blue Tail Fly. U.C.L.A. Certified by George Savage, Theatre Arts Department.
	Gary Gardner: Just Like in the Movies; Purgatory on a Saturday Night. U.C.L.A. Certified by John Couble, Theatre Division.
$200 2d Prize	David Seiffer: If I Ruled the World. New York University. Certified by Lowell Swastzell, Associate Professor.
$100 3d Prize	Allison Giglio: Home Again, Home Again. Penn State University. Certified by Ronald Kross, Instructor.
	BIOGRAPHY
$250 1st Prize	Charles Coe: First Combat. U.C.L.A. Certified by Professor William W. Johnson, Journalism.
$150 2d Prize	Theresa Stephens: Vision Through a Veil. University of Arizona. Certified by Arthur A. Paul, Lecturer, Speech/Journalism.
$100 3d Prize	Patricia Wagoner: The Termagant Duchess. Trinity College, Hartford, Connecticut. Certified by Borden W. Painter, Jr., Department of History.
	ESSAY
$250 1st Prize	Barbara Jean Savery: Pilgrimage to Mecca. Stanford University. Certified by Jacques Kornberg.
$150 2d Prize	Chris Dickon: San Francisco: Sundial by the Sea. Western Reserve University, Cleveland. Certified by Margaret Barnes, Education Counselor.
$100 3d Prize	Sylvia G. Barclay: Time of Surrender. Muskegon County Community College, Muskegon, Michigan. Certified by Wilma Kyvig, Professor of English.

JOURNALISM

$200 1st Prize — David L. Bieber: LSD at Kent State. Kent State University, Kent, Ohio. Certified by Charles Brill, Assistant Professor of Journalism.

$150 2d Prize — Barry Herem: A One-Time Trip. University of Washington. Certified by L. G. S. Willis, Faculty Advisor.

$100 3d Prize shared — John Polich: Laura Bernstein. Arizona State University. Certified by Gordon C. Jones, Professor.

Schrader, Paul: Life at the Top, criticism. Calvin College, Grand Rapids, Michigan. Certified by S. M. Wiersma, Professor of English.

MOTION PICTURES

$500 1st Prize — David B. Jones: Neither Here Nor There. Stanford University. Certified by Janet Voelker, Instructor.

$250 2d Prize — Mike Shannon: Untitled Film Script. San Francisco State. Certified by C. L. Earlenbaugh, Registrar.

$100 3d Prize — Paul Petlewski: The Ripper. University of Detroit. Certified by John Schmittroth, Associate Professor of English.

TELEVISION

$250 1st Prize — Salvador de Usabel: Does the Empress Always Smile? San Francisco State. Certified by George E. Steiner, Professor, Radio-TV-Film.

$150 2d Prize — Herb McCabe: Bridge Night. Loyola University, Los Angeles. Certified by Bernard Abbene.

PHOTO ESSAY

$200 1st Prize — Irving Fitzig: Hospital for Animals. Brooklyn College. Certified by Andrew Ciofolo, Instructor, Department of English.

$150 2d Prize — Gary Goodwin: A Fishing Village in India. St. Lawrence University, Canton, New York. Certified by Robert Helsabeck, Assistant Dean of Men.

$100 3d Prize — Robert Sheffield: The Lovin' Spoonful. University of Michigan. Certified by Philip Dsuro.

$100 COLLEGE NEWSPAPER INITIATIVE AWARD

Daily Kent Stater: Kent State University, Kent, Ohio. For publication of LSD on the Campus, a series by David L. Bieber.

CARTOON

The quality of submissions was not deemed up to Award standards. This category will be continued one more year and if cartoonists of originality are not discovered, the category will be discontinued.

ADDITIONAL

$50 Honorable Mention Publication Awards for Short Stories

Michael L. Brannon: Chastain On The X-Axis . . . University of Alabama. Certified by W. O. Hopper, Department of English.

Ernest Brawley: The Chicken. San Francisco State. Certified by William Wiegand, Director, Creative Writing.

Derek Harris: Time For Reason. San Diego State College. Certified by Elizabeth Chater, Assistant Professor of English.

John F. Hathaway: Barrel. San Diego State College. Certified by Elizabeth Chater, Assistant Professor of English.

Charlotte Schupan: The Slap. Western Michigan University, Kalamazoo, Michigan. Certified by Robert Larue, Assistant Professor of English.

David Walton: Madelaine. Bowling Green State University, Bowling Green, Ohio. Certified by Donald Winkelman, English Department.

ADDITIONAL

$25 Honorable Mention Publication Awards for Poetry

Angel Abitua: This Old Man. Pan-American College, Edinburgh, Texas. Certified by Bill Skinner, Communications Department.

Marjorie Allegro: A Time For Moving. College of Notre Dame of Maryland. Certified by Sister Maura, Professor, Advanced Writing.

Marsha Brody: In A Summer Room. Louisiana State University. Certified by Cooper Mackin, Chairman, Department.

Marianne Confalone: Le Cadeau. College of Notre Dame of Maryland. Certified by Sister Maura, Professor, Advanced Writing.

Peter Fellowes: To Jim . . . Dead in Vietnam. Johns Hopkins University. Certified by Professor Elliott Coleman.

Cynthia Henderson: If; There was Something. Marygrove College, Detroit. Certified by Registrar.

Geof Hewitt: Letter to His Wife. Johns Hopkins University. Certified by Elliott Coleman, Writing Seminar.

Olivia Hogue: Poem for China, Ode To Emily. University of Tulsa. Certified by Winston Weathers, Associate Professor.

Lawrence Kistler: Scouting Party. Boston College. Certified by D. R. Dunbar, English Department.

D. W. McGinnis: After the Death of My Granduncle Joseph Patsey. University of Washington. Certified by Father Gould, Professor of English.

Richard Mathews: Cedar Key. University of Florida. Certified by F. E. Gehan, Associate Professor of English.

Marion Pendleton: Ballad of A Triangle. Community College, Muskegon, Michigan. Certified by Wilma Kyvig, Department of English.

Rene Rickabaugh: The Cooking Tips of Julia Child; Somewhere Under an Unknown Length of Love. Museum Art School, Portland, Oregon. Certified by George Cummings, Faculty.

Patricia Schneidhorst: Poem To e.e.; Love in the Western World, Lesson 12; Tuesday. Ohio Northern University, Ada, Ohio. Certified by Richard Arthur, Instructor.

Hillel Schwartz: Whittling; The French Doors. Brandeis University. Certified by Eugene C. Black, Professor.

Mary Slowick: Hawkweed and Aster. Marygrove College, Detroit. Certified by Sister Janice Marie.

Beverly Sopp: The Giant Years. College of Notre Dame of Maryland. Certified by Sister Maura, Professor of Advanced Writing.

Thomas Wayman: Pregnant Street; The Capes of Horn. Writing Center, University of California, Berkeley. Certified by S. Cohen, Associate in English.

Award Winners and Honor Roll

The following authors, in their various categories, have been singled out by the judges and editors of this annual for degrees of excellence indicated by asterisks: ***indicating the highest distinction; * * indicating distinction in both material and treatment; and * indicating distinction in either material or treatment or both surpassing that of hundreds of other submitted entries. Prize Award Winners published in this volume are listed (STORY 1968) and HRPA, STORY 1968 means winners of special Honor Roll Publication Awards in the short story and poetry categories. The editors regret space prevented us from including in this book all prize winners in every category.

THE STORY TELLERS

AYERS, MARY ALICE
***The Flavor of God. New School for Social Research, New York, N.Y.
ALBRIGHT, CARLETON
*Blood, White and Blue. U. of Iowa
ALDRIDGE, MARY CAMILLE
**Christopher. Mt. Holyoke Coll.
ALSOP, ELIZABETH
*Dominus Vobiscum
*Mister Lester. Sarah Lawrence Coll.
ANDERSON, DENNIS R.
**Merry-Go-Round. San Diego St. Coll.

BEALL, OWEN D.
**September Myth. Hobart Coll.
BIRD, RICHARD
*Discipline
*Preparation for War. No. Michigan U., Marquette
BOYD, BLANCHE M.
**And Uncle R. T. Made Coffee. Pomona Coll.
BRANNON, MICHAEL
***Chastain on the X-Axis, Stebbins on the Y-Axis. HRPA, STORY 1968. U. of Ala.
BRAWLEY, ERNEST
***The Chicken. HRPA, STORY 1968
*Samsara. San Francisco St. Coll.

CARLISLE, BARBARA
**Paul, Do You Remember the Island? Sonoma St. Coll., Rohnert Park, Calif.
CARR, PATRICIA
*Journey South. U. of Houston
CLIFFORD, JOHN
*The Sun Still Shines. Calif. Concordia Coll., Oakland
CLINE, JERENE
*The Octopus. U. of Calif., Irvine
CORCORAN, ELIZABETH
*The Victory. Skidmore Coll.

DEFOE, MARK
**The Hunter. Okla. St. U.
DE GRAW, PAT
*Inside Mother. U.C.L.A.
DOGGETT, JOE
**A Dot of Yellow. U. of Houston

ELDER, ELIZABETH
**The Bus Stopped in Fairgale. Skidmore Coll.

GAGE, EDWIN, III
**The Two-Pronged Hook. U. of Mich.
GLASER, ELTON
**The Timely Marriage
**Rubber Cheeks. La. St. U.
GOHN, DAVID MICHAEL
*The Stopover. U. of Washington
GOSHORN, MARGARET
**Net Contents of This Package. Villa Madonna Coll., Covington, Ky.
GRANT, LOUIS T.
*Dead End. St. U. of N.Y., Stony Brook
**The Insured

HALL, MICHAEL
*Off Broadway. U. of Texas
HARRIS, DEREK
***A Time for Reason. HRPA, STORY 1968. San Diego St. Coll.
HATHAWAY, JOHN F.
***Barrel. HRPA, STORY 1968. San Diego St. Coll.
HIGGINS, JAMES J.
**Sky Blue Gerry. La Salle Coll., Philadelphia
HOEY, IRENE
*The Acolyte. San Diego St. Coll.

JOHNSEN (SEREDIN), NORMA
**Hector, Tamer of Horses. U. of Ariz.

KENFIELD, KAY
*The Miracle. Chico St. Coll., Chico, Calif.
KOUROUS, SHARON
**Where Does A Circle Begin? U. of Toledo

LAKIN, R. D.
*A Question of Philosophy. Colo. St. U.
LECKEY, HUGO
*The First Mate. Brown U.
LELAND, RUTH D.
*The Covert of Thy Wings. Harvard U.
LESKOSKY, RICHARD J.
*The Dark of Dreams, The Gold of Death. Boston Coll.

LITTKE, LAEL
*The Dream. Pasadena City Coll.
LOGAN, LOUIS
***The Bill Collector. 2d Prize, STORY 1968. Stanford U.
LUDWIG, MYLES ERIC
*Snowy Egrets Melt in Summer. U. of N.C.
LYNCH, BOBBIE BENNETT
*Whirling Around. Richmond Prof. Inst., Va.

MACGILLIS, DONALD
**Vandals of the St. Anthony School. Yale U.
MALMROS, RICHARD S.
**The Time Between. Wesleyan U.
MCKENZIE, CLIFFORD A.
*The Love-In. San Diego St. Coll.
MÉNDEZ, CHARLOTTE WALKER
***Monserrate. 3d Prize, STORY 1968.
***But God Will Not Forgive You. Syracuse U.
MEYER, DAVID
***The Last Summer of the Mill Sisters. Cornell Coll., Mt. Vernon, Iowa
MUELLER, LAVONNE
*The Isolates. No. Ill. U., DeKalb
MURRAY, JANE
*The Thank-God Crack. Pasadena City Coll.

PETERSEN, THOMAS
***The American at Scazzeriera. Humboldt St. Coll., Arcata, Calif.
PHEGLEY, MICHAEL
*One Fine Place. U. of Mo., St. Louis, Mo.
PUMILIA, JOSEPH
*Ark of the Covenant
*Night Thing. U. of Houston

RUSSELL, RODNEY G.
*A Touch of Cinnamon. So. Methodist U.

SAWAYA, RICHARD
*To Win. Boston Coll.
SCHRADER, PAUL
**What Makes Wayne Foster. Calvin Coll., Grand Rapids, Mich.
SCHUPAN, CHARLOTTE
***The Slap. HRPA, STORY 1968. W. Mich. U., Kalamazoo
SEARS, ANNA
*Kristin. U. of Wash.
SHACKELFORD, R.
*Big Wheel Turn Around, Around. U. of So. Ala., Mobile
SHIELDS, GWENDOLYN
*A Sense of Order. Yale U.
STEVOVICH, ANDREW V.
*Ritualistic Balloon. R.I. School of Design, Providence
STIGLER, BARRY
*Ti Aunalao. U. of Ill.
STUART, DORIS
*Progress. U. of Mo., Kansas City, Mo.

TAGGART, ELLEN
*Rain. Wilkes College, Wilkes-Barre, Pa.
THELWELL, MIKE
***The Organizer. 1st Prize, STORY 1968. U. of Mass.
TILLOTSON, RICHARD
***On the Citrus
**Dithyramb. U. of Wash.
TOLER, PATRICIA
*The Witness. U. of Ala.
TOLNAY, THOMAS
**The Miracle of Uncle Stavros

VAN DER VOORT, RICHARD
**The Night of the Big Blow-up. U. of N. Mexico

WAGONER, JOYCE
*The Trouble With Westlake. U. of Toledo
WAGONER, PATRICIA GARROTT
**Honor. Trinity Coll., Hartford
WALTON, DAVID
***Madelaine. HRPA, STORY 1968. Bowling Green St. U., Ohio
WHITE, VALERIE
**Four-thirty in the Morning. New Paltz State University Coll., N.Y.
WILD, BILL
*Death and the Baseball Game. U. of Houston
WINFREY, LEE
*The Nine Ball Players. U. of Iowa
WOODWORTH, DAVID A.
**May One Ask These Questions Of The Girl Sitting Next to Me? Northwestern U.

ZACHEK, ELAINE MARIE
*Faces. Coll. of St. Elizabeth, Convent Sta., N.J.

POETS†

ABITUA, ANGEL
***This Old Man. STORY 1968. Pan American U., Edinburgh, Tex.
ALLEGRO, MARJORIE
***A Time for Moving. STORY 1968
*Prokofiev Without Benefit of Concert Hall. Coll. of Notre Dame of Md.

BAREFOOT, THOMAS E., III
**Requitas for T. S. Eliot. Tufts U.
BEREN, PETER
*Think. Tufts U.
BOJESKI, TOM
**Among the Statues
**A Supper of Goose
**Soliloquy in a Greenhouse. No. Ill. U., DeKalb
BRODY, MARSHA
***In a Summer Room. STORY 1968
**The Watermelon Man. La. St. U.
BROWNBACK, GLENDA
**Venus on the Half Shell
**The Chant of a Young Girl. U. of Houston
BURKE, KAREN
***Fugue: To J. S. Bach
***Requiem. 3d Prize, STORY 1968. Skidmore Coll.

CARROLL, DAVID
*The Quest. U. of Calif., Riverside
CONFALONE, MARIANNE
***The Fisherman. STORY 1968
**Three Pictures of a Child
**The Roar of Gulls. Coll. of Notre Dame of Md.

†Excepting Wait, Herem and Burke, the three prize winners, all poets listed as STORY 1968 were recipients of Special Honor Roll Publication Awards.

Fellowes, Peter
***To Jim . . . dead in Vietnam. STORY 1968. Johns Hopkins U.
Grimmer, Karen
**Persephone. San Diego St. Coll.
Grimmett, Gerald
**Amplification. Idaho St. U.

Henderson, Cynthia
***There Was Something. STORY 1968
***If. STORY 1968. Marygrove Coll., Detroit
Herem, Barry
***At Twelve
***Whales
***Gather Me
*Tokyo. 1st & 2d Prizes shared (Wait) STORY 1968. U. of Wash.
Hewitt, Geof
***Letter to His Wife. STORY 1968. Johns Hopkins U.
Hogue, Olivia
***Poem for China. STORY 1968
***Ode to Emily. U. of Tulsa

Kistler, Lawrence
***Scouting Party. STORY 1968. Boston Coll.

Lagen, John W.
***Patterns. Humboldt St. Coll., Arcata, Calif.

Martin, Grace B.
**Thirty-One-O-Eight. State U., Buffalo
Mathews, Richard
***Cedar Key. STORY 1968. U. of Florida
McGinnis, D. W.
***After the Death of my Granduncle Joseph Patsey. STORY 1968
***A Return to the Ho-Had-Huns. U. of Wash.

Pendleton, Marion
***Ballad of a Triangle. STORY 1968. Comm. Coll., Muskegon, Mich.

Rickabaugh, Rene
***Somewhere Under an Unknown Length of Love. STORY 1968
***I Shall Now Inherit the Bones
***The Cooking-Tips of Julia Child. STORY 1968. Museum Art School, Portland, Ore.

Schneidhorst, Patricia
***Poem to e.e.
***Love in the Western World . . .
***Tuesday. STORY 1968
**Advice to a Sister. Ohio No. U., Ada
Schwartz, Hillel
***Whittling
***The French Doors. STORY 1968. Brandeis U., Waltham, Mass.
Slowick, Mary
***Hawkweed and Asters. STORY 1968. Marygrove Coll., Detroit
Sopp, Beverly
***The Giant Years. STORY 1968. Coll. of Notre Dame of Md.

Wait, Eleanor
***Playground
***Ellie: An Inventory of Being. 1st & 2d Prizes shared (Herem), STORY 1968
**December 22. Chatham Coll., Pittsburgh
Wayman, Tom
***Capes of Horn. STORY 1968
***Pregnant Street. Writing Center of U. of Calif., Berkeley

DRAMA

Albright, Carlton
*Torba and the Tone. U. of Iowa
Aldridge, Mary Camillo
**You Know What Happens to Little Boys. Mt. Holyoke Coll.

Delgado, Ramon
*Brother of Dragons. Yale School of Drama

Felton, Keith Spencer
***The Blue Tail Fly.
***The Last Lost Weekend of Missionary Peale. 1st Prize shared, STORY 1968. U.C.L.A.

Gardner, Gary
***Purgatory on a Saturday Night
***Just Like in the Movies. 1st Prize shared, STORY 1968. U.C.L.A.
Giglio, Allison
***Home Again, Home Again. 3d Prize. Penn State U.
Goheen, Eugene
*Dust to Diamond. Syracuse U.
Grainger, Tom
***The Kill. Yale U.

Karp, David
**Varnedoe. San Francisco St.

McIlvaine, Nancy
**Glesingl. Carnegie Tech.

Pelke, Wayne
**Walls. U. of Calif., Irvine

Rogers, James Case
*The Arroyo. Yale

Seiffer, David
***If I Ruled the World. 2d Prize. N.Y.U.

BIOGRAPHY

Adams, Don P.
***The Green Years. U. of Texas

Coe, Charles
***First Combat. 1st Prize, STORY 1968
**R & R. U.C.L.A.

Fisher, Jerome
**Cold Soup For a Hot Tea Taster. U. of Md.

Shoemaker, Thomas
**The Darkness of a Dead Man's Eyes. Cabrillo Coll., Aptos, Calif.
Stephens, Theresa
***Vision Through a Veil, 2d Prize, STORY 1968. U. of Ariz.

Wagoner, Patricia
***The Termagant Duchess, 3d Prize. Trinity Coll., Hartford, Conn.

Zuckerman, Edward B.
**The Day Trip. Cornell U.

ESSAY

Barclay, Sylvia G.
***Time of Surrender. 3d Prize. Muskegon Co. Comm. Coll., Mich.
Barefoot, Thomas E. III
*Balance in "Rhapsody on a Windy Night." Tufts U.

DICKON, CHRIS
***San Francisco: Sundial by the Sea. 2d Prize, STORY 1968. Western Reserve U.

FENSCH, THOMAS
*More Questions Than Answers. Iowa U.

HELD, GEORGE
**Frost's "All Revelation." Rutgers U.
HEREM, BARRY G.
***Logic in Nonsense: U. of Wash.
HORSTMAN, LEE
**Sodomy and Schizophrenia in *Huckleberry Finn*. Rice U.

LENKE, HAL
**An Introduction to Free Universities
*We Must Connive for Peace. Antioch Coll.
LINTON, MARIE-PIERRE
**Wild Plums and an End of Halvard Solness. Marymount College, Palos Verdes, Calif.

SAVERY, BARBARA JEAN
***Pilgrimage to Mecca, 1st Prize, STORY 1968. Stanford U.
SCHULTZ, DIANA E.
***Don Quixote* and *On the Road*. U. of Chicago

TIMMERMAN, JOHN
*Shelley, Prophet of Mysticism. Calvin Coll., Mich.
TULSKY, LIZBETH
*The Fable of the Crystal World. Lawrence U., Wis.

WOO, CYNTHIA
**The Case Against Economic Anti-Semitism. Stanford U.

YOUNG, AL
**The Compensation Claimant. Stanford U.

JOURNALISM

ANDREWS, LOUIE
*Major Wood. Gulf Coast Jr. Coll., Fla.

BIEBER, DAVID L.
***LSD at Kent State. 1st Prize, STORY 1968. *Daily Kent Stater*. Initiative Award. Kent State, Ohio

DICKON, CHRIS
**The Voice Speaks of the Times. Western Reserve U.

GREENFIELD, ROBERT
***Observation on Obsession. Brooklyn Coll.

HALPER, JACKIE
**The Medium is the Massage
**Psychedelic Sound. San Diego State Coll.
HEREM, BARRY G.
***The One-time Trip. 2d Prize. U. of Wash.

LAWSON, TODD
*Anti-Defamation League. Mankato State Coll., Minn.

PARCHMAN, FRANK
**Who is the Real Stokely Carmichael? Ore. State U.
POLICH, JOHN
***Laura Bernstein, 3d Prize. Ariz. State U.
POLZIN, JOAN AND LAWSON, TODD
*The Firehouse Theatre. Mankato State Coll., Minn.

ROBINSON, T. SUMNER
***Brill Tolls Post Mortem for Sex. American U., Washington, D.C.

SCHRADER, PAUL
***"Life at the Top." Calvin Coll., Mich.
SHATZMAN, MARCIA
**Baseball's No. 1 Fan. Temple U.
SHIELDS, GWENDOLYN
*Virginia Graham. Yale Writers' Workshop
SILVA, JOHN W.
*Welfare in Tulare County. Fresno State Coll., Calif.

WAGNER, ARLO T.
*Brammer Kills Self. U. of Cincinnati

MOTION PICTURES

JONES, DAVID B.
***Neither Here Nor There, from a sketch by Kafka. 1st Prize, STORY 1968. Stanford U.

KOWINSKI, WILLIAM
**Morning, Byrd! Knox Coll., Ill.

MCBEATH, LEE J.
**Vestibule. Ill. State U.

PETLEWSKI, PAUL
***The Ripper. 3d Prize. U. of Detroit

SHANNON, MIKE
***Untitled Film Script. 2d Prize, San Francisco State

TELEVISION

MCCABE, HERB
*Bridge Night. 2d Prize. Loyola U., Los Angeles

USABEL, SALVADOR DE
**Does the Empress Always Smile? 1st Prize. San Francisco State

PHOTO ESSAY

BELINOFF, ROBERT
**Mollie. U. of Ill.

BRASCOLL, JAMES
**Flight. San Jose St. Coll.

CAMPBELL, JUDY
**Nursery School. U. of Florida

FITZIG, IRVING
***Hospital for Animals. 1st Prize. Brooklyn Coll.

GOODWIN, GARY
***A Fishing Village in India. 2d Prize. St. Lawrence U., Canton, N. Y.

NICHOLS, JAMES
**Promotional Booklet. U. of Florida

SHEFFIELD, ROBERT
***The Lovin' Spoonful. 3d Prize. U. of Michigan

WALLIS, HELEN
**Summer on the Coast of Maine
**Coffee House of Nick Kavouklis. U. of Florida

The Judges

SHORT FICTION
Hallie Burnett, novelist, formerly of Sarah Lawrence faculty
Dr. Riley Hughes, Georgetown University

POETRY
Marianne Moore, poet
Richard Eberhart, poet
Clark Mills, poet, publisher, and Fairleigh Dickinson faculty
Assisted by John Pope, Four Winds Press

DRAMA
Stanley Richards, playwright, editor Best One Act Plays, etc.
Assisted by Nancy Nicholas, Language Arts Books, Scholastic Magazines

BIOGRAPHY
J. Donald Adams, biographer, *The New York Times*
Assisted by Eleanor Van Zandt, Language Arts Books, Scholastic Magazines

ESSAY
J. Donald Adams
Assisted by Eleanor Van Zandt, Language Arts Books, Scholastic Magazines

JOURNALISM
John Luter, Co-ordinator of Advanced International Reporting Program, Columbia Graduate School of Journalism
Assisted by Whit Burnett, chairman Program Council, Overseas Press Club of America

MOTION PICTURES
Tad Mosel, playwright, screen writer
Assisted by Margaret Ronan, Language Arts Books, Scholastic Magazines

TELEVISION
Tad Mosel, playwright, television writer
Assisted by Margaret Ronan, Language Arts Books, Scholastic Magazines

PHOTO-ESSAY
Lucy Evankow, photo procurement, librarian, Scholastic Magazines
John Carter, Scholastic Magazines
Mary Jane Dunton, art editor, Scholastic Magazines
Russell D'Anna, Language Arts art editor, Scholastic Magazines